Richard C

MINING GEOPHYSICS

SERIES

Methods in Geochemistry and Geophysics

Methods in Geochemistry and Geophysics

3

MINING GEOPHYSICS

BY

D.S. PARASNIS

Professor of Applied Geophysics
University of Lulea, Lulea, Sweden

Second revised and up-dated edition

ELSEVIER SCIENTIFIC PUBLISHING COMPANY
AMSTERDAM/OXFORD/NEW YORK
1975

ELSEVIER SCIENTIFIC PUBLISHING COMPANY
335 JAN VAN GALENSTRAAT, P.O. BOX 211, AMSTERDAM

AMERICAN ELSEVIER PUBLISHING COMPANY, INC.
52 VANDERBILT AVENUE, NEW YORK, N.Y. 10017

First published 1966
First reprinted 1970
Second revised edition 1973
First reprinted 1975

LIBRARY OF CONGRESS CATALOG CARD NUMBER 72-87961
ISBN: 0-444-41077-5 (hardbound)
ISBN: 0-444-41324-3 (paperback)

WITH 131 ILLUSTRATIONS AND 11 TABLES

PRINTED IN THE NETHERLANDS

"Malmletning, även i sin mest inskränkta utöfning ar före-
mål för bemödanden, hvilka ej sällan åtföljas af ett nit,
hvars belöning oftare önskas, än ernås." (Lagerhjelm-
Rothoff, Förslag till ändringar och stadganden uti Bergs-
författningarne, 1832, cited by H. Carlsborg.)

"Ore prospecting, even in its most restricted practice, is
the object of efforts, which are not seldom accompanied
by a zeal the reward of which is more often desired than
achieved." (Lagerhjelm-Rothoff, Proposal for amend-
ments and enactments of mining statutes.)

To my father

The most unforgettable character I have met.

Preface to the First Edition

This book is intended as an introduction to the geophysical methods of ore prospecting and is written primarily for geologists and mining engineers. I hope, however, that others may also find it useful. Considering that the day-to-day mathematical equipment of geologists and mining engineers does not, in general, go beyond elementary algebra and trigonometry, I have avoided the use of higher mathematics in the main text. However, for the reader who is interested in knowing the basis of geophysical formulas, a few appendices on selected topics are included but even these do not require more than elementary knowledge of the calculus for their understanding.

Several texts on applied geophysics exist at approximately the same introductory level as the present one, for example, Dobrin's *Introduction to Geophysical Prospecting* or Eve and Keys' *Applied Geophysics in the Search for Minerals*. Therefore, it should be of some interest to point out in what manner the present book differs from its predecessors.

It appears in the first place that this is the first modern book devoted exclusively to mining geophysics and, as such, it treats several topics which are not treated, or at best mentioned only cursorily, in the older books of its class. Among these may be mentioned electromagnetic moving source—receiver methods, induced polarization, minimax estimates in gravity interpretation, mass estimates from gravity data, and airborne electromagnetic work.

The second point of difference is the relative emphasis on the various methods. In Dobrin's book, for example, the gravity and seismic methods occupy about 25 percent of the book each, while the self-potential, electromagnetic and electrical methods together receive only 7 percent of the book. While this proportion may meet the requirements of oil prospecting it is unsatisfactory from the point of view of ore prospecting in which the latter class of methods is, at least at present, of very much greater importance than the seismic method. The present book redresses the balance in favour of the geoelectrical methods without, however, sacrificing the gravity method which continues to enjoy the share appropriately due to it.

At several places in this book reference is made to a previous monograph of mine *Principles of Applied Geophysics*, especially in regard to certain master curves and theoretical points of general interest. As both books cover a certain amount of common ground, and my previous monograph, being of recent date, is readily available, this course seemed to me a more sensible one than a mere repetition for the sake of completeness of the present volume. The space thus set free has been utilized in the discussion of case histories and of topics of specific interest to mining geophysics. However, either book has its well defined separate point of view and is self-sufficient as far as it goes.

No attempt is made in this book to describe the details of calculating theoretical anomalies in interpreting geophysical data. Firstly, an adequate account of the technique of such computation can hardly be given within the scope of this book. Secondly, the fundamental problem of geophysical interpretation is not that of making subtle adjustments of the various parameters in order to secure an agreement between theoretical and observed anomalies to some very high degree of accuracy, but that of understanding physical phenomena and of manipulating physical magnitudes in order to arrive at a working hypothesis concerning the structure of the subsurface, a hypothesis that is reasonable in the light of physical theories as well as geological knowledge.

With the above in mind, I have laid great stress on the physical principles behind each geophysical method and in so doing sometimes started at a point which may appear to many readers as elementary. However, the consultations which I had with geologists during the planning stages of this book, lead me to believe that most geologists and mining engineers would welcome a revision of their knowledge of the elementary concepts of physics in reading about geophysical methods.

The reader will notice that a very large number of practical examples of mining geophysical work in this book are drawn from Swedish ore fields. The object of field examples is to illustrate certain principles and to show the variety of geophysical anomaly patterns and phenomena which are obtained in practice.

It would perhaps have been more "impressive" if the examples were distributed in several parts of the globe but I doubt that this would have carried any special pedagogic advantage at the introductory level of this book. A compensating circumstance is that the examples are fresh. The much hackneyed illustrations, like the celebrated Kursk anomaly, the Lundberg equipotential survey of the Kristineberg ore or Tagg's (now almost ancient) electric drilling determination, which occur in wellnigh every geophysical text, are avoided here. In fact, the majority of field examples in this book have never appeared in papers or texts in the English language and quite a large number have never been published until now.

Many sections of the book are built around short, succinct case histories. The interpretation of the maps and profiles presented in them is deliberately kept sketchy, although in several instances it could be carried through in very great detail, in the belief that many teachers using this book would like to treat these examples as exercises for their students.

Finally, it should be mentioned that the book makes no pretence at being comprehensive in the sense of including, every major and minor variant of a geophysical method. Many other topics like demagnetization factors, resolution of e.m. anomalies (a tricky question!) will also be found to have been omitted. However, it is hoped that the geologist encountering an unfamiliar or a less common geophysical technique will be able to follow it by reference to the principles described in this book. In fact, if the book helps the geologist and the mining engineer to see through the jargon of the geophysicist it will have served its purpose.

Many of the line drawings are adapted from existing drawings in the internal reports of the Boliden Mining Company, Sweden. The source of these drawings is acknowledged in the captions by the letters BGAB. Other drawings were supplied to me by the Swedish Geo-

logical Survey, Geophysics Section, while yet others were kindly prepared for me by Mrs. L. König of Stockholm.

My thanks are due to the following organizations and persons: the
Boliden Mining Company for allowing me to publish the data in its
archives, to Dr. E. Grip of the Company for his encouraging attitude
towards this book, to Dr. D. Malmqvist of the Company for a fruitful
exchange of ideas, especially in connection with the Swedish two-
frame and Turam techniques; to Dr. S. Werner of the Swedish Geological Survey for supplying certain field examples; the ABEM Company
of Stockholm for photographs of geophysical equipments manufactured by them; to Dr. H. O. Seigel of E.J. Sharpe Instruments of
Canada Ltd., Downsview, Canada for photographs of geophysical
equipment and field examples most willingly supplied; and Mr. E.
Carlsson, Falun, Sweden for supplying two magnetic profiles from the
records of the Stora Kopparbergs Bergslags Aktiebolag, Falun.

The source of drawings published in the literature before is indicated at the appropriate place in each case.

Boliden, Sweden   D.S. PARASNIS

Preface to the Second Edition

When the occasion arose for a third printing of this book it was decided to revise and enlarge the book. The present edition preserves the plan and contents of the first one but possesses the new features mentioned below.

The Système Internationale (SI) units are used throughout in the text and formulas, even for magnetic quantities. However, to avoid redrawing a number of figures (especially in the chapter on gravity methods) the old units have been retained in some figures and instead a note on the conversion to SI is added in the caption.

The section on fundamental concepts of magnetism in Chapter 3 contains additional matter explaining the units Weber/m^2 and Ampere/m. The idea of magnetic susceptibility is also explained in more detail than before. A catalogue is given of type curves of magnetic vertical field anomalies over broad zones for use in northern as well as southern magnetic latitudes.

Vector diagrams are included in Chapter 5 for the interpretation of electromagnetic anomalies over sheet-like conductors. Two entirely new sections in this chapter deal respectively with the H-mode VLF method and with the effect of magnetic permeability.

The chapter on induced polarization has been extended while that on airborne methods now also contains descriptions of the INPUT and Radiophase methods.

Appendix 10 deals with elliptic polarization. FORTRAN source-programs for magnetic and gravity calculations are provided in Appendix 11.

New material has also been added to the sections dealing with mise-à-la-masse measurements, refraction seismics and radioactive spectrometers.

A few ambiguities that appeared in the text of the first edition have been removed and references brought up to date. Towards this end the "Notas del traductor" appended by Prof. Ernesto Orellana to his Spanish translation of the first edition have been most helpful.

As before my special thanks are due to the Boliden Company for allowing me to make liberal use of the material in its archives for illustrations (acknowledged in the captions by the letters BGAB).

Boliden, Sweden.   D.S. PARASNIS

Contents

CHAPTER 1

The Role of Geophysics in Ore Prospecting

Mining has been an activity of man since ancient times and the continual search for new ore deposits, as those already known became exhausted, must have been as much a major concern of the miners of yesterday as it is of the miners of today. Evidence of the thoroughness and diligence with which this search was conducted in olden times can be found in many places, such as the ancient workings of Laurion in Greece or, coming nearer to our age, those of Saxony in Germany and Bergslagen in Sweden, to take but a few examples.

Scholastic controversies as to the origin of ores probably did not seriously distract the old prospectors in their search, whose chief guiding principle was analogy. It is a valuable and indispensable principle of ore prospecting even today. One must look for more ore where ore has already been found and in districts with natural conditions similar to those in the known district. If the ore of a district is associated with, say, limestone then we should follow that limestone, or if a mineral is known to occur predominantly in granite, every granite is suspect from this point of view and in looking for new deposits of the mineral, we should start by looking for granite masses.

The principle of analogy narrows the prospector's field considerably, which is necessary because orebodies are relatively rare, small-scale structures and the search for them would otherwise be a hopeless undertaking. The study of the interrelation, in space as well as in time, of different rocks, their inferred behaviour in the past, the study of the minerals in ordinary rocks and in ores — in short the application of geology and mineralogy — can further restrict the area for prospecting. However, the area may still be too large for investigations, such as digging and drilling, to be practical and economical, and further restrictions on it may be desirable. Moreover, both geology and mineralogy depend upon exposures of rocks which are not always available. If available, they may not be sufficiently abundant for the course of the ore-bearing formations to be predicted with reasonable certainty. Again, even if the ore-bearing formations be well known, the deposits may be concealed at a smaller or greater depth below the surface accessible for direct geological or mineralogical study. In fact, this is very often the case in modern prospecting because outcropping ores have long since been discovered and, in many cases, worked out. The scope of surface geological examiniation, therefore, naturally decreases with the development of the mining industry.

It is here that geophysics — the application of physics to the study of the earth — enters the picture. Ore bodies frequently differ in physical properties (magnetic susceptibility, electric conductivity, density etc.) from the rocks in which they are found embedded. By suitably observing the variations in the physical properties of the ground, and by carefully interpreting the results, we can eliminate large areas as being unlikely to bear specific types of ores, and direct further detailed search after such ores to certain limited areas.

The choice of the original area for geophysical observations is often dictated by geological considerations. The portions that geophysics can eliminate are, in very general terms, those within which the relevant physical property of the ground shows no significant variations (anomalies), while the portions selected for further work are those in which it does show appreciable variations which can reasonably be attributed to subsurface masses differing in that property from the surrounding rocks. In this sense the geophysical search after ores is a direct search, in contrast to that after oil which is indirect. In oil prospecting we cannot exploit any physical property of oil itself but must look instead for geological structures that may be acting as reservoirs of oil.

It is not possible to decide from geophysical data alone whether the anomalous masses indicated by them are ore deposits or not. However, combining these data with geological and other information, as well as past experience, we can often select some of the indications as being particularly likely to be caused by ore. The costly exploratory operations like drilling, trenching and shaft-sinking, which alone can provide the ultimate proof of ore, can then be concentrated at these few places. Moreover, the detailed interpretation of geophysical anomalies frequently yields reliable estimates of the probable depth, length, breadth, attitude etcetera of the anomalous masses. Such estimates provide further help in planning a rational and economical exploration programme, in assessing the quantity and value of a possible orebody and in taking decisions concerning its exploitation.

Thus, the primary purpose of geophysics in prospecting is to separate areas which appear to be barren from those which appear to hold a promise of ore. Since orebodies are relatively rare occurrences, the barren areas are naturally very much more numerous than the promising ones and the results of most geophysical surveys, as of most geological surveys also, will be (correctly) negative. Consequently, the success of a well-conducted geophysical survey is not to be measured by the number of orebodies discovered or by the number of recommended drill holes that struck ore, but by the time, effort and money which the survey has saved in eliminating ground which would otherwise have to be eliminated by more expensive methods.

It is important to realize that the elimination of barren ground can only be made within the limitations of the geophysical method, or methods, used and is not an "absolute elimination". In a recent electromagnetic survey in Newfoundland, for instance, no significant indications were obtained within a certain area. Properly speaking, the survey eliminated the possibility of subsurface electric conductors only down to the depth to which the particular electromagnetic method is able to detect them, namely about 25 m. To give a classic example, areas in central Sweden, which in all probability were thoroughly investigated magnetically in the seventeenth and eighteenth centuries by the mine compass and eliminated as barren, proved in many cases to be ore-bearing when the more accurate Thalén-Tiberg magnetometer was employed in the nineteenth century. Similarly, many areas discarded in the nineteenth century have revealed large iron-ore bodies during the present century and especially during the last twenty years, as a result of surveys with modern accurate magnetometers and improved interpretation techniques.

If an orebody is discovered as a result of recommendations based mainly on geophysical work, we can often talk of a "returns-ratio" for the geophysical work. This figure, which represents the ratio of the estimated value of the ore to the cost of the geophysical work, is not meaningful unless the cost of the geophysical work on barren ground in the same campaign is also included. Mining geophysics has shown very impressive returns-ratios, of the order of several hundred to one. In an exceptional instance, a mining company in central Sweden reported the discovery of 5,800 dollars worth of ore for every dollar spent by it on geophysical work (only magnetic) during a period of fifteen years (Hedström, 1957). Other instances can be quoted.

The returns-ratio is sometimes called the success ratio of a geophysical survey, but this is inappropriate as the success and returns of a geophysical survey are two different concepts. The distinction between them is essential for the proper understanding of the role of geophysics in ore exploration and for the efficient planning and execution of a geophysical survey.

A survey can be successful even if no geophysical indication is obtained or, if any is obtained, no ore is found after drilling and trenching. The criterion and measure of the success is simply the estimated saving in costs effected through the use of geophysical methods in eliminating barren ground. (In estimating this saving, the cost of work, like drilling carried out specifically to test the survey results, must of course be included in the cost of the survey.) On the other hand, there can be no question of a returns-ratio before an orebody has actually been ascertained by drilling and its value adjudged. The returns-ratio may vary somewhat with time because the market value of the orebody will not, in general, be the same at some later date as at the time of its discovery. In fact, the "exact" returns-ratio of a geophysical survey (or, for that matter, of the entire exploration campaign) cannot be calculated before all the mineable ore discovered by it has been worked out and sold.

In recent years attempts have been made to apply advanced statistical theory to the problem of optimum planning of ore exploration campaigns (for example, by Slichter, 1955) but a discussion of these lies outside the scope of this book.

CHAPTER 2

General Aspects of the Collection and Presentation of Geophysical Data

In this chapter we shall consider certain general aspects common to all geophysical methods used in ore exploration. As a matter of fact, many of these considerations apply in other branched of geophysics as well, pure or applied, but we shall be concerned here specifically with ore prospecting.

A necessary condition for the detection of an orebody by geophysical methods is that the ore should possess some physical property than can influence the relevant measurements. More precisely, it is necessary that the particular property of the ore should differ sufficiently from that of the host rock. If the ore itself has no such property, geophysical prospecting for it can sometimes be carried out in an indirect way, provided some associated mineral or geological formation possesses it.

CLASSIFICATION OF GEOPHYSICAL METHODS

The only ordinary properties of matter that can conceivably be utilized in geophysical exploration are the magnetic susceptibility, the electric conductivity, density, elasticity and the thermal conductivity. Of these, the first three are by far the most important in ore prospecting while the last is of extremely limited significance. Electrochemical phenomena in the ground form the basis of two geophysical methods but they also depend ultimately on the measurement of electric quantities.

All the above properties have been used to devise methods for the study of the earth and, in particular, for locating small-scale structures such as orebodies. These methods may be conveniently classified as follows.

In the first place we have the *static methods* based on detecting and measuring accurately the distortions produced in a stationary field of force, by ores (or by other inhomogeneities) in the earth's crust. Their essential feature is that the fields concerned, whether natural or artificial, do not vary with time. The magnetic and gravity fields of the earth are examples of stationary natural fields of force and so is the electric field observed in the vicinity of certain ores. The field, due to an electric direct current injected into the ground, is an instance of an artificial stationary field.

In contrast to the above class we have the *dynamic methods* in which the fields measured are not stationary but vary with time. This class comprises the electromagnetic and seismic methods which too can exploit either natural or artificial phenomena. Among the electromagnetic methods are some of the most important methods of ore prospecting. So far, the seismic methods have been used little in ore exploration but they are likely to grow in importance in the future.

Next, we have the *relaxation methods*. They are electrical methods which may be said to lie between the artificial static and artificial dynamic methods. To this class belong the induced polarization or overvoltage methods.

There is a significant difference between the natural field methods on the one hand and the artificial ones on the other. In the artificial methods the depth of exploration can be controlled within certain limits by appropriately choosing the relative positions of the source and the detectors of the field, but such control is not possible in the natural field methods.

No one of the above methods can be said to be the "ideal" one in the search after ore since each has its own scope and limitations, its own advantages and disadvantages, and very often the best results are to be obtained by judiciously combining the use of two or more methods. It is nevertheless possible to rank the methods in other ways, for example with regard to simplicity of operation, ease of data interpretation, importance as aids in geological work etc. The order in which they will be dealt with in this book is a result of weighing such considerations against each other.

The magnetic and electromagnetic methods can be adapted to measurements from the air while all, except the gravitational methods, can also be used in boreholes. Considerable research has, however, gone into adapting the gravitational methods to borehole and aerial work (Goodell and Fay, 1964), but the accuracy at present available in them falls far short of that required for ore exploration.

RADIOACTIVITY

All the physical properties referred to above (magnetic susceptibility, electric conductivity etc.) originate in the electronic structure of matter and, in fact, almost entirely in the so-called outer electronic shells. All substances of our experience possess them, although to different degrees. On the other hand, only one property, depending on the *nuclear* constitution of matter, is at present known to have any significance in exploration geophysics. This is radioactivity. However, only a few of the naturally occurring nuclei on the earth exhibit it so that radioactive methods have a rather limited application. In particular, the nuclei of the common metals of industry, and hence the corresponding ores, are not radioactive. We shall deal with radio-activity methods in a separate chapter.

COLLECTION OF PRELIMINARY INFORMATION

One of the first steps in planning a geophysical survey is to collect the available topographical, geological and mineralogical information about the area concerned to find out what rocks and minerals we are likely to encounter within it and how they are likely to be interre-lated. At least some information of this sort is nowadays almost al-ways to be had for any but the most inaccessible regions of the earth. It is also a sound policy to procure, if possible, some rock samples from the area and measure their physical properties in the laboratory before starting large-scale geophysical operations. The results of such preliminary investigations should decide whether geophysical methods should be used in the area at all and, if they are used, which of them would be the most suitable. The criteria for such a decision will appear later in the book.

If neither the mineralization sought nor any of the associated minerals or rocks have suitable physical properties, geophysical methods cannot be used profitably in the search for ore. In such cases, the areas for prospecting can hardly be narrowed down, short of extensive geological examination, and correlation of the rocks ascertained in systematic diggings, trenchings, drillings etc.

There is another situation which may also tell against the use of geophysics. The data of geophysical methods need corrections for topographic irregularities. Generally these corrections are small and fairly easy to evaluate, but in areas of rugged topography they are often such that the interpretation of the geophysical data can become very uncertain. Under such circumstances, the value of geophysical methods may also be doubtful.

TRIAL SURVEYS

There are no universally applicable simple rules for deciding whether geophysical surveys can be usefully undertaken within an area or not, and every case has to be considered carefully in the light of the available information. In doubtful situations, a trial survey can often help in taking a decision. Actually, a trial survey ought always to be carried out before launching a large-scale geophysical campaign in a completely new or an ill-known area. Such a survey helps one to form some idea of the geophysical indications to be expected from the various rocks and minerals within the area, as well as those expected due to topography and overburden variations. A trial survey may also indicate any modifications necessary in the field operations for obtaining the best possible results.

STAKING AN AREA

A number of different considerations lead to the choice of a particular area for geophysical prospecting. Chief among these are the known occurrences of ore and the geological surroundings. In many parts of the world the initial prospecting is nowadays often carried out with airborne apparatus and the indications obtained thereby are then examined more closely on the ground. As, however, ground work is by far the more important for directing an exploration programme in detail, we shall consider here the course of a ground survey only, reserving airborne prospecting for a special chapter.

When the area of investigation has been selected it must be staked before starting the geophysical measurements. The purpose of staking is to establish a coordinate system in which every observation station is clearly and uniquely marked.

Staking enables us to identify the position of eventual indications so that the follow-up work, like drilling, can be directed to the proper places. Secondly, if geophysical measurements with more than one method are found desirable, staking helps us to reoccupy exactly the same observation stations so that a comparison of the results of the various methods is rendered reliable.

Staking is an important basic operation and should be carried out accurately.

A well-defined convenient point of the area is chosen and a straight 'base line' is laid out from it, preferably by means of a theodolite, in a direction approximately parallel to the known or presumed geological strike. The line should be clearly marked by wooden stakes, about 1 m long, driven firmly in the ground at suitable intervals. It is advisable to tie in the base line securely with a good topographical map of the area by taking the theodolite bearings of some prominent point, marked on the map, from suitable points on the line. If, as it sometimes happens, a reliable map is not available, it may be necessary to determine the orientation of the base line with respect to the true north by means of pole-star observations with an astronomical transit instrument.

The base line having been laid out, a set of parallel lines, usually called profiles, are staked at right angles to it. An interval of 100 or 200 m between adjacent profiles is generally quite satisfactory for reconnaissance surveys in ore prospecting but a somewhat more convenient interval to start with is 160 (or 80) m. If intermediate profiles are needed for more detailed work, this spacing can be successively halved to 80, 40, 20, 10 and 5 m. In 'non-metric' countries initial profile intervals of 400–1,000 ft. are commonly used.

A good steel tape should be employed for measuring distances and care must be taken to hold it taut between two points. Even so, the tape will sag somewhat but the correction for sagging is negligible for most purposes.

The direction of at least two or three well-separated profiles should be fixed by means of a theodolite so that these profiles can serve as checks on the staking, if necessary. For orientating the remaining profiles a pocket prismatic angle-finder will usually suffice. There are several such gadgets on the market. It is not safe to rely on the magnetic compass for accurate staking unless the area is known to be reasonably free from local magnetic disturbances. For rough direction-finding and for staking a few isolated profiles, the compass is, however, a handy and rapid instrument.

A series of points at which the geophysical measurements are to be made are marked off along each profile at some suitable interval, for example, 40 or 20 m. The interval must be chosen with regard to the anticipated depth of the orebodies and the detail of anomalies required. For instance, if the expected depth is small the interval should be reduced, because the anomalies of shallow ores fall off very quickly with the distance, so that in using a large point-separation one runs the risk of missing a significant anomaly. In magnetic and electromagnetic work on shallow ores it is sometimes necessary to place the points as close as 1 or 2 m from each other to obtain an adequate picture of the anomaly trends.

Probably the best way to mark a point is by means of a stick, about 50 cm long, on which are written (1) a number or symbol representing the profile to which the point belongs and (2) the distance of the point from the base line, together with a symbol N, SE etc. showing the direction (north, southeast etc.) in which the point lies from te base line.

Profiles are sometimes marked A,B,C,D... or I,II,III... etc. but there is little to recommend this practice when the terrain allows a regular staking network. The alphabet is soon exhausted in staking a large area and furthermore the marking of intermediate profiles becomes inconvenient with such systems.

The rational way to designate a profile is by its distance and direction from a "zero profile", for example, as Profile 100W(est), Profile 200N(orth)E(ast) etc. Sometimes, if the points along the profiles are marked in metres (or feet), the profiles themselves are marked in tens of metres (or feet) so as to distinguish between the two sets of numbers. Actually, such a hybrid system ultimately becomes confusing rather than convenient, and it is hardly necessary to resort to it because the direction symbol after a number on a stake clearly indicates whether the distance meant is parallel or perpendicular to the base line.

Profiles should be sufficiently long by which is meant that they should not merely cover the area of expected anomalies but extend well outside it into the less disturbed peripheral regions so that the flanks of any anomalies obtained are adequately ascertained. To ensure this it may be necessary to lengthen some or all profiles during a survey.

The setting-up of a rectangular coordinate system for staking is fairly straightforward in areas with gentle topographic relief, although dense bush, wood or jungle may be a great hindrance at times for cutting the lines. But in mountain areas with rough topography dissected by numerous hill tops and river valleys, the staking of a regular network of straight lines often becomes impractical. Access to such areas is sometimes impossible, except along river valleys, gulleys, passes, mountain roads etc., and the course of these is irregular. A good large-scale topographical map to mark the observation points is indispensable for work in such areas because the geophysical survey must necessarily be made in a somewhat disjointed fashion.

FIELD MEASUREMENTS

The exact routine of geophysical field measurements with the various methods is a topic that we shall deal with in later chapters. However, certain general remarks can be made here.

Most commercially available present-day instruments have been constructed with special attention to speed, accuracy, portability, dependability, robustness and a minimum of maintenance. Moreover, the operation of many of them has been made "fool-proof" to such an extent that semi-skilled personnel can be readily trained to make accurate observations in almost all the methods, and to carry out minor instrument repairs in the field.

It is convenient to record the field observations on standardized blank pages with printed columns and lines. On the top of every page, adequate space should be indicated (in print) for general information such as date, name of area, method, instrument, observer and page number. In addition, it may be necessary to record some special information depending upon the method used, for example, electrode separation in resistivity methods or frequency in electromagnetic ones.

In the first column are usually noted the profile and the point of observation, in the second the time and in the third the instrument reading. The reading of time is imperative only in certain methods. The remaining columns are required for noting corrections, readings converted to appropriate units, etc. One column should be reserved for "remarks". Apart from the making of notes likely to be of significance for judging an observation (for example, "stand shaky due to wind"), this column can also be used for noting special details about the topography (for example, "rock exposure at point . . .", "road (brook) at point . . ." etc.). A fair amount of topographic detail should be recorded without burdening the journal too much, as this is useful in coordinating the staking system with a map of the area, not to say that topography can have a direct bearing on the interpretation of abnormal readings and on the placing of eventual drillholes.

GEOPHYSICAL MAPS

When the readings have been converted to appropriate units, if necessary, and corrected as called for by their nature, they are plotted on a map at points representing the corresponding observation stations. Large, ruled graph-paper sheets greatly facilitate the preparation of a geophysical map.

The scale chosen for the map will naturally depend on how close the observation points are to each other. Scales of 1 : 1,000 (1 cm = 10 m) and 1 : 2,000 (1 cm = 20 m) suffice for most purposes and yet allow a reasonable accuracy (0.5–1 m) in reading off topographic distances from the map. In non-metric countries scales of 1 : 1,200 (1 inch = 100 ft.) or 1 : 2,400 (1 inch = 200 ft.) are often used.

It is useful to have important topographic details (roads, houses, rock exposures, mine dumps, power lines etc.) put on the geophysical map. Their position can be taken from the field journal.

ISOANOMALY CURVES OR CONTOURS

The primary information on a geophysical map comprises a large set of numbers, each one the result of a physical observation, and cannot be grasped easily and immediately in its entirety. Clearly, it would be useful to summarize this information in some fashion and we achieve this object by drawing on the map a set of discrete curves, each of which purports to be a path along which the observations have some constant value, usually chosen to be a "round" number for convenience. Such curves are called *isoanomaly curves* or *contours*. Thus, for example, we may draw on a magnetic map one curve joining points at which the field intensity is estimated to be 100 units, another at which it is 200 units and so on.

Evidently, in drawing isoanomaly lines, we are concentrating our attention on points at which the observations take (or are judged to take) certain selected values, and the isoanomalous lines show how these points are distributed within the area. More precisely, we are demarcating a number of sub-areas (between two successive isoanomaly curves) such that within each area the observations are greater than some value A but less than some value B.

It is important to realize that isoanomaly curves constitute a summary of the observations and *not* their interpretation. Large or un-

wieldy numerical data can be concisely presented simply as isoanomaly charts, as is done, for example, at several places in this book.
Such charts are, therefore, more convenient than the numerical observations themselves for studying the anomaly trends and also in comparing the results of different methods; but in detailed interpretation
we must go back to the primary data.

In this instance, there will be very few points, if any at all, at which
the observations will have convenient "round" values like 1,2,3. . . or
500, 1,000. . . etc. In constructing isoanomaly charts we are, therefore, required to interpolate between adjacent observations to estimate where such round values would occur if measurements were
made at intermediate positions.

It is generally adequate to interpolate linearly between two observations. Linear interpolation implies that an observation increases or
decreases at a constant rate from one station to the adjacent one.
Thus, if the observations at two adjacent stations are, say, 172 and
284 we assume that halfway between them the observation would also
be halfway, that is, 228 and so on. It is possible to improve on the
simple linearity assumption by well-known methods in the mathematical theory of interpolation and, although this may be sometimes
desirable, the need for it seldom arises. With some practice, quite
accurate interpolation can be quickly done in the head while drawing
an isoanomaly line.

No general rule can be framed in respect of the interval between
successive isoanomaly curves but the interval should allow the curves
to bring forth the main trends of the anomalies within the area. A too
large interval will not summarize the data adequately, while a too
close interval tends to bring minor variations into relief and may lead
to a confusing or "patchy" picture.

Finally, a few properties of isoanomaly curves, obvious from the
definition of the curves, may be mentioned. It is helpful to keep them
before the mind in drawing isoanomaly curves.

Isoanomaly curves, corresponding to different observation values,
cannot cross each other. However, one and the same isoanomaly curve
can cross (or touch) itself any number of times. Every isoanomaly
curve either closes on itself or goes out to the edge of the map.

If there are insufficient observations or if the anomaly relief in an area is low, it may not always be possible to draw the isoanomaly curves in a unique manner. The proper course in these circumstances is to accumulate more data or to make more accurate observations. To adjust the isoanomaly lines to "fit" to the available geological information is to bias the insufficient or insufficiently accurate data and is clearly an unscientific procedure.

PROFILE DRAWING

Another way of presenting and studying the data of geophysical measurements is to take the observation stations as abscissas and the anomaly values at them as ordinates on an ordinary graph paper. The points thus plotted are then joined by straight lines or by a smooth curve, and a profile is obtained.

While isoanomaly charts are of great help for visualizing the general trends of various indications, profiles are better adapted to visualizing the continuous variation of anomalies. Further, the positions of true anomaly peaks, maximum gradients and other characteristics are more easily determined from profiles than from isoanomaly maps. Quantitative interpretation of geophysical data generally aims at calculating theoretical curves which resemble a number of selected profiles as closely as possible.

Isoanomaly maps and profiles are complementary ways of summarizing and presenting geophysical data.

Digital computers and automatic plotters are nowadays often resorted to for preparing geophysical maps and for contour drawing. However, in small-scale mining geophysical surveys on the ground the use of computers and automatic plotters for this purpose is not always as economic (or even time-saving) as one is inclined to believe from the start. The processing of large-scale survey data on the other hand is, of course, considerably facilitated by computers and plotters.

INTERPRETATION

Certain qualitative conclusions can be readily drawn from an isoanomaly chart. Thus, for instance, closed isoanomaly curves, with the values increasing (or decreasing) towards a "centre", indicate an anomalous subsurface mass. The direction of elongation of the isoanomaly curves may be identified at this stage of the interpretation as approximately that of the length of the mass. It coincides very often with the geological strike. Asymmetry in the anomaly flanks (most clearly discerned when profiles are drawn) might give clues about the direction of the dip.

Great care must, however, be exercised in inferring the strike of masses from the magnetic anomalies, particularly in low magnetic latitudes, because the contours often tend to align themselves east-west regardless of the strike of the mass (see p.44).

A rapid variation of anomalies at right angles to the strike is often due to shallow features, while a broad anomaly reflects a relatively large depth to the subsurface mass, but this may also be due to a shallow mass of great width.

With experience it is possible to extract considerable qualitative information of the above sort from a careful study of the isoanomaly charts and the profiles.

The quantitative interpretation of geophysical data naturally involves a certain amount of computational work. Recent theoretical researches and publication of extensive catalogues of master curves, tables, nomograms, computer programs etc., have greatly widened the scope of quantitative interpretation. Consequently, a good deal of such information can be obtained by relatively simple calculations and from rules-of-thumb which need machinery no more complicated than a slide rule and a desk calculator. Nevertheless, the serious practitioner of geophysics must not shun a certain amount of computational labour if he wishes to gain an insight into geophysical interpretation. Fortunately, the electronic digital computer has greatly facilitated the task of mathematical computations for geophysical interpretation. Programs for magnetic and gravity calculations will be considered later in the book.

The details of how the data of geophysical measurements can be interpreted in combination with geological information will be the subject of the next few chapters.

CHAPTER 3

Magnetic Methods

INTRODUCTION

Certain types of ore, especially magnetite, ilmenite and pyrrhotite-bearing sulphide deposits, produce distortions in the earth's magnetic field which can be used to locate such ores. Besides this direct application, the magnetic methods of prospecting can also be used for tracing ore-bearing formations and geologic features like faults, contact zones, intrusions etc.

Magnetic methods have a long history behind them. Recent historical researches (Carlsborg, 1963) prove beyond doubt that they were in use in Sweden, in the search for magnetic ore, as far back as 1640. Naturally, these were primitive applications employing only the ordinary, mariner's declination compass, which was subsequently replaced by the mine compass in the early nineteenth century. The latter measured the variations in the inclination of the magnetic field.

The magnetic methods are among the cheapest geophysical methods and, from the operational point of view, also among the easiest and fastest. The applicability of magnetic methods is, moreover, so wide that it is generally a sound policy to include a magnetic survey in every comprehensive geophysical campaign.

The success of magnetic methods in discovering shallow as well as deep-seated magnetic iron orebodies has been outstanding. Discoveries have been reported in which the depth to the bodies was as much as 700–1,000 m and there is little doubt that careful analysis of precision data could, under favourable circumstances, double or even quadruple these figures.

Magnetic methods have also been used extensively in prospecting for manganese and chromite ores owing to the fact that these ores are often found to display strong magnetic properties. However, the magnetism of manganese as well as chromite ores is highly irregular and magnetic methods are, in reality, of very limited advantage in this connection. They are certainly not sufficient by themselves for locating these ores.

Among the more unusual applications of the magnetic method may be mentioned the investigations of Bahnemann (1951) for locating the emery deposits on the island of Naxos in Greece.

RECALLING SOME FUNDAMENTAL CONCEPTS

A magnet is perhaps most satisfactorily defined as an object which experiences a mechanical force in the vicinity of an electric current and one which exerts a converse mechanical force on the current. The peculiar field of force that surrounds electric currents, and evidently also magnets, is called a magnetic field.

Within a long solenoid of n closely spaced turns, whose length is l metre and which is carrying an electric current i (A), there is a magnetic field. The quantity ni/l (A/m), which is the cause of the magnetic field, is called the magnetizing force and often denoted by H. This force is defined in the present instance to be acting parallel to the axis of the solenoid.

It is fruitful to describe the state of the medium within the solenoid by imagining that, as a result of the magnetizing force, the solenoid is threaded by an incessant flow or flux entering through one face and leaving through the other. The density of this flux (flux per square metre perpendicular to the direction of flow) is called the magnetic field and denoted by B. We shall presently see how it can be measured. Thus the flux across a small, flat coil of effective area $A(\text{m}^2)$, placed perpendicular to the solenoid axis, is BA.

If now we vary the current in the solenoid at a constant rate, a constant voltage E develops between the ends of the coil, whatever the medium within the solenoid, although its magnitude depends on the medium. This experimental fact is known as Lenz's law of induction, which is more generally expressed by the words: The time rate of change of magnetic flux associated with a circuit is equal to the electromotive force developed in it. Obviously, if a flux N decreases to zero in t seconds, *at a constant rate*, the voltage developed in the coil will have the constant magnitude E volt, throughout the duration t. In other words, $N = Et$ (Vsec).

The magnetic flux can therefore be measured in Volt-seconds (Vsec) and the flux density in $Vsec/m^2$ or $Weber/m^2$ (Wb/m^2), since one Volt-second is called one Weber. For almost all media, the flux density B is found to be proportional to the magnetizing force H (A/m), to which it is due, and their relation can therefore be written as:

$$B = \mu H \quad Wb/m^2$$

where μ is called the permeability of the medium on which H is acting. It is evident that the dimensions of μ are:

$$\frac{Vsec}{m^2} \bigg/ \frac{A}{m} = Ohm\text{-}sec/m$$

The permeability of vacuum is denoted by μ_0. Its value in the system of units known as Système Internationale (SI), based on the metre, the kilogramme, the second and the ampere, is $4\pi \cdot 10^{-7}$ Ohm-sec/m. Thus, in vacuum, the flux density due to a magnetizing force H will be:

$$B_0 = \mu_0 H \quad Wb/m^2$$

The permeability of air, water, soils and many other substances may for many practical purposes be taken to be equal to μ_0.

If a bar magnet is suspended anywhere on the earth so as to swing freely in a horizontal plane, one and the same end of it always points (approximately) towards the north. This end is called the north pole of the magnet, the opposite end being called the south pole. By definition, the direction of any magnetic field whatsoever is the direction in which the north pole of a small, freely suspended magnet points when the magnet is placed in that field.

If a magnet is turned out of its alignment with the field, the north pole experiences a force in the direction of the field, and the south pole a force in the opposite direction so that the magnet as a whole experiences a turning moment.

A continuous curve, such that the tangent at any point of it gives the local direction of the magnetic field, is called a *line of force*. A very short magnetic needle will orientate itself along the tangent when placed at that point.

The lines of force of the magnetic field (flux density) due to a bar

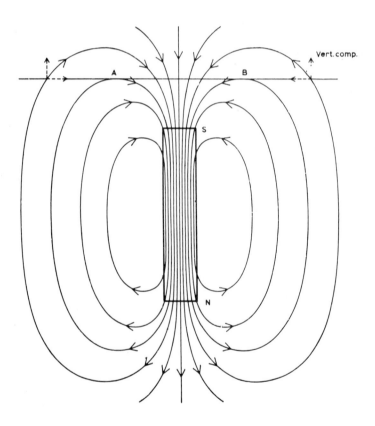

Fig. 1. Lines of force due to a bar magnet. (For significance of the horizontal line see p. 38.)

magnet are shown in Fig. 1. The lines seem to start from the north pole (N) and end on the south pole (S) of the magnet but actually they continue within the magnet as shown and form closed loops. Thus, there is a magnetic field (flux density) within a magnet also. It is often called the induction and is associated, at every internal point, with an *intensity of magnetization* (I) directed in the same sense as this internal field.

In fact, the intensity of magnetization is the magnetizing force that gives rise to the flux density within the magnet. It is measured therefore in A/m. The corresponding electric currents may be conceived of as minute electric circuits of atomic dimensions.

If V is the volume of the magnet, the product:

$$M = I \cdot V \tag{3.1}$$

is known as the (dipole) magnetic moment of the magnet. Eq. (3.1) also defines the intensity of magnetization I as the magnetic moment per unit volume. Being directly measurable, the magnetic moment is the most important quantity relating to a magnet. A fundamental method of determining it is as follows (Kohlrausch, 1947, pp.96–113; Starling, 1945, pp.22–28).

A small magnetic needle is allowed to come to rest in a magnetic field F and the magnet whose moment is to be measured is then placed near it. The deflection of the needle under the joint influence of F and the field of the magnet is a measure of the ratio M/F. A second experiment measures the time of oscillation of the magnet in the field F and yields the product MF. Multiplication of the two quantities gives M^2 while division gives F^2. The experiment has thus also simultaneously succeeded in measuring a magnetic field.

The SI unit of magnetic moment is evidently Am^2 (ampere times metre squared). This agrees with the magnetic moment of a small, plane electric current loop, which is defined as the current in the loop times the loop-area.

In the electromagnetic centimetre-gramme-second (c.g.s.) system of measurements, in which one unit of electric current (the absolute ampere) is 10 ordinary amperes, magnetic field is expressed in the unit gauss (G), in honour of the mathematician Gauss who was the first scientist to devise a method for the quantitative measurement of a magnetic field. For geophysical purposes, a sub-unit, the gamma (γ), which is 1/100,000 of a gauss, turns out to be more convenient. Thus $1 \gamma = 10^{-5}$ G.

The SI unit of magnetic field, Wb/m^2, equals 10,000 G. Conversely 1 G $= 10^{-4}$ Wb/m^2. It follows that $1 \gamma = 10^{-9}$ $Wb/m^2 = 1$ nano– Wb/m^2. This simple numerical relationship admits the gamma as a convenient sub-unit of the magnetic flux density in the Système Internationale. The strength of the earth's total magnetic field is about 0.6 G or 60,000 γ. The associated magnetizing force is $(60,000 \cdot 10^{-9})$ $/\mu_0 = (60,000 \cdot 10^{-9}) / (4\pi \cdot 10^{-7}) = 47.8$ A/m since, as has been mentioned previously, the permeability of air may be taken to be equal to that of vacuum, namely μ_0. Orebodies may produce fields of the order of hundreds of gamma to thousands of gamma (several gauss) which are superimposed on the earth's field.

The unit oersted is sometimes used for expressing the magnetic field in the sense of flux density. For reasons into which we shall not enter, this usage must be regarded as incorrect, but the matter is not of great practical consequence since the gauss and the oersted are numerically equal in "non-magnetic" media, such as air or water.

At the end faces of a magnet the medium through which the lines of force traverse changes from the material of the magnet to air. As a result, there is a "free" intensity of magnetization at points in the end faces. If A is the area of an end face, the product:

$$m = J \cdot A \qquad (3.2)$$

is known as the *pole strength* of the magnet. The pole strength is defined to be positive at the north pole of the magnet and negative at the south pole. Pole strength is to be expressed as ampere · metre.

For many purposes it is sufficient to treat the magnetic field outside an elongate magnet as if it were caused by a pair of isolated *point* poles of strength $+m$ and $-m$, situated at its ends but slightly towards the inside although, of course, the intensity of magnetization is actually distributed over an area. The distance between the virtual poles may be taken to be about 5/6 of the length of the magnet, a fact which is of relevance while inferring the position of the top surface of orebodies from magnetic anomalies.

Each pole of a magnet is supposed to create its own field (flux density) of strength $\mu_0 m/(4\pi r^2)$ along the line joining the pole to a point distant r from the pole. The north pole creates a field away from itself and the south pole towards itself.

INDUCED AND PERMANENT MAGNETISM

All substances when subjected to a magnetizing force, such as that which exists in a magnetic field acquire a certain intensity of magnetization which they lose on being removed from it. Such magnetism is said to be induced by the field. On the other hand, some substances, for example, iron, cobalt, nickel, certain alloys, some magnetite, pyrrhotite, chromite or manganese ores etc., can show a magnetic action even when they are not subjected to an external field. They are then said to possess permanent, remanent or spontaneous magnetization.

The induced intensity of magnetization, that is, the magnetic moment per unit volume, acquired by a body on which is acting a magnetizing force H can be written as:

$$I = \kappa H \tag{3.3}$$

The factor κ is called the volume susceptibility of the body.

The induced intensity constitutes an additional magnetizing force. If H is the magnetizing force in a region of vacuum (or air) the flux density in that region is $B_0 = \mu_0 H \, \mathrm{Wb/m^2}$. When a body is brought in this region the induced intensity of magnetization I creates an additional flux density $\mu_0 I = \mu_0 \kappa H$ in the region now occupied by the body. The total flux density within the body therefore becomes:

$$\begin{aligned} B &= \mu_0 H + \mu_0 \kappa H \\ &= (1 + \kappa)\,\mu_0 H \\ &= (1 + \kappa)\,B_0 \end{aligned} \tag{3.3a}$$

The factor $1 + \kappa$ is denoted by μ_r and called the relative magnetic permeability. Like κ, it is a pure number. The quantity $\mu_0\mu_r = \mu$, on the other hand, is known as the absolute permeability (Ohm-sec/m).

As a consequence of the induced intensity, a body develops north and south poles on its surfaces and the field due to these everywhere modifies the original field. The greater the susceptibility of the body, the greater is the magnitude of the extra field. The susceptibility may be positive or negative. Moreover, for some substances it is constant, while for others it depends on the field and history of the sample.

If the north poles are developed in the direction of the field and the south poles in the opposite direction the susceptibility is said to be positive. This is the case of greatest practical importance in geophysics. In the reverse case κ is negative.

If a so-called unrationalized system of units is used, the value of κ expressed in it is $(1/4\pi)$ times that expressed in a rationalised system. Conversely, the value of κ expressed in a rationalised system is 4π times that expressed in an unrationalized system. The value of μ_r is, however, the same irrespective of the system used since μ_r is obviously (cf. eq.3.3a) the ratio of the actual flux density within the body to the flux density existing in that region before the introduction of the body.

GENERAL MAGNETIC PROPERTIES OF ROCKS

The magnetism of practically all rocks is controlled by their content of ferromagnetic minerals. These are substances possessing a relatively high susceptibility and capable of acquiring permanent magnetization. Chemically, they are either iron oxides belonging to the system $FeO-Fe_2O_3-TiO_2$ or sulphides belonging to the troilite—pyrrhotite series. The oxides enter into solid solutions with each other, for example, Fe_3O_4 (magnetite) with Fe_2TiO_4 (ulvöspinel), α-Fe_2O_3 (haematite) with $FeTiO_3$ (ilmenite), and Fe_3O_4 with γ-Fe_2O_3 (maghemite). The nature of the solid solutions plays a vital role in determining the magnetic properties. However, besides the chemical composition, the size and shape of the ferromagnetic grains are also of importance.

The general formula of the members of the troilite—pyrrhotite series is usually written as $FeS_{1+x}(0 \leqslant x \leqslant 0.25)$, although $Fe_{1-y}S$ is more appropriate in view of the crystal structure, which reveals regularly distributed vacancies in the iron ion positions rather than an excess of sulphur. If $x \geqslant 0.08$, the vacancies lead to ferromagnetic properties while for $x \leqslant 0.08$ the members display low susceptibility and no ability to acquire permanent magnetization.

The mineralogy of rock magnetism is a very complex phenomenon and for further details of it reference should be made to articles by Nicholls (1955) and Néel (1955). An elementary account is to be found in Parasnis (1961) and Lee (1963).

SUSCEPTIBILITIES OF ROCKS

Of the various ferromagnetic constituents that affect the susceptibility of rocks, magnetite is undoubtedly the most important on account of its widespread occurrence and its relatively large susceptibility.

Many quantitative relations have been suggested for the dependence of susceptibility of rocks on their Fe_3O_4 content. For example, measurements by Balsley and Buddington (1958) on the metamorphic rocks from the Adirondack mountains, U.S.A., containing about $0.01-80\%$ magnetite by volume (v), indicate the formula:

$$\kappa = 0.033v^{1.33} \quad \text{(rationalised SI)} \quad (3.4)$$

while Jahren (1963) found a relation:

$$\kappa = 0.0145v^{1.39} \quad \text{(rationalised SI)} \quad (3.5)$$

Fig.2 is reproduced after Jahren. Many other relations have also been suggested which make it clear that no universally valid relation between the susceptibility and the Fe_3O_4 content of rocks exists. Furthermore, where a relation does exist, the same susceptibility value may correspond to different Fe_3O_4 contents and vice versa so that great caution must be exercised in predicting one from the other. It is therefore advisable to directly determine the susceptibilities of rocks

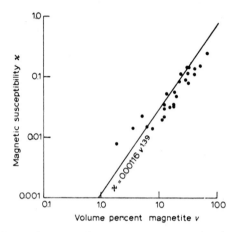

Fig.2. Dependence of susceptibility on magnetite content. The line fits other data than those shown and is drawn in this figure (and also in the original) for comparison. (After Jahren, 1963.) Susceptibility in this figure is in unrationalized units. To convert to SI multiply by 4π.

and ores within the area of interest and not rely on formulas of the above type.

In the case of sulphide ores and certain igneous rocks, notably dolerites, syenites and gabbros, the amount of accessory pyrrhotite undoubtedly affects the κ-value. However, no general formulas seem to be published in this respect.

On account of the well-established dependence of susceptibility on the amount of ferromagnetic minerals, it is rather misleading to assign susceptibility values to rocks considered merely as petrographic or lithologic units. The ranges in Table I should, therefore, be looked upon as representative of particular sets of samples rather than of given rock types.

Although the variation of susceptibilities is considerable we can say that, very broadly, magnetite, pyrrhotite, ilmenite and some chromite and manganese ores have large susceptibilities while pyrite, haematite, zinc blende and galena have low ones. Among the rocks, basalts and diabases as well as skarn and some granulites are much more magnetic than limestones, sandstones and slates.

The susceptibilities of pyrite, haematite, etc. are in fact so low that ores of these minerals acquire very weak intensities of magnetization in the earth's field and cannot distort it to such an extent that their detection by means of magnetic measurements is feasible. The situation is, of course, otherwise if they contain appreciable amounts of pyrrhotite or magnetite.

The susceptibilities of rocks are relevant because the magnetic detection of an orebody depends essentially upon the difference between its susceptibility and the susceptibility of its host rocks, and not merely upon its own susceptibility. Also, the susceptibility variations in rock formations cause a background of anomalies which may mask the anomalies due to weakly magnetic or deepseated ores.

PERMANENT MAGNETIZATION (REMANENCE) OF ROCKS

Besides the intensity of magnetization induced by the earth's field, rocks possess a permanent intensity which is due to the remanent magnetism of their constituent ferromagnetic grains. A volume cut out of such a rock is, in fact, a weak magnet having north and south poles.

Researches all over the world have abundantly shown that the remanence of rocks is a very widespread and common property. In a number of rocks (e.g. basalts, gabbros, diorites etc.) and ores (e.g. manganese, chromite, ilmenite etc.) the remanent intensity of magnetization often completely dominates the induced one and serious errors in the calculated dip, breadth, volume etc. of an orebody or rock mass can arise if remanence is neglected. The subject of the remanent magnetization of rocks has been extensively treated in recent geophysical literature to which the interested reader could refer with advantage (Balsley and Buddington, 1958; Jahren, 1963; Green, 1960; Bath, 1962; Hood, 1963).

A curious instance of remanence has been reported by Carmichael (1963). He found that a deposit in the Allard lake region of Quebec, Canada, despite its high content of iron oxide (up to 20%), produces no effect detectable by the magnetometer. The explanation is as

TABLE I

SUSCEPTIBILITIES OF SAMPLES OF ROCKS AND ORES
(Rationalised units)

Rocks	Susceptibility $\times 10^6$	Locality	Observer	Remarks
Limestone	500–750	Berggiesshübel, Germany	Neumann (1932)	some Fe_3O_4
Limestone	12.5–24,700	Various, Sweden	Werner (1945)	
Diabase tuffs	50,000–245,000	South Bahrtal, Germany	Neumann (1932)	metamorphic
Diabase tuffs	1,900–2,380	North Bahrtal, Germany	Neumann (1932)	metamorphic
Diabase	10,000–150,000		Mooney and Bleifuss (1953)	0–3.4% magnetite
				0–0.9% ilmenite
Basalt	250–105,000		Mooney and Bleifuss (1953)	0–2.5% magnetite
				0–0.6% ilmenite
Rhyolite	250–9,500		Mooney and Bleifuss (1953)	0–0.4% magnetite
Gabbro	1,000–76,000		Mooney and Bleifuss (1953)	0–0.9% magnetite
				0–0.2% ilmenite
Granite	0–49,500		Mooney and Bleifuss (1953)	0–1.3% magnetite
Greenstone	500–11,000		Mooney and Bleifuss (1953)	0–0.2% magnetite
Slates	0–1,250		Mooney and Bleifuss (1953)	0–0.2% magnetite
Skarn	500–5,300	Ställberg, Sweden	Werner (1945)	
Granulite	88–46,300	Persberg, Sweden	Werner (1945)	
Porphyry	225–210,000	Kiruna, Sweden	Werner (1945)	

TABLE I *(continued)*

Ores	Susceptibility × 10^6	Locality	Observer	Remarks
Brown iron ore	1,000–1,750	Berggiesshübel, Germany	Neumann (1932)	haematite
Haematite	6,630	Långban, Sweden	Werner (1945)	rich, very low magn.
Haematite	4,110–9,860	Striberg, Sweden	Werner (1945)	low magn.
Magnetite ore	71,000–97,000	Berggiesshübel, Germany	Neumann (1932)	
Magnetite ore	$3.0 \times 10^6 - 6.15 \times 10^6$	Ställberg, Sweden	Werner (1945)	31.1–63.3% magnetite
Magnetite ore	$1.25 \times 10^7 - 1.4 \times 10^7$	Grängesberg, Sweden	Werner (1945)	86.1–94.6% magnetite
Chromite ore	$7,500 - 1.2 \times 10^6$	Various	Hawkes (1951)	26.76–58.40% Fe
Iron ore	$6.5 \times 10^5 - 1.53 \times 10^6$	Biwabik and Soudan, U.S.A.	Mooney and Bleifuss (1953)	15.4–26.1% magnetite
Haussmannite	1,650	Långban, Sweden	Werner (1945)	Mn_3O_4
Jacobsite	25,000	India	Bhimasankaram and Rao (1958)	$(MnFe)_3O_4$
Pyrite ore	5,300	Kankberg, Sweden	Malmqvist (1960)	compact
Pyrrhotite	750	Kankberg, Sweden	Malmqvist (1960)	compact

follows. The deposit contains crystals of pure magnetite and exsolved hemoilmenite. The former are magnetized permanently in one direction (in that of the earth's field) but the hemoilmenite is magnetized in the opposite direction. Further, the magnetization intensities are exactly equal so that the deposit as a whole shows no net magnetization.

By and large, the permanent magnetization of rocks, especially that of igneous rocks and ores, is extremely stable and seldom undergoes significant change due to weathering effects alone. Hammering, drilling and cutting also have little effect on the permanent magnetic intensity of most igneous and metamorphic rocks. Some ores may, however, show a predominantly unstable remanent magnetization, as is evident from the fact that such magnetization is easily removed by subjecting them to alternating current or mechanical action.

The permanent magnetization of rocks which have not been disturbed reflects the direction of the earth's field at the time of their formation. It may or may not agree with the present direction of the field at the locality concerned, if the rock has been disturbed or if the earth's field has undergone a change of direction after the formation of the rock. Mineralogical factors are also of importance in this connection. Consequently, the induced and remanent magnetization intensities in a rock may not be in the same direction.

The remanence of a rock formation of ores is seldom uniform within the entire mass but varies in direction as well as magnitude, that is, equal volumes cut out of a mass are not magnets of equal strength, nor are the north and south poles of such virtual magnets orientated in the same direction. The remanence variations in a rock mass also contribute to more or less random magnetic anomalies.

MEASUREMENT OF SUSCEPTIBILITY AND REMANENCE

The accurate determination of the susceptibility and remanence of rock samples has been discussed in great detail by several authors (Puzicha, 1942; Mooney, 1952; Mooney and Bleifuss, 1953; Werner, 1945). Naturally, it requires recourse to special experimental arrangements. Rough determinations of the susceptibility and remanence can, however, be made relatively easily with a vertical field magnetometer by the simple procedure described in Appendix 1.

Convenient, small instruments for directly reading the susceptibility of samples of definite shapes and of rocks in situ have been constructed. One such instrument, operating on high frequency current (10 Kc/sec), is the ABEM kappameter designed for large samples with a flat surface (e.g., a smooth rock exposure) or long drillcores.

THE GEOMAGNETIC FIELD

As the magnetic method of prospecting depends on detecting the deviations (anomalies) in the earth's field, it is necessary to have an idea of the normal character of this field.

The vector of the earth's field is completely specified at any point by its "elements", the horizontal intensity H, the declination D of H,* east or west of true north and the vertical intensity Z. By convention,

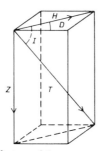

Fig. 3. Vectors of the geomagnetic field.

Z is reckoned positive downwards and negative upwards. The magnitude of the total flux density is $T = \sqrt{(H^2 + Z^2)}$, obtained by the application of Pythagoras' theorem, and its direction in the vertical plane is given by its angle of inclination $I = \tan^{-1}(Z/H)$ with the horizontal (Fig.3). Since H on the earth's surface is always directed from the south to the north (local irregularities excepted), I is

* This H, which is a flux density, is not to be confused with a magnetizing force which also is often denoted by the same letter.

reckoned positive or negative according as Z is positive or negative, i.e., downwards or upwards.

The imaginary line, joining points at which the vertical flux density on the earth's surface is zero, is called the magnetic equator. It runs close to the geographical equator but is not parallel to it. South of the magnetic equator the north pole of a free magnetic needle will point upwards, north of it downwards.

The points on the earth's surface at which the total magnetic field is directed vertically downwards ($I = +90°$) or upwards ($I = -90°$) are called the magnetic dip poles. The earth has two principal dip poles, the north one in the Baffin Islands in the northern hemisphere and the south one in Antarctica in the southern hemisphere. As we go from the magnetic equator to the magnetic poles, the horizontal intensity decreases and the vertical one increases. At the dip poles there is no horizontal intensity.

For the values of H, Z, and D at different places a standard book of physical constants should be consulted. A short table is also given in Parasnis (1972).

When the earth's field is downwards, an orebody placed in it acquires north poles on its lower surface and south poles on its upper surface, provided the body has a positive susceptibility. This is the case, generally speaking, in the northern hemisphere. In the southern hemisphere a body with positive susceptibility will acquire north poles on the upper and south ones on the lower surface. As for its lateral faces, a body acquires north poles on the more northward face and south poles on the more southward face, irrespective of whether it is situated north of the magnetic equator or south of it. This is because the horizontal component of the earth's field, which gives rise to the lateral poles, is, as mentioned above, always directed from the south to the north.

MAGNETOMETERS

Magnetic measurements in ore prospecting are carried out most conveniently by means of magnetometers, as relative determinations. The value of an element of the magnetic field at any point is then expressed as a difference from its value at a suitably chosen base point.

The element most commonly used for the purpose is the vertical intensity, the anomalies in which are denoted by ΔZ. The anomalies in the other elements, ΔH, ΔD, ΔI and those in the magnitude of the total field (ΔT) can also be measured, but the ΔZ anomalies are as a rule the easiest to interpret in terms of the possible geometry of the

Fig.4. Askania magnetometer for vertical intensity measurements. (Courtesy BGAB.)

subsurface masses disturbing the earth's field. Unless specifically otherwise mentioned, magnetic intensities in this book are vertical field (flux density) anomalies.

Most magnetometers depend for their action on the fact that a magnetic needle which is suitably balanced at the reference station deflects on being taken to another station. Either the angle of deflection itself or the compensating force necessary to restore the needle to

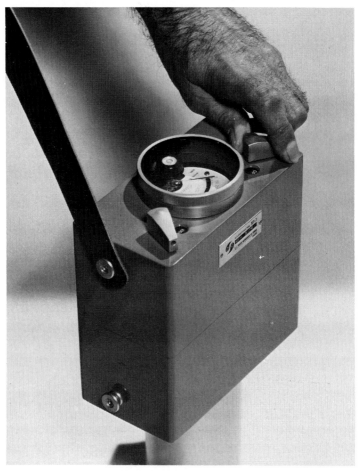

Fig. 5.   Flux-gate   reconnaissance   magnetometer.   (Courtesy   of   Scintrex,
Downsview, Canada.)

its reference position can be used as a measure of the change in the field. The calibration constant of the instrument enables this change to be expressed in the appropriate unit gamma.

Brief descriptions of various types of magnetometers will be found in Parasnis (1972) and Heiland (1946), and are not included here on account of limitations of space. A photograph of one of the common instruments is shown in Fig.4. Magnetometers are readily available on the market. For example, deflection variometers are manufactured by Askania Werke (Berlin), by Hilger and Watts (Cambridge, England) and by Ruska (U.S.A.); compensation variometers are manufactured by Askania Werke. Variometers are available for the measurement of horizontal as well as vertical intensity anomalies.

The accuracy of precision magnetometers is of the order of 1–5 gamma and their speed is such that a single man can cover about 200 points per day in normal terrain, assuming the point separation to be 20 m.

The ordinary magnetometers must be accurately levelled before taking a reading so that a tripod for fixing them is indispensable in field work. The need for handier instruments, even at the expense of some accuracy, is often felt, for instance in laying profiles for rapid reconnaissance across indications, or for following up geological key horizons. One such instrument is the flux-gate magnetometer (Fig.5) manufactured by Scintrex of Downsview, Ontario, Canada. The accuracy of such reconnaissance instruments is naturally considerably less than that of precision instruments.

FIELD WORK

Certain precautions must be taken in carrying out all magnetic field work. The observer must remove from his wearing apparel iron and steel objects like his wrist-watch, keys, penknife etc. Some less obvious objects which can often vitiate the readings are steel wires in spectacle frames, zip-fasteners, buckles in belts, nails in field shoes etc.

Magnetometer observations must be corrected for the diurnal variations of the earth's magnetic field. This may be accomplished by one of two alternative procedures or minor modifications of them.

In one procedure the reading at the base station (or at any pre-viously occupied station) is repeated after an interval T of about $1-2$ h. If the repeat reading shows an increase d, every reading taken during that interval is diminished by the amount $d \cdot t/T$ where t is the time at which it was taken after the initial base reading. This amounts to assuming that the change d, which strictly speaking includes not only the diurnal variation but also the drift of the instrument and its temperature coefficient, occurred at a constant rate during the time T.

The alternative procedure is to automatically record the readings of an auxiliary base instrument to obtain a continuous registration of the diurnal variation, with a view to securing better accuracy in the appli-cation of the diurnal correction as the variation is often irregular (Fig.6). The diurnal change at any instant is directly read off the record, and the necessary correction added to or substracted from the station reading. Unless the field instrument is known to be sufficiently free from drift it must be re-read at the base at intervals and an appropriate drift-correction must also be applied, if necessary.

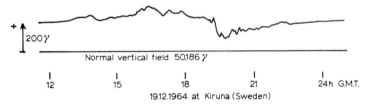

Fig.6. Diurnal variation of the earth's magnetic field.

The first procedure of diurnal correction is sufficiently accurate for most prospecting surveys, while the accuracy of the second is often more illusory than real, unless additional precautions are taken for controlling such factors as the temperature correction, the height of the field instrument above ground during measurement, freedom of base instrument from drift, etc.

Besides the diurnal variation, magnetic storms (sudden and violent variations in the geomagnetic field) also affect magnetometer readings but there is no satisfactory method of correcting for them. The safest course is to discontinue the field measurements and resume them when the storm is over. A trained observer can easily detect the signs of an approaching magnetic storm during a survey, as the readings of the magnetometer start to fluctuate.

THE ZERO LEVEL

An important point in considering the magnetic anomalies in an area is the zero level, that is, the reading of the magnetometer at points where there are no appreciable disturbances from subsurface masses so that only the normal geomagnetic field is present. It is not usually possible to decide ab initio upon a suitable zero level; therefore a "working zero" is used to start with and all the readings are corrected at the end of the survey by adding to or subtracting from all of them a constant amount arrived at from the study of the anomalies obtained.

If the readings remain constant over a fairly large part of the area or vary within it so as to suggest a background effect only (Fig.7A), the mean reading of the instrument within this part may be considered to be the zero reading. The readings at all other stations are then expressed as positive or negative departures from this reading.

When distinct anomalies, due to a subsurface ore, are evident in the area, the zero level can generally be inferred from the flanks of the anomaly curve because these approach the zero level asymptotically (Fig.7B,C).

The interpretation of magnetic anomalies depends considerably on the zero level selected. When the relief is not very much greater than the uncertainty in the zero level, the magnitude of the anomalies, and hence the estimate of the size of an orebody, may be greatly affected by the choice of the zero level. Similarly, the magnitude of the negative side-minima as in Fig.7B depends on the zero level and as these minima are diagnostic of the lower surface of the disturbing body, the choice of the zero level may seriously affect the depth-extent estimates.

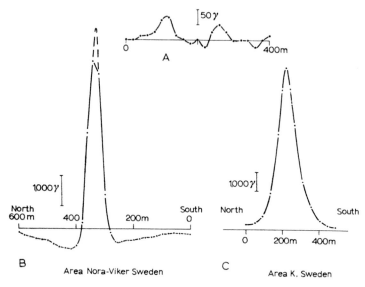

Fig. 7. Determination of the magnetic zero level.

AN OREBODY AS A MAGNET

Consider a vertical, pencil-shaped orebody as in Fig.8. The component Z/μ_0 of the earth's vertical magnetizing force induces in it an intensity of magnetization in the vertical direction so that if Z/μ_0 is directed downwards and the susceptibility is positive, as is the case for all ores, a north pole develops on the lower surface and a south pole on the upper surface of the body. The body also acquires a horizontal intensity of magnetization and corresponding poles on the lateral surface but, for the present, we shall neglect this "transverse or cross magnetization".

Such an orebody resembles a large bar magnet and the pattern of its lines of force in space is similar to that shown in Fig.1. If the horizontal line in Fig.1 represents the earth's surface we find that directly above the magnet, at the epicentre, the anomalous field is vertically downwards and hence positive. The field of the ore has no horizontal component here.

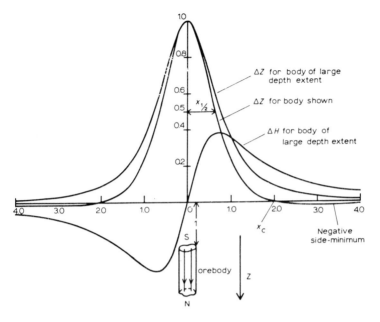

Fig. 8. Orebody as a magnet.

Between the epicentre and the points A,B the field still has a downward vertical component but also a horizontal component directed towards the epicentre. At A and B the vertical component vanishes, and beyond these points it is directed upwards so that the corresponding anomaly is negative. However, the horizontal component continues to be directed towards the epicentre even beyond A and B.

If the susceptibility of the ore is κ, the vertical induced intensity of magnetization is $I = \kappa Z/\mu_0$. By eq. (3.2) each pole of the ore has then a strength of $\kappa Z A/\mu_0$ where A (m²) is the cross-sectional area of the body. The poles may be considered to be points if the linear dimensions of the cross-section are not too large compared to the depth, and the ore may be replaced, from the magnetic point of view, by two point poles. The anomalies of such a double pole system with one pole vertically below the other are easily calculated (see Appendix 2).

Fig. 8 shows typical vertical and horizontal field anomalies (ΔZ and

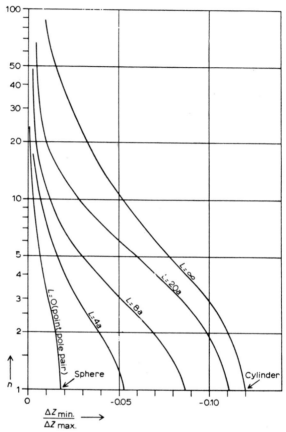

Fig. 9. Ratio $\Delta Z_{min.}/\Delta Z_{max.}$ for thin bodies of different length L; a denotes the depth to the upper surface.

ΔH) along profiles going through the epicentre. Here, the horizontal component is reckoned positive when directed towards the right and negative when directed towards the left. The distances in figures like the present one are often plotted in terms of the depth of the upper pole, and the anomalies often in terms of the maximum value of ΔZ. By appropriately stretching or contracting the vertical and horizontal scales, such "master" curves can therefore be readily brought into a size suitable for comparison with an observed anomaly curve. When the true distances are plotted against the measured anomaly, we find that the anomaly curve becomes broader as the depth of the ore increases. On the other hand, shallow ores show sharp anomaly curves.

As the depth extent of the orebody increases, the influence of the lower pole decreases so that the ΔZ-anomaly falls off less rapidly from its maximum value. The result is that the position of the point at which the anomaly passes through zero (the point at which the fields of the upper and lower poles cancel each other) shifts farther away from the maximum. Similarly, the positions of the negative side-minima shift outwards, while the magnitude of the minima decreases. These positions, as well as the magnitude of the side-minima, can be used to estimate the depth extent (cf. Fig.9).

If the magnet is inclined the negative minimum on the dip side is greater in magnitude than that on the opposite side. However, in most cases, the transverse magnetization referred to above plays an important role and estimates of dip, based on this simple observation concerning a two-pole system, can be grossly in error (see under the heading *Transverse magnetization*).

The magnetic isoanomaly lines on the earth's surface due to a vertical double pole system, like a pencil-shaped ore, will be circles. Generally, of course, the contours will be elongated in practice indicating line poles rather than point poles.

INTERPRETATION OF MAGNETIC ANOMALIES

The ultimate object of magnetic interpretation is to deduce the geometry of magnetic bodies causing a given set of anomalies. Unfortunately, however, infinitely many different subsurface distributions of magnetization can, in principle, be found to explain a set of magnetic field observations on the earth's surface, even if the field were known with perfect precision at every point on the surface. It follows that magnetic anomalies alone are not sufficient for unambiguously determining the bodies or structures to which they are due.

Normally, therefore, the interpretation must proceed in an indirect way, by trial and error, assuming a body of a plausible form and calculating its anomalies for comparison with the observed anomalies. The parameters of the body like depth, length, breadth, dip etc., are adjusted until the two anomalies agree with each other satisfactorily. The form to be assumed for the body will depend very much on the available geological information.

The problem of quantitative magnetic interpretation is made tractable in practice owing to the fact that a very large number of orebodies and other structures can be geometrically classified as thin or thick sheets, or as plugs resembling cylinders. For a thin body, the simplest approach in interpretation is to replace the upper and lower surfaces of the body by equal and opposite magnetic poles of appropriate length, at suitable depths, and calculate their resultant field on the surface. Dip can be simulated by moving the poles sideways with respect to each other. Thick bodies need a somewhat different treatment.

The parameters of an orebody, which the pole theory is able to supply estimates of, are: (1) depth to the top surface, (2) length along strike, (3) attitude, (4) depth extent (depth of lower face), (5) width or cross-sectional area, and (6) magnetization intensity (assumed constant throughout the body).

Of these parameters, the depth, width and magnetization intensity are estimated from the magnitude of the observed anomalies, while the length, dip, pitch and depth extent are estimated from the *pattern* of the anomalies, that is, from the shapes of isoanomaly curves and profiles. The width (or cross-sectional area) and magnetization intensity should, properly speaking, be bracketed together because the magnetic measurements provide an estimate of their product only and not their values separately.

It must not be imagined that the various parameters can be estimated from magnetic measurements independently of each other. Actually, the estimates of any one (or more) affect the estimates of the remaining ones.

The right combination of parameters to start the trial calculations would be difficult to find if it were not for the circumstance that certain guiding rules can be obtained from an analysis of the theoretical anomalies of magnetic pole systems. The rules discussed below apply to thin ore bodies and are valid for more or less well separated anomaly features. If the effects of two or more bodies are overlapping they must first be isolated in some plausible manner.

Depth

The depth to the top surface can be estimated from a magnetic profile at right angles to the strike, and traversing an anomaly centre or its immediate neighbourhood. As a first approximation, the depth is of the order of the "half-width" of the profile curve, i.e., the distance from the maximum at which the vertical field anomaly falls to half the maximum value. This distance is marked by $x_{1/2}$ in Fig.8. In general, $x_{1/2}$ must be multiplied by a factor between 1 and 2, depending upon the length of the body and its depth extent, to obtain the estimate of the depth to the upper pole of the body.

TABLE II

DEPTH TO THE MAGNETIC UPPER POLE OF SHEET-LIKE BODIES

Strike length	Depth extent	
	great	small
Great	$1.0-1.1\ x_{\frac{1}{2}}$	$1.4-1.7\ x_{\frac{1}{2}}$
Small	$1.2-1.3\ x_{\frac{1}{2}}$	

Table II indicates, in a schematic manner, the necessary multiplying factors. A more complete table will be found in Parasnis (1972). The depth rules for thin bodies of very great depth extent have been critically reviewed by Hutchison (1958).

Strike length

This can be fairly accurately estimated for relatively long bodies from the magnetic profile in the strike direction, going through the anomaly centre. The length is approximately equal to the distance between two points, one on each side of the maximum, at which the anomaly falls to half the maximum value. This distance is often denoted by $2y_{1/2}$.

The estimate of the strike length of thin ore sheets is nearly independent of the depth-extent and the depth to the top surface.

When the length of a body and the depth to its top are about equal, the length must be estimated from a diagram showing its dependence on the ratio $x_{1/2} : y_{1/2}$. Such a diagram is given in Parasnis (1972).

The above procedure and many a one in the following paragraphs are generally applicable only in relatively high magnetic latitudes where the magnetic anomaly contours tend to be orientated in the direction of the length. In low latitudes, as well as in high ones in case there is a strong horizontal magnetization along the length, the magnetic contours tend to be orientated at right angles to the body! The effect is due to the fact that, the strong horizontal magnetization develops a north pole at one end of the body and a south pole at the opposite end so that the body becomes a horizontal rather than a vertical bar magnet as in Fig.8.

The ends of the body may then be inferred as being approximately beneath the two anomaly centres, one positive and the other negative, which manifest themselves in such a case, and the length of the body may be estimated at this stage of the interpretation as being equal to the distance between the two centres.

Dip and pitch

The direction of dip can be inferred from the asymmetry in the magnetic profiles at right angles to the strike, that of the pitch from the asymmetry in profiles parallel to the strike. Roughly speaking, magnetic anomalies fall off more slowly on the down-dip side of a body than on the up-dip side. However, the effect of the poles on the lower surface of a body as well as the effects of remanent and cross-magnetizations may create complications. What the magnetic data can determine is the direction of the resultant intensity of magnetization in an orebody, but this may or may not have relevance to the actual attitude of the body.

Depth-extent

We have already noted (see under the heading *An orebody as a magnet*) that estimates of the depth-extent of a body can be based upon one, or both, of two features of an observed anomaly curve. We can either use the cross-over point marked x_c in Fig.8, at which the anomaly changes sign, or the magnitude of the negative side-minimum, $\Delta Z_{min.}$

If the negative side-minimum is well developed and the body is dipping steeply, fairly accurate estimates of the depth-extent are possible from the ratio $\Delta Z_{min.}/\Delta Z_{max.}$. Strictly speaking, the depth-extent of a pole system can only be estimated as the ratio (n) of the lower-pole depth to the upper-pole depth. Fig.9 shows a diagram in which n is plotted against $\Delta Z_{min.}/\Delta Z_{max.}$ for thin, steep, sheet-like bodies of different length.

Size and magnetization

Magnetic measurements can provide an estimate of the product $b \cdot I$, of the width b (m) and the intensity of magnetization I (A/m) of a thin sheet.

For long bodies of great depth-extent:

$$b \cdot I = 0.5 \cdot 4\pi \cdot a \frac{\Delta Z_{max.}}{\mu_0} \qquad (3.6)$$

where a(m) is the estimate of the depth to the top, I is in A/m, $\Delta Z_{max.}$ is expressed in Wb/m^2 and μ_0 is the permeability of vacuum. If $\Delta Z_{max.}$ is expressed in gamma, then:

$$b \cdot I = 0.5 \cdot 10^{-2} a \Delta Z_{max.} \qquad (3.6a)$$

If the body is short, the factor 0.5 must be replaced by a somewhat greater number while if the depth-extent is small the factor approaches 1.0.

If the intensity of magnetization is more or less vertical, we may write $I = \kappa Z/\mu_0$ where κ is the susceptibility and Z the normal vertical field (Wb/m^2) of the earth at the place so that the width will be given by:

$$b = f \frac{4\pi a \Delta Z_{max.}}{\kappa Z} \qquad (f = 0.5-1.0) \qquad (3.7)$$

For plug-like, steeply dipping bodies, we have a similar formula for the cross-section:

$$A = g \, \frac{4\pi a^2 \, \Delta Z_{\max.}}{\kappa Z} \qquad (g = 1.0 - 2.0) \qquad (3.8)$$

where the factor $g \doteq 1.0$ is valid for a large depth-extent and 2.0 for a small one.

In general, the magnetization of an orebody will be, in part, the induced magnetization $\kappa Z / \mu_0$ and, in part, the remanent one I_r, in which case ΔZ and Z must be expressed in Wb/m^2 and I_r in A/m. We recall that 1 gamma = 10^{-9} Wb/m^2 and $\mu_0 = 4\pi \cdot 10^{-7}$ ohm−s/m. If the two magnetizations are in the same direction, κZ in the denominator of eq. (3.7) and (3.8) must be replaced by $\kappa Z + \mu_0 I_r$ and, if they are oppositely directed, by $\kappa Z - \mu_0 I_r$. It is easy to see that neglecting the remanence will overestimate the size in the first case and underestimate it in the second. If the remanent magnetism is much stronger than the induced one, but is neglected, the size of the body determined from eq. (3.7) or (3.8) will be greatly in error.

A SIMPLE EXAMPLE OF A MAGNETIC SURVEY
(U-DAL, CENTRAL SWEDEN)

Fig.10A shows the results of a magnetic survey in an area of predominantly granulite rocks. There is a distinct main magnetic indication, with maximum values above 1,600γ, which occupies the central part of the area, but, besides this, a line of anomaly centres appears on the western margin of the map.

The anomalies in the western row fall to half their maximum values within a distance of some 20 m or less, which indicates a fairly shallow depth to their cause. Other "shallow anomalies" are also discernible on the map.

The main indication is almost circular but shows a distinct northwest−southeast strike, parallelling the shallow western anomalies. The anomalies along the profile AA$'$ going roughly at right angles to the strike, are plotted in Fig.10B.

There is an area on the map, around 100S/360E, and another one around 120N/360E, bounded by the 50γ contour, within which the anomalies reach minimum values of the order of 20γ. Both areas are parallel to the trend of the main indication and there is little doubt that we have here a negative side-minimum although the values measured as such are positive. The zero level thus appears to be slightly in error and in Fig.10B a dashed horizontal line has been drawn representing the level that is accepted as the correct level for the purposes of the interpretation. It is 40γ higher, which means that all the observed anomaly values ought to be reduced by this amount. The negative minimum then turns out to be about -20γ.

The solid curve through the filled circles in Fig.10B represents the observed anomaly, and the two dashed curves the anomalies calculated on two different hypotheses. In either case, however, it is assumed that the length of the body is short enough for the upper and lower surfaces of the body to be considered as point magnetic poles. The depth of the upper pole is assumed to be 150 m.

The open rings represent the anomaly of a point pole pair, with the south pole at the top and the north pole vertically below it at a depth of 225 m. The rings with a cross show the calculated anomalies of a system in which the line joining the poles dips towards the northeast at an angle of $70°$ with the horizontal, the distance between the poles being 300 m. It is obvious that the latter anomalies fit better to the observed curve.

It seems, therefore, that the body is dipping towards the northeast, although the angle of dip ($70°$) should not be regarded as more than a rough estimate. The direction of dip agrees with that expected from geological observations in nearby areas.

The results of boreholes, shown in Fig.10A, check well with the magnetic interpretation.

Fig.10C shows the anomalies along the profile BB' in the strike direction. Besides the main magnetic high it indicates a minor one at about 580 m from B. On subtracting the calculated anomaly of a point pole pair (dashed curve) representing the effect of the orebody discussed above, the difference (maximum 450γ) can be explained by means of another and a smaller body with its upper pole also at a depth of 150 m (continuous curve). Note that the isoanomaly curves in Fig.10A are less densely packed in the corresponding region and also suggest the occurrence of a second mass.

As has been mentioned there is some uncertainty in the zero level, and hence in the magnitude of the negative minimum and the inferred depth-extent. The proper zero level can only be determined by extending the profiles to the nortwest and southeast beyond the present edges of the survey.

Assuming that the body as a whole has negligible remanence, the product "cross-sectional area x susceptibility" can be estimated from eq. (3.8) to be:

$$A\kappa = 2 \times 4\pi \times 150^2 \times \frac{1,600}{47,000}$$

$$\approx 19,000 \ m^2$$

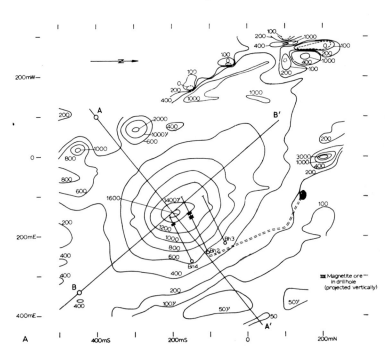

Fig.10A. Magnetic isoanomaly map of the U-dal area, central Sweden. (Courtesy of BGAB.)

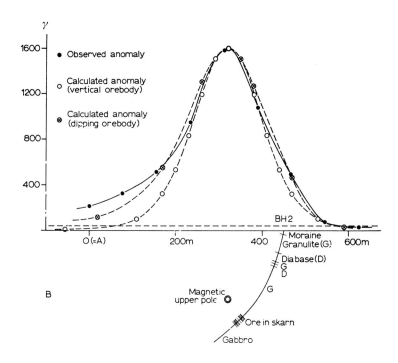

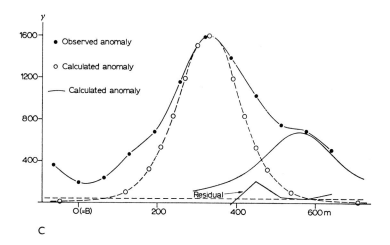

Fig.10B. Profile AA′ in part A. C. Profile BB′ in part A.

(The vertical component of the geomagnetic flux density is about 47,000γ in the area.)

The susceptibility and remanence may be determined in the present case by measurements on drill cores so that the cross-sectional area can be separately estimated.

It is possible to refine the above calculations considerably to secure better agreement with the observed and calculated anomalies, and to obtain more detailed information about the possible structure and alternatives to it. However, we shall not pursue the matter further.

It is in esting to note the large difference in this example between the depths to the bodies causing the main indication and the depths to those causing the string of anomalies to the west. Does this indicate a fault, approximately parallel to the strike direction? We may speculate, and certainly one topographic observation does suggest an affirmative answer. The shallow indications occur on the top of a high ridge and the deep ones on low ground, the slope between being very steep and, in some parts, an inaccessible, almost vertical cliff.

MAGNETIC SURVEY IN THE E-O OREFIELD
(CENTRAL SWEDEN)

A somewhat more complicated example of magnetic anomalies than the one in the last section is shown in Fig.11A, which is a map based on a square observation net of 10 m in the central portion and 20 m in the peripheral ones. The map shows a magnetic indication, about 1 km long, in a district where the magnetic ores are known to occur as sheet-like bodies sub-outcropping under a relatively shallow moraine cover. The country rock is layered pre-Cambrian granulite with a dip of about $70-80°$ towards the northeast.

It is evident that the cause of the indication is not one ore lens but several ore lenses occurring in two groups, one south and the other north of the line 100S. Four principal lenses (A,B,C,D) have been demarcated as shown, their lengths being estimated from the points at which the anomalies along the strike fall to half the respective maxima.

The narrow anomaly-tail north of about 100N, where the maximum anomalies are less than 3,000γ as compared to 10,000–30,000γ in the central portion, indicates that weak magnetic impregnation continues in this direction, probably as a thin band.

The broadening of the isoanomaly curves in the extreme south could be due to several causes, for example, some magnetic body or bodies beyond 300S disturbing the anomalies between 400S and 500S, or the lens A's pitching to the southeast. The latter explanation seems to be the more plausible one since the bodies C and D also seem to pitch to the southeast, as judged from the displacement of the negative side-minimum with respect to the positive maximum.

Table III lists the estimates of the depth to the top obtained from the half-widths of the anomaly profiles perpendicular to the strike.

It is difficult to estimate the depth extents of the various bodies owing to the marked asymmetry between the negative side-minima on the NE and the SW flanks (the latter minima outside the figure), the NE minima being greater in magnitude. Using the mean of the two minima for entering the diagram in Fig.9, we get estimates of $n = 5-8$ for C and D. The depth extents of A and B cannot be estimated in this manner, however, because no negative minima attributable to the effects of these two bodies can be discerned.

The calculation of theoretical anomalies is a rather tedious procedure in the present case as the overlapping effects of the various bodies as well as the effects of dip and pitch must be allowed for. An

TABLE III

ESTIMATES OF THE DEPTH TO THE TOP OF OREBODIES IN FIG.11A

Body	Depth estimate (m)
A	15
B	14
C	12
D	11

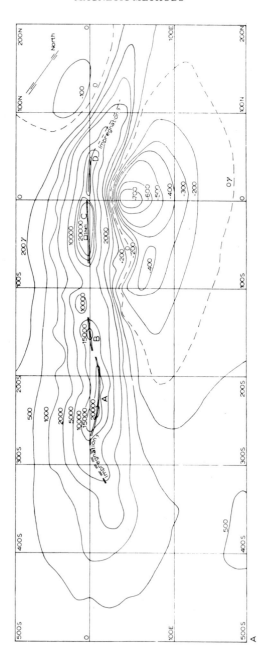

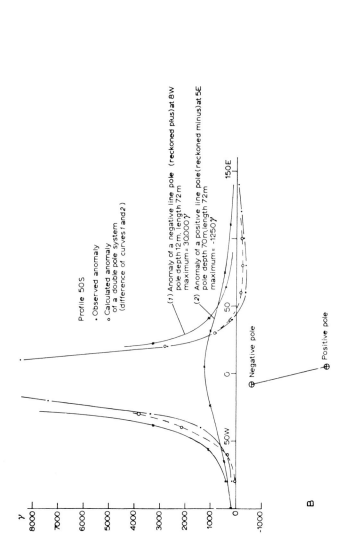

Fig.11.A. Magnetic vertical intensity map of the E-O area, central Sweden. B. Trial calculation across body C in part A. (Coordinates in m.)

example of a trial calculation along profile 50S across the body C is shown in Fig.11B. Only the flanks of the curve are shown as they are more sensitive indicators of the agreement between the calculated and observed curves than the region around the maximum.

The filled circles represent the observed anomalies. The dashed curve *1* is the calculated anomaly of a positive magnetic line pole at 12 m depth, representing the upper edge of the sheet-like ore. Curve *2* is the anomaly of a parallel pole at a depth of 70 m, corresponding to the lower surface of the sheet, but displaced some 13 m towards the NE to allow for an assumed dip of 77°, an assumption which is in accord with the geological data.

These calculations have been made using the formula derived in Appendix 2. The circles represent the difference between the two curves and it will be seen that the agreement with the observed values is fairly satisfactory, except for one point (40W) on the footwall side where the calculated value is about 56% higher.

TRANSVERSE MAGNETIZATION

We have so far considered the magnetization of an orebody to be entirely along it but this is not, in general, true.

Fig.12A shows a long orebody in plan, striking at an angle β with the *magnetic* north. While the vertical component of the earth's field produces south and north poles on the upper and lower faces of the body, the component of the horizontal field transverse to the body (H') produces south and north poles on its lateral surfaces. The presence of these poles is known as the (induced) transverse magnetization.

Clearly, the transverse magnetization in a long, vertical ore sheet is negligible when the sheet strikes along the magnetic north-south direction. It is maximum when the strike is east-west since the entire horizontal field is then transverse to the sheet.

Fig.12B is a section through a line such as AA' perpendicular to the body, whose dip is here assumed to be vertical. The solid curve in this figure represents the ΔZ field produced by the poles on the upper and

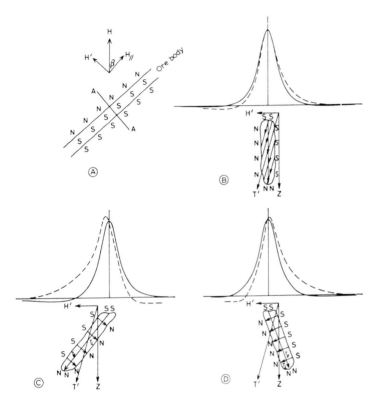

Fig. 12. Effect of transverse magnetization on the shape of vertical intensity profiles.

lower surfaces and is analogous to the ΔZ curve in Fig. 8. The lateral north poles contribute an additional field on the ground, whose vertical component is negative since the field is directed away from the poles and hence upwards. Conversely, the lateral south poles produce a vertical component that is positive. However, on the left flank, the negative field is greater than the positive one because the north poles are somewhat nearer to this flank than the south ones.

The net effect is that the ΔZ-anomaly is reduced on the north-ward side, its gradient becomes steeper and the negative side-minimum deepens. Conversely, the ΔZ curve is lifted up on the southern flank.

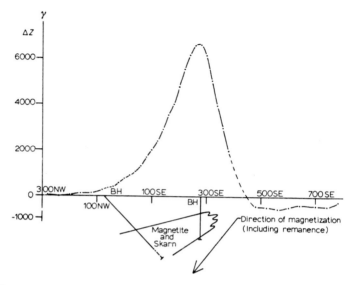

Fig. 13. Profile across Hasselbacken magnetite mass, Sweden, showing effect of transverse magnetization. (Courtesy of E. Carlsson, Falun, Sweden.)

The resulting anomaly is thus asymmetric, although the orebody is actually vertical[1].

If the body is dipping (Fig. 12C and D), the resultant field:

$$T' = \sqrt{Z^2 + H'^2}$$

can be resolved into a component $T_\perp$ along it and a component $T_\parallel$ transverse to it. In either case the ΔZ-curve is lifted up on the down-dip flank and dragged down on the up-dip flank. If the effect of transverse magnetization is neglected and the orebody is treated as a bar magnet, the direction of dip inferred from the relative magnitudes of the negative side-minima will be opposite to the true direction!

If the strike and dip of the ore are such that T' is approximately parallel to it, there is no transverse magnetization and the direction of

[1] This explanation, which is essentially valid for thick bodies, cannot be made rigorous for thin bodies with strong transverse magnetization without recourse to the concept of the magnetic dipole.

true dip may well coincide with that indicated by the greater of the two negative minima. This happens to be the case in the example of the last section.

Another important consequence of transverse magnetization is that the maximum in the ΔZ-anomaly does not necessarily indicate the top of the orebody. In fact, the maximum is sometimes shifted considerably to one side. Fig.13 is a profile across a plug-like magnetic mass (magnetite in skarn) of roughly circular cross-section. The effect of transverse magnetization is clearly seen here in the gently falling NW flank and the displacement of the maximum with respect to the top of the body.

A SIMPLE GEOMETRICAL CONSTRUCTION FOR DETERMINING THE POSITION OF AN ORE SHEET

There may be considerable difficulty in inferring the position of an ore sheet when the transverse magnetization is appreciable, which is often the case with gently dipping orebodies or with bodies not striking exactly along the magnetic north-south. For a long, thin ore sheet this difficulty may be overcome by means of a simple geometrical construction devised by Werner (1955).

We first determine the angle i' which the magnetic field T' in the vertical plane of the profile makes with the horizontal. This angle is given by:

$$\tan i' = \frac{Z}{H'} = \frac{Z}{H \sin \beta}$$

where Z and H are the vertical and horizontal components of the earth's flux density, and β is the strike angle (Fig.12A).

Connect the points M and m (Fig.14), at which the anomaly attains a maximum and minimum respectively, by a straight line. Let C be the intersection of Mm with the zero line. The position of x_0 (the epicentre) is now obtained by marking off from A, the "cross-over" point, the distance AC in the opposite direction.

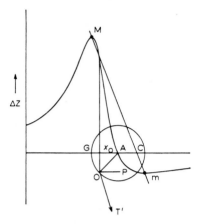

Fig. 14. Geometrical construction for determining the position of an ore sheet from the magnetic vertical intensity anomaly. (After Werner, 1955.)

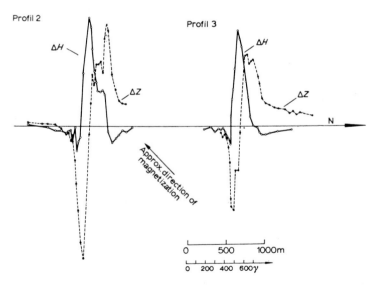

Fig. 15. ΔZ and ΔH profiles across the Martin orebody in Saxony, Germany, illustrating the effect of strong remanence in the direction of the arrow. (After Neumann, 1932.)

Next describe a circle with centre A and radius AG where G is the coordinate of the maximum. This circle cuts the vertical line through x_0 in O which point gives the position of the top edge of the ore sheet.

Finally, rotate the pair of angles x_0OA and AOP (OP is parallel to the x-axis) rigidly around the common apex O until OA coincides with T', with A pointing in the direction of T'. Then the position of the sheet is given by the line OP if the anomaly plotted is the vertical field anomaly ΔZ.

In the discussion of transverse magnetization hitherto we have considered only the induced magnetization but, actually, it is the resultant of the induced and the remanent magnetization that determines the shape of the anomaly curve. If the remanent intensity is strong and differs in direction from the induced one, intriguing effects are sometimes obtained.

Fig.15 shows parallel ΔZ and ΔH profiles across the Martin orebody (magnetite beds in metamorphosed Devonian diabase tuffs) in the Berggieshübel district of Saxony in Germany (Neumann, 1932). On comparing the figure with Fig.8 we find that the shapes of the ΔZ and ΔH curves are exactly interchanged. Since the inclination of the earth's field in Saxony is not far from the vertical (about $67°$) and the ore dips fairly steeply ($55°$), induction in the earth's field fails to explain the shapes. The explanation is, in fact, that the ore has an almost horizontal total magnetization, in the direction shown by the arrow, which is the result of a strong remanent intensity differing in direction from the induced one.

MAGNETIC EFFECTS OF BROAD ZONES

So far we have mainly considered thin, sheet-like orebodies, but the case of thick, broad zones is also of great importance in practice. The reason is twofold. Firstly, many ores, among them also magnetite and pyrrhotite bearing ones, occur as more or less uniform mineralizations over wide areas. Secondly, the practical tactical problem in ore prospecting can be often reduced to one of tracing and mapping geo-

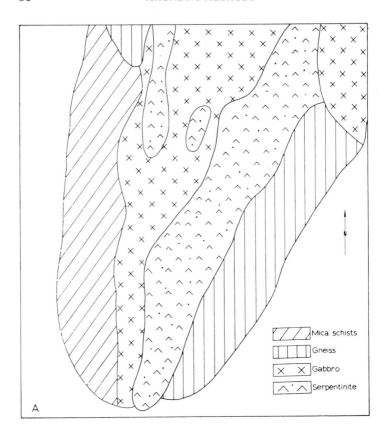

Fig. 16A. Geological map of the Siebenlehn serpentinite massif, Germany.

logical formations, some of which may be very broad and magnetic although the ores sought may be non-magnetic or weakly magnetic.

For example, it is apparent from Fig.16A and B that the extensive, nickel-bearing, gabbro–serpentinite massif in Siebenlehn (Germany) is very well delineated by its magnetic anomaly. A closer study of the whole area indicates that the magnetic anomalies on the gabbroid part are relatively uniform and smooth, while those on the serpentinite are highly irregular. A distinction between these two formations is therefore possible to some extent, a fact of great significance since the nickel ore here is of the hydrosilicate type and occurs in weathered

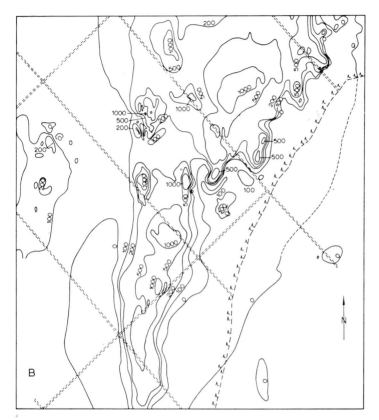

Fig. 16B. Magnetic vertical intensity map of the Siebenlehn massif in part A. (After Lauterbach, 1956.)

serpentinite (Lauterbach, 1956). Similar problems also arise in chromite prospecting.

For the purposes of magnetic calculations, we formally define a magnetic zone or dike as broad when its horizontal dimensions are large compared with the depth to the top surface. The magnetic anomaly over such a zone has a characteristic shape. It is nearly constant above the central portions of the zone but falls sharply across the edges. If the walls of the zone have a vertical or steep dip the anomaly above the edges is almost exactly half that at the centre. The boundaries of a broad magnetic zone can therefore be located relatively easily in many cases from the magnetic anomalies (cf. Fig.16B, 102, 126B). If there is an appreciable dip the anomalies may not fall as sharply on the hanging-wall side as on the footwall one, and the corresponding edge may be difficult to locate.

The vertical field anomaly of a block such as that shown in Fig.17A, where the strike-length is assumed to be very great, is given by:

$$\Delta Z = 200I_z \ \{(\alpha_1-\alpha_2)-(\alpha_3-\alpha_4)-k\ln(r_1r_4/r_2r_3)\} \qquad (3.9a)$$

where ΔZ is in gamma and I_z (A/m) is the magnetization intensity of the block in the vertical direction; the angles α, shown in the figure, are measured in radians ($1° = \pi/180 = 0.0175$ rad); ln is the logarithm to the base e ($2.303 \cdot$ logarithm to the base 10); and $k = \tan(\theta-i')$ is the ratio of the transverse to the vertical magnetization in the block.

If the difference $\theta-i'$ between the dip and the angle i' (p.57) is almost $\pm 90°$ (e.g., for a vertical block situated very near the magnetic equator and possessing only induced magnetization), it is of computational advantage to use the following expression for ΔZ instead of (3.9a):

$$\Delta Z = 200I_h \ [(1/k) \ \{(\alpha_1-\alpha_2)-(\alpha_3-\alpha_4)\} \\ -\ln(r_1r_4/r_2r_3)] \qquad (3.9b)$$

where I_h is the *horizontal* magnetization intensity in the block.

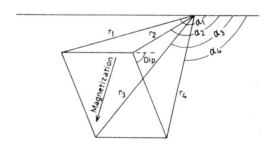

Fig.17A. Prism with sloping sides and striking perpendicular to the figure.

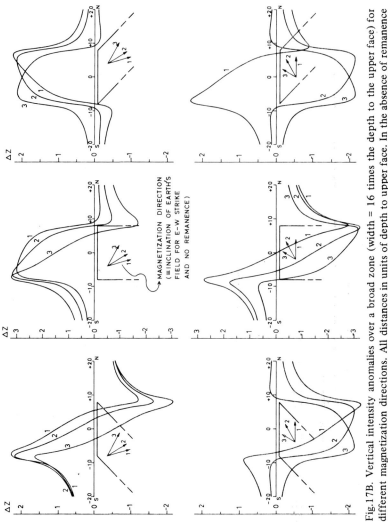

Fig.17B. Vertical intensity anomalies over a broad zone (width = 16 times the depth to the upper face) for different magnetization directions. All distances in units of depth to upper face. In the absence of remanence the upper set is valid north of the magnetic equator, the lower set at (arrow 1) or south of (arrows 2,3) the magnetic equator.

It should be noted that i' is the angle (lying between $-90°$ and $+90°$) made by the *net* magnetization intensity with the horizontal. Only in the absence of remanence is i' equal to $\tan^{-1}(Z/H\sin\beta)$.

From the algebraic point of view eq. (3.9a) or (3.9b) is a generalized form of the anomaly of a line pole.

If the depth-extent of the block in Fig.17A is very great, $\alpha_3 \approx \alpha_4$ and $r_3 \approx r_4$ and we get:

$$\Delta Z = 200 I_z \ \{(\alpha_1 - \alpha_2) - k\ln(r_1/r_2)\}. \qquad (3.9c)$$

This equation, which now represents the anomaly of a dike of infinite depth extent, has been discussed in detail by many authors (Hutchison, 1958; Werner, 1955; Hall, 1959; Gay, 1963).

Fig.17B shows a set of ΔZ profiles across long, broad dikes or magnetic zones, each having a width equal to 16 times the depth of the upper surface and striking east—west, it being assumed that the net magnetization is in the direction of T' (p.55), the component of the earth's total field in the plane of the figure. The upper set of profiles is therefore valid north of the magnetic equator, the lower set at and south of it. In the lower set is also shown the case when the magnetization of the zone is entirely horizontal. It should be particularly noted that even for this case there is a strong peak-to-peak ΔZ anomaly. The reader should guard against the fallacious statement sometimes made that vertical intensity anomalies are non-existent or negligible in low magnetic latitudes or that horizontal ones are negligible in high magnetic latitudes.

Usually, k cannot be determined a priori but there is nothing to prevent our using any reasonable value for it in the formula for the purpose of securing a satisfactory agreement between the observed and calculated anomalies. Similarly I is also unknown but for trial calculations a first approximation to it (to be adjusted subsequently) may be obtained from the rule that:

$$I \approx 10^{-2} \frac{\Delta Z_{max.}}{2\pi} = 1.59 \cdot 10^{-3} \Delta Z_{max.} \qquad (3.10)$$

where I is in A/m and $\Delta Z_{max.}$ in gamma.

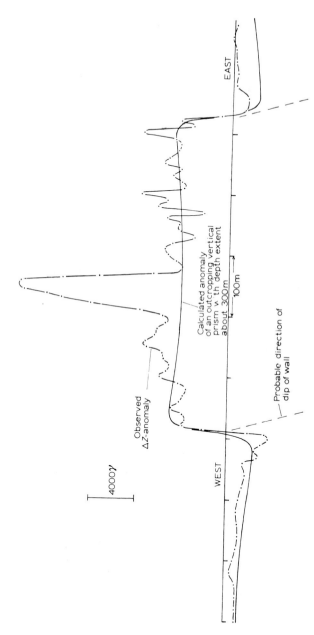

Fig.18. Magnetic vertical intensity profile across a broad zone (Melkogruvan, northern Sweden) and calculated curve (continuous line) for a prism of finite depth-extent. Note weak saddle point in the centre of the calculated curve. (Courtesy of E. Carlsson, Falun and ABEM Company, Stockholm.)

This rule follows from the following reasoning. If the strike of the block is such that the transverse magnetization and hence the factor k are zero (cf. under the heading *Transverse magnetization*) then the anomaly is simply proportional to the difference between the two "angles of sight", $(\alpha_1 - \alpha_2)$ and $(\alpha_3 - \alpha_4)$, at which the lower and the upper surfaces of the block are viewed from the point of observation. Above the centre of a broad block, the former angle of sight is almost $180° = \pi$ radian, while the latter angle will be zero if the block has a great depth-extent, in which case:

$$\Delta Z_{max.} = 200\pi I$$

The anomaly over a block with steep sides and finite depth-extent does not attain its maximum at the centre but at two points slightly inside of the edges, while at the centre there is a shallow saddle in the profile curve (Fig.18). In practice, broad magnetic zones are often irregularly impregnated with magnetic material and the anomalies over them show local variations swamping this effect, which therefore is seldom discerned.

From the value of k that gives the best fit between the observed anomalies and those calculated according to eqs. (3.9a), (3.9b) or (3.9c) the dip of the sides of the block may be determined from the equation:

$$\theta = \tan^{-1} k + i'$$

This formula is adequate for determining the dip of formations of weak susceptibility (e.g., greenstone zones, diabase dikes etc.), provided the remanent magnetization is negligible, but it must be modified in the case of bodies having a high susceptibility (e.g., magnetite ore) to take into account demagnetizing forces. The poles induced on the surfaces of the prism in Fig.17A produce internal magnetizing forces within the body, as a result of which the induced magnetization is no longer parallel to T' but is deflected so as to become more nearly parallel to the dip than otherwise. Consequently, k no longer represents the difference $\theta - i'$ (see Gay, 1963, who, however, uses unrationalized units for the susceptibility).

THE GREENSTONE AREA OF LOOS (SWEDEN)

This example of a magnetic survey over a broad zone in the province of Hälsingland in Sweden is selected here as it illustrates some of the above principles, and also because the anomalies show a peculiar subsidiary feature.

The Loos greenstone zone, several kilometres long, seems to be built of basaltic lava beds between which there sometimes occur agglomerates. It contains a number of minerals, notably pyrrhotite, pyrite, chalcopyrite and smaltite, but zinc blende, galena, arsenopyrite, gersdorffite, native bismuth, bismuth glance and nickelin were also deposited in connection with the albitization of the basalt by late magmatic solutions within the basalt magma itself.

The massif is almost totally overlain by glacial moraine with average thickness of about 5 m. No direct observations of the dip are available.

Fig.19A is a magnetic map of a part of the area; the magnetic zone is nearly 350–400 m wide and strikes in the north–south direction. The eastern edge of the massif is well marked by a sharp anomaly gradient but the western one is rather diffuse. This difference and the negative zone to the east, which is considerably stronger than the zone to the west, can be accounted for by a westerly dip.

Within the broad zone there occur a number of local "pockets" of high anomalies but none of them seem to indicate any sizeable orebody. Of considerably greater interest, however, is the narrow strip of low anomalies that runs from the north to the south through the centre of the area. It probably marks an agglomerate bed devoid of, or very poor in, magnetic material, and therefore having a weaker intensity than the adjoining greenstone.

The triangles to the extreme south in the approximate continuation of the strip represent a string of sulphide boulder floats. This string was one of the primary indications of the occurrence of sulphide ore in this part of the massif. Subsequent electrical surveys have revealed the presence of electrical conductors within this strip and a number of drill holes have confirmed the presence of copper and lead mineralizations, which are good conductors of electricity. The metal values and widths are generally low.

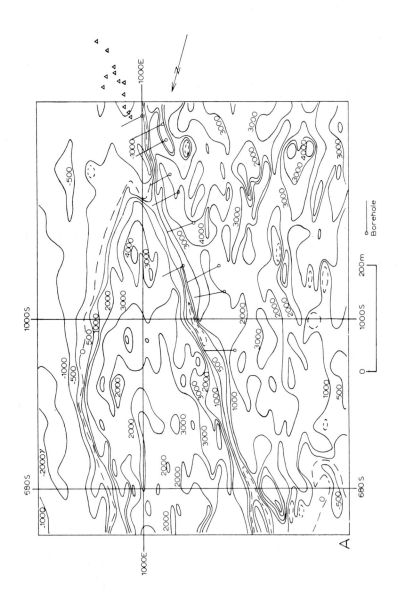

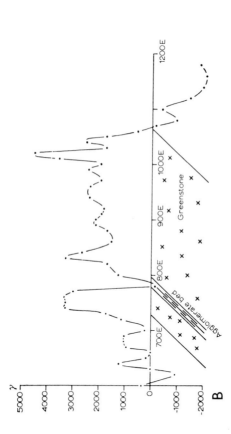

Fig. 19A. Magnetic isoanomaly map of the broad greenstone massif of Loos, Sweden. (Contours in γ.) B. Magnetic profile across the Loos massif and schematic interpretation. (Courtesy of BGAB.)

VECTOR MEASUREMENTS

In the remainder of this chapter we shall consider two special techniques which are sometimes found useful in magnetic prospecting. One of these (vector measurements) is actually an old technique that was extensively used before the development of the modern vertical

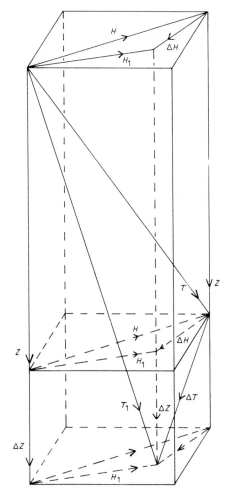

Fig.20A. Anomalous vector of the magnetic field.

field magnetometer, especially in Swedish mines, while the other
(borehole logging) is of more recent origin.

The principle of vector measurements is illustrated in Fig.20A
where H and Z denote the normal horizontal and vertical components
of the geomagnetic field. Their resultant T is the normal total-field
vector (cf. Fig.3). Suppose that there is an extra horizontal compo-

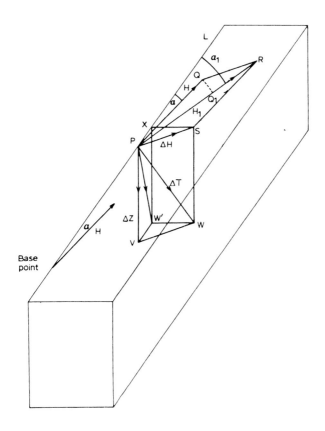

Fig.20B. Principle of magnetic vector measurements.

nent of magnitude ΔH due to an ore. In general, it will differ in
direction from H so that the actual horizontal component at the point
will be H_1 obtained by completing the parallelogram having H and ΔH
as sides and drawing its diagonal through the point of observation.

Similarly, if the ore produces a vertical field ΔZ, the actual vertical
component will be Z_1. The resultant of H_1 and Z_1 is the total-field
vector T_1. The line joining the extremities of T and T_1 represents the
anomalous total-field vector ΔT, in direction and magnitude, due to
the orebody.

The aim of vector measurements is to determine the vector ΔT.
This aim is achieved in two stages: (1) determination of ΔH, and (2)
determination of ΔZ.

The procedure for determining ΔH is as follows. First we draw a
line PQ (Fig.20B) on some suitable scale (say 1 cm = 1,000γ) representing the magnitude of the normal horizontal field. The line is
drawn at the appropriate angle α which the field makes with a fixed
direction, say, the direction of an adit or of the profile of measurement. The angle α is simply the angle which a compass needle, free to
swing in the horizontal plane, makes with the reference direction, at
some base point where the geomagnetic field is known to be reasonably free from disturbances. The magnitude of the normal horizontal
field must, however, be determined by a separate physical experiment
or obtained from a nearby magnetic observatory.

We then measure the angle α_1 at which the compass needle comes
to rest at the observation point P. This gives us the direction of the
local horizontal field H_1. The magnitude of H_1, represented by the
length PR, can be obtained by means of a horizontal force magnetometer, which determines, not H_1 itself but, the amount Q_1R by
which H_1 differs from $H(= PQ = PQ_1$ in Fig.20). The line QR or, on
completing the parallelogram PQRS, the line PS represents the magnitude ΔH of the anomalous horizontal field at P, the direction being
from P to S.

In the vertical plane through PS we draw the vertical line PV representing the anomaly ΔZ which, of course, can be measured on a
vertical force magnetometer in the usual manner. On completing the
rectangle PVWS we get PW as the anomalous vector ΔT. The azimuth

of the anomalous vector is given by the angle LPS and its inclination
with the horizontal plane by the angle SPW.

In general, the ΔT vectors at different points along the line of
measurement will not lie in the vertical plane through it, so that it is
not possible to obtain an adequate picture of the anomalous vectors
short of constructing a three dimensional model. On a two-dimensional figure a partial picture can be obtained by studying the projection PW$'$ of ΔT on the vertical plane through the line of measurement.
PW$'$ can also be determined by taking the projection PX of ΔH
on the line, and compounding it with PV.

EXAMPLE OF VECTOR MEASUREMENTS

This example from Logn (1964) comes from the Fosdalen iron ore
mine in Norway. The ores in this field occur as very long, thin sheets
and at least two of the principal orebodies lie with their upper surface
at a depth of some 800 m below the ground. As the position of one of
these was not known with certainty, underground vector measurements were carried out at intervals along an exploratory adit while it
was being driven from January 1952 to January 1954. The object was
to minimize the adit length.

The results of the vector measurements are shown in Fig.21. It is
evident that the upper pole of the body was passed between January
1953 and January 1954 since the vector starts turning "backwards"
If the vertical field anomaly alone were measured along the adit with
the object of locating the pole, an ambiguity would have persisted as
to whether an eventual maximum in the anomaly was due to a south
pole (upper surface of an ore) below the adit level or a north pole
(lower surface of an ore) above it, because in either case the anomaly
would be positive. The ambiguity is resolved here owing to the additional information provided by the horizontal component.

For comparison, a vector profile on the surface is also shown. The
tendency of the surface vectors to converge towards points rather near
the surface is indicative of the south poles of shallow ore lenses, but
the vectors in the centre seem to point towards the deeper south pole
on the upper surface of the main orebody.

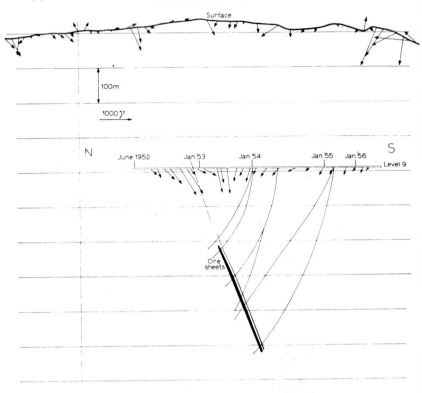

Fig. 21. Magnetic vector measurements on the surface and in an underground adit in the Fosdalen mine, Norway. (Courtesy of O. Logn.)

Reference to Fig. 1 will show that had the effect of the lower, that is, the north pole, of the orebody been sufficiently strong, the flank vectors along the adit would have pointed upwards at some stage. Their actual behaviour indicates, either that the lower surface of the ore lies very deep, or that the vectors are being disturbed by a north pole above the adit level, possibly the lower surface of one (or more) of the shallow lenses mentioned above.

In interpreting vector measurements great caution should be exercised in identifying the points of convergence of the vectors as the positions of magnetic poles. The poles may actually lie quite far from such areas, the reason being that since the lines of force of a magnet are not straight but curved, a vector does not point directly to a pole.

Finally, it must be emphasized that vector determinations do not resolve the inherent ambiguity in magnetic interpretation, namely the existence of a number of alternative distributions of magnetization explaining a given set of anomalies. It can also be shown that vector measurements are unwarranted in surface work because all the information about a magnetic field is implicit in sufficiently detailed measurements of the vertical component of the field (Parasnis, 1972, pp.54–59).

BOREHOLE MEASUREMENTS

Magnetic measurements in boreholes have been undertaken in recent years on an increasing scale. Three main systems have been proposed for the purpose: (1) measurement of the magnetic intensity along the borehole, (2) measurement of the total intensity at points in the hole, and (3) determination of three mutually perpendicular components of the magnetic field for determining the total vector at discrete points in the hole. (Usually one of the measured components is that along the hole.)

Of these schemes, the last one naturally gives the maximum information. A photograph of an apparatus using this scheme is shown in Fig.22. The magnetic vector in a borehole is simply given by the body-diagonal of the rectangular parallelepiped, the sides of which represent the three measured mutually perpendicular components. A vector representing the earth's normal field is then drawn at the point of measurement, and the line from its extremity to the extremity of the actual vector gives the direction and magnitude of the anomalous vector as in Fig.20.

The true directions of the measured components will, of course, be uncertain if the curvature of the borehole in space is not known so that accurate borehole magnetic measurements must be accompanied by determinations of the borehole geometry. The technique of such determinations has been discussed by Holm (1964).

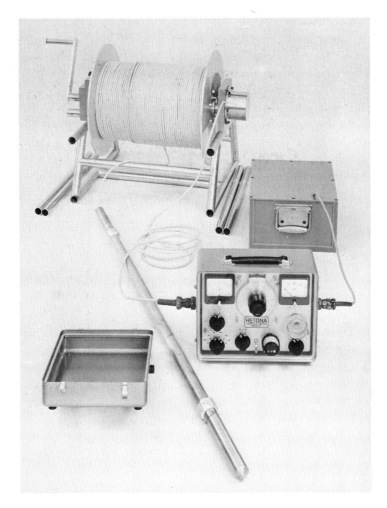

Fig. 22. Hetona borehole magnetometer equipment. (Courtesy of AB Hetona, Stockholm.)

There are no standard methods of interpreting borehole measurements. Some attempts at developing qualitative procedures were made by Levanto (1959). In recent years the mathematical theory of interpreting borehole data has been highly developed in the U.S.S.R. (Volocyka and Safronova, 1971). However, one or two general com-

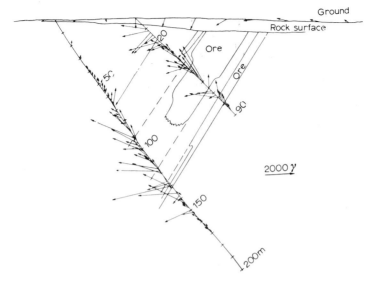

Fig.23A. Anomalous magnetic vectors in a drillhole through the Kankberg pyrite-pyrrhotite orebody, northern Sweden. (After Malmqvist, 1958.)

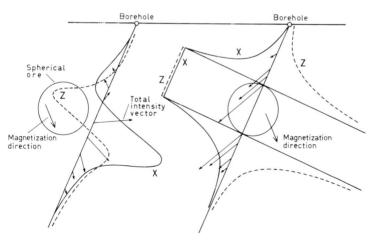

Fig.23B. Magnetic anomalies in boreholes (Z, anomaly in the direction of the hole (downhole anomaly); X, anomaly perpendicular to the hole).

ments seem to be called for even at the present stage.

In the first place, only a three-dimensional model will in general give an adequate picture of the tendencies of the measured vectors so that the methods of interpretation are bound to be somewhat more complicated than for conventional surface measurements.

Secondly, when a borehole passes through a magnetic zone (such as a magnetite or pyrrhotite bearing mass) local variations in the permanent and induced magnetization within it are such that borehole measurements often provide no useful information, at any rate no information that can be interpreted without unreasonable labour.

Nevertheless, borehole magnetic measurements seem to be a promising auxiliary method of geophysical investigations, especially for locating an ore mass that a hole has failed to encounter but in whose vicinity it is suspected to pass.

An example of the anomalous vectors measured in a borehole through a pyrrhotite-bearing orebody is shown in Fig.23A.

The complications that arise in the interpretation of borehole magnetic measurements will be appreciated from Fig.23B. We consider here a homogeneously magnetized spherical orebody. On the left-hand side are shown the fields, Z in the direction of the hole and X perpendicular thereto and in the plane of the figure, as well as the vectors, that will be measured in a hole passing in the neighbourhood of the body but not cutting it. On the right-hand side are shown the fields and the vectors in a hole passing through the centre of the spherical body. We notice that in the second case Z increases continuously as we approach the body but shows a discontinuity when we cross the boundary of the sphere. Within the sphere Z is directed oppositely, that is, up the hole and is moreover constant throughout the body. Similarly X is also constant within the orebody.

The pictures in the two cases when the hole does and does not cut the body are thus very different from each other.

NOTE ON REVERSE VERTICAL FIELD MAGNETIC ANOMALIES

From the discussion in the section *An orebody as a magnet* it is clear that the principal anomaly of a magnetic ore will normally be positive if the body is situated north of the magnetic equator. South of the magnetic equator the anomaly will be normally negative. However, large reverse magnetic anomalies (that is, negative ones in the northern hemisphere and positive ones in the southern) are often encountered and the possible causes of such anomalies should be kept in mind during the interpretation of the field data.

In the first place it should be noted that in the vicinity of mine dumps, houses, cars, iron junk, etc., the magnetic anomalies are generally negative in the northern hemisphere and positive in the southern. This fact will be readily understood if in Fig.1 we draw a horizontal line flush with the lower surface of the magnet which, in this case, represents an "artificial" feature like a mine dump resting on the ground.

Secondly, positive anomalies in the northern hemisphere are often flanked by negative ones, sometimes quite strong, which are due to the effect of the north poles on the lower end of a body. In the southern hemisphere the normal negative anomalies will be surrounded by areas of positive ones which are due to the south poles on the lower end of the causative body. Similarly, transverse magnetization effects also produce "legitimate", and sometimes strong, reverse anomalies (see Fig.17B).

Another condition giving rise to reverse anomalies is topographic relief. It can happen that when measurements are made in areas of appreciable topographic relief, strong negative anomalies are obtained (in the northern hemisphere) at stations in valleys and depressions, if a magnetic ore happens to outcrop above the station. This situation will be appreciated again from a study of Fig.1 if the horizontal line in it is drawn below the north pole of the magnet. Conditions in the southern hemisphere will, of course, be the reverse.

Unless the possibility of reverse anomalies being due to the above and similar causes is eliminated, the hypothesis of a reverse remanent magnetization of the subsurface rocks and ores to explain the reverse anomalies obtained in an area can hardly be entertained in magnetic interpretation.

CHAPTER 4

The Self-Potential Method

INTRODUCTION

If two metal stakes or two non-polarizable electrodes are driven anywhere into the ground and connected to the terminals of a sensitive
voltmeter, an electric voltage is found to exist between them. Such
voltages normally range from a few millivolt to a few tens of millivolt
but above some sulphide bodies, notably those containing pyrite, chalcopyrite and pyrrhotite, and above graphite they may attain values as
high as several hundred millivolt to a volt. It should be recalled for
comparison that the voltage across the terminals of a flash-light cell is
about 1.5 V (1,500 mV). Large voltages have also been reported over
pyrolusite, psilomelane, magnetite and anthracite coal.

Like the magnetic method, the self-potential (SP) method, as the
method exploiting the spontaneous or natural voltages in the ground
is called, is also a simple, easy and cheap geophysical aid in prospecting. As self-potentials do not depend on any definite physical
property but are due to differences in chemical activity in the ground,
they give no clue (at least at present) about any distinct physical
parameter associated with the body causing them. Further, it is not
possible to say from SP anomalies alone whether they are due to
sulphides, oxides, graphite or something else. The clue to this must be
obtained through geological and other studies within the area.

As the measurement of self-potentials requires a direct electrical
connection with the ground, the method cannot be employed in areas
where the surface layer is a bad electric conductor, for example, dry
crystalline rock, frozen ground etc.

ORIGIN OF SELF-POTENTIALS

The self-potentials observed on the ground can be broadly divided into two classes: (*1*) the small "background potentials" ranging from a fraction of a millivolt to a few or few tens of millivolt, and (*2*) the "mineralization potentials" with maximum values of the order of a few hundred to several hundred millivolt showing a systematic pattern.

The background potentials may be positive as well as negative but the mineralization potentials are exclusively negative, although it must be remembered that high positive potentials of the order of 100–200 mV are also encountered but these are not associated with ores.

The background potentials seem to originate in several well-understood ways. For example, it is known that between two electrolytes of differing concentration in contact with each other, there exists an electrical voltage. Some of the background self-potentials must be due to the variations in the concentrations of the electrolytes in the ground (humic acid, ground water with dissolved salts etc.). Again, it is known that when an electrolyte flows through a capillary, a small voltage difference is created between the ends of the capillary. Some self-potentials can be attributed to this cause if water is streaming through the pores of the rocks, especially the surface layers. Other electrochemical phenomena no doubt also contribute to the background variations of self-potentials.

The mineralization potentials are, however, difficult to explain and several theories for their origin have been proposed. It has been commonly believed that the oxidation of the top surface of an orebody creates a potential difference between the upper and lower ends of the body so that it becomes a large battery cell sending currents in the ground. These currents would give rise to the observed natural potentials above an orebody.

If this theory were true the orebody will be consumed in due course owing to the constant dissipation of energy needed to maintain the electric currents through actual oxidation of the body. Further, the theory does not fit graphite which, although it undergoes no oxidation, often shows strong self-potentials. A more fatal objection to the theory is that because oxidation entails the loss of electrons, which are negatively charged particles, the top surface of an orebody would become positively charged with respect to the surroundings, but, in fact, the reverse is found to be the case.

Sato and Mooney (1960), who carefully examined the various theories of sulphide and graphite self-potentials in detail, came to the conclusion that self-potentials cannot be due to the oxidation of an orebody as such but to the difference in the oxidation capacity of the waters near the upper and the lower surface of an orebody, the electrical conduction in which takes place by electrons. Among such bodies may be mentioned pyrite, chalcopyrite, pyrrhotite, galena, magnetite and graphite. At the top and bottom of the orebody an exchange of ionic and electronic charges takes place, with the orebody serving to transport electrons from the lower surface to the upper until electrochemical equilibrium is reached. The upper surface therefore becomes negatively charged and the lower one positively charged, as is found to be the case in nature.

One consequence of the self-potential mechanism proposed by Sato and Mooney seems to be that electrically conducting orebodies would be expected to show self-potentials under a wider variety of climatic and other conditions than those admitted by the oxidation theories. This in turn means that the SP method has a wider scope in ore prospecting than has hitherto been supposed. There is, therefore, a strong plea for using the method more extensively than at present. It seems unlikely, however, that the method will be able to detect very deep lying ores even if considerable refinements were to be made in the technique of measurement itself.

Besides the background effects, there may be large local disturbances due to buried iron pipes, electrical earthings, chemical fertilizers, mine slags, topography, groundwater drainage, etc., for which allowance must be made in the interpretation of SP anomalies. Otherwise, the qualitative interpretation of SP anomalies presents few complications and is fairly straightforward in the sense that strong negative anomalies indicate mineralization. Attempts at quantitative interpretation of SP anomalies have also been made (Edge and Laby, 1931; Yüngül, 1950) but it cannot be said that these have so far met with much success in routine interpretation.

MEASUREMENT OF SELF-POTENTIALS

The apparatus required for SP measurements is essentially simple and comprises only: (*a*) electrodes, (*b*) cable, and (*c*) voltmeter. SP outfits are also commercially available.

Electrodes

Although metal rods, for example, of copper or stainless steel, sometimes function satisfactorily for SP work, it is not generally advisable to employ them directly for this purpose because electrolytic action sets up a variable potential difference between two metal electrodes in contact with the ground. This phenomenon, known as polarization, tends to obscure the natural potential difference between the electrodes.

Non-polarizable electrodes are therefore to be preferred and one of the simplest electrodes of this type is obtained by placing a copper rod in a porous pot containing saturated $CuSO_4$-solution, the contact with the ground being made through the pot. Another convenient non-polarizable electrode is the commercially available $KCl–HgCl_2$ (calomel) electrode used in pH-measurements. Fig.24A illustrates the calomel electrode manufactured by Ingold (Switzerland). When securely mounted in a cylindrical plastic tube of suitable length, fitted with a thoroughly moist porous wooden plug at the bottom (Fig.24B), it makes a robust and dependable electrode for SP work.

Cable

Practically the only requirements on the cable to be used in SP measurements are that it should have a good insulation cover and be light in weight. Almost any type of a sheathed, multistrand copper wire will suit.

Voltmeter

Self-potentials are measured by connecting the electrodes to a voltmeter. Two types of instruments are available for the purpose: a direct-reading and a compensating.

If a direct-reading voltmeter is used, one with a sufficiently high internal resistance should be chosen to ensure that when it is connected across the electrodes it draws no appreciable part of the natural ground current so that the measured potential difference is that actually existing between the electrodes in the absence of the voltmeter. If $Cu/CuSO_4$ electrodes are used voltmeters with input

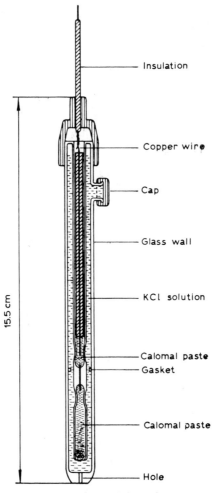

Fig. 24A. Calomel electrode.

impedances of the order of 20,000–50,000 Ohm serve well, while calomel electrodes call for instruments with very high impedances, of the order of one to several megohm or more.

A type of voltmeter that has a very high impedance and is there-

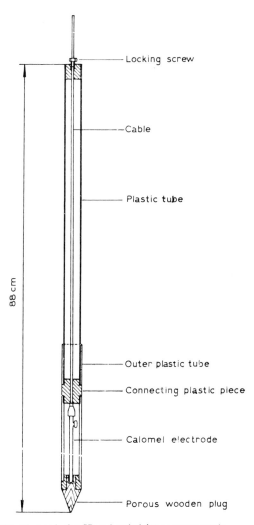

Fig. 24B. Electrode for SP and resistivity measurements.

fore suitable for work with $Cu/CuSO_4$ as well as calomel electrodes, is the electronic vacuum-tube voltmeter. Some of the commercially available pH-meters, such as the Beckman model N or Philips, are essentially vacuum-tube voltmeters. When housed in a small wooden case to be carried by the observer, both these meters are very well suited for SP work apart from the fact that their scales are graduated in pH numbers. However, it is easy to construct a table of pH values and the voltages they represent (Kaye and Laby, 1959). One pH unit is approximately equal to 54–60 mV depending upon the temperature.

The voltage between SP electrodes can also be determined by balancing it against a known voltage. This is the principle of the compensation voltmeter, also called a potentiometer or d.c. compensator, illustrated schematically in Fig.25. Many commercially available SP outfits employ a d.c. compensator. A standard battery (b) sends a current through a fixed resistance R_0 and a variable resistance R_1 in series. On closing the switch the resistance R_1 is first adjusted so that the meter (a) shows a standard (usually full-scale) deflection corresponding to a definite current in the circuit, irrespective of reasonable variations in the battery voltage due to ageing etc. There is then a fixed voltage drop across the ends of R_0.

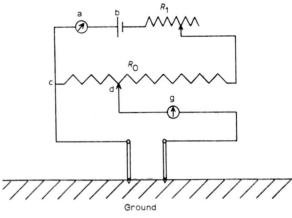

Fig. 25. Principle of direct-current compensator for voltage measurements.

One of the electrodes is now connected to the end (c) of R_0 while the other electrode is allowed, through the galvanometer G, to make a contact along R_0. The galvanometer will show no deflection when the contact is at a point d such that the voltage drop across the portion cd of R_0 balances the voltage difference between the electrodes. The positions along the resistance can be calibrated directly in volts (or mV).

FIELD PROCEDURE

Two alternative procedures can be used for SP surveys. In the first of these, one electrode is kept fixed at a base station while the other electrode, together with the cable reel and the voltmeter, is carried to different points as the cable is laid off, and the electric potential of each point with respect to the base is read on the voltmeter. Care must be taken to note the sign of the potential. The simple rule is that it is the sign of the voltmeter-terminal to which the *moving* electrode must be connected in order to obtain a positive deflection on the meter.

When the cable length is exhausted a new base station is chosen and its potential Δ with respect to the first base is determined by a few repeated observations or by measuring the potentials at five or six convenient points from the old as well as the new base. If Δ_1, Δ_2, Δ_3 ... etc., are the potentials with respect to the first base and Δ_1', Δ_2', Δ_3' ... those with respect to the new base, the mean of $\Delta_1 - \Delta_1'$, $\Delta_2 - \Delta_2'$, $\Delta_3 - \Delta_3'$ ... etc., gives the required difference Δ between the two bases. A potential with respect to the new base is referred to the first base by merely adding the amount Δ to it.

The zero level of the self-potentials is determined in essentially the same manner as the zero in magnetic work (see Chapter 3, under the heading *The zero level*), i.e., by an inspection of the observed anomalies.

In the second, and less frequently used, procedure of SP surveys, the two electrodes have a constant mutual separation s, say, of 10–50 m (or, say, 20–100 ft.) and they are advanced together along the line of measurements in steps equal to the mutual separation, so that the rear electrode 1 each time occupies the position previously occupied by the front electrode 2. If the potential difference between the electrodes is $\Delta_2 - \Delta_1$, then $(\Delta_2 - \Delta_1)/s$ is approximately the gradient of the potential or the electric field (mV/m) at the point midway between the electrodes.

A convention regarding the sign of the gradient must be fixed at the start of the work. For example, if the meter shows a positive deflection when the more northward (or the more eastwards etc.) electrode is connected to the positive terminal, the gradient is reckoned positive. If then the electrode connections have to be interchanged at a station to obtain a positive deflection, the gradient must be reckoned negative. If centre-zero voltmeters are used the deflection of the voltmeter can be immediately read off as positive or negative without having to interchange the terminals. The sign convention should be fixed with respect to a geographical direction and not with respect to the concepts "rear" and "front" electrode, to avoid confusion when measurements are made, as is usual, in a zig-zag manner.

The point midway between the electrodes is reckoned as the observation point in gradient measurements.

By successive addition of the measured differences $\Delta_2 - \Delta_1$, $\Delta_3 - \Delta_2$, $\Delta_4 - \Delta_3$ etc., we can obtain the potential of any point occupied by the front electrode. However, if the potentials are desired, a direct measurement of them is preferable because successive addition tends to accumulate the errors of difference measurements. Conversely, the gradients can be obtained from the potential data by taking the differences between the potentials at adjacent points.

In principle, the two procedures are therefore equivalent. However, gradient measurements have the advantage that their operational range is unlimited. The range of potential measurements is governed by the maximum cable length that can be conveniently carried on the reel. On the other hand, the chances of discovering a weak SP anomaly which varies slowly with distance are greater if the potentials are observed directly.

What is to be considered as an SP indication depends on whether we are measuring the potentials or the gradients.

If the potentials are measured, high negative potentials within a

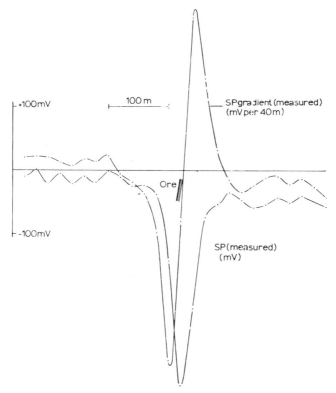

Fig. 26. Self-potential and self-potential gradient along a profile across the orebody in Fig. 27.

large area may be considered to be an indication. If the gradients are measured, an indication will consist of a high positive and a high negative measurement flanking a zero gradient, i.e., of an inflection point (Fig. 26). Potential maps are easier to interpret than the gradient maps.

EXAMPLES OF SP SURVEYS

The Kimheden orebody

This sulphide orebody (predominantly pyrite) occurs in the Skellefte orefield in northern Sweden. The country rock is sericite-quartzite overlain by moraine of thickness 1–2 m within the area in question. The ore lenses occur along a ridge, in the form of steeply dipping sheets. Drillings have indicated weathered sericite-quartzite in the western part of the area shown on the map in Fig.27; elsewhere the rock appears to be fresh. The upper surfaces of the various lenses lie at a depth of about 10 m or less.

SP measurements in the area reveal a number of distinct elongated anomaly centres with maximum potentials between −300 and −450 mV in magnitude. The map also shows the cross-sections of the various ore lenses as ascertained by extensive drilling. The SP anomalies are seen to agree reasonably well with the drilling results. In particular, the anomalies within the −300 mV contour between 600E and 1050E closely follow the ore lens to which they are undoubtedly due. The lens is thicker in the middle than at the extremities, but there is no correlation between the variations in the width and those in the maximum anomalies above the lens. Nor can the anomaly variations be correlated with the Cu-content (average 1–2%).

The dent in the −300 mV contour at about 850E probably corresponds to a local break in the ore along its strike which is indicated by the drillings.

The ore lens with the centre at approximately 640E/220N also shows up on the SP map with the maximum observed potential (−400

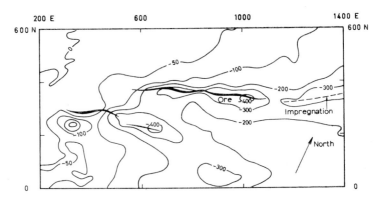

Fig. 27. Self-potential map of the Kimheden pyrite orebody, northern Sweden. Coordinates in m, contours in mV. (Courtesy of BGAB.)

mV). Further west, there appears a third ore lens, about 200 m long, but with no SP anomaly to indicate its presence, unless it be the anomaly with the centre at 320E/240N. However, this would mean a displacement of about 60 m between the anomaly and the ore lens, which seems to be too large to be accounted for by topographic effects or the known dip. A possible explanation why the ore lens between 300E and 500E fails to show an SP anomaly may be that the ore lens has a very high electrical resistivity.

The Gransjö orefield, central Sweden

This field is situated in an area of precambrian granulite rocks which occasionally grade into mica schists. The strike is northeast–southwest and the dip about 80° to the southeast. Bands of limestone interbedded in the granulite are quite common. The overburden is glacial moraine.

The mineralization zone is approximately 100–200 m broad and contains galena, zinc blende, pyrite, pyrrhotite and, in places, chalcopyrite. The metal contents are generally low, Pb ranging from about 1 to 7% and Zn from about 2 to 10%.

The SP measurements in the area (Fig.28A) show a distinct anomaly with maximum observed potentials exceeding −400 mV at several points. The picture is irregular in detail probably due to the fact that the mineralization itself is irregular. However, it is found that the ore zone may be delineated approximately as the area enclosed by the −200 mV contour.

A striking feature of the map is the extensive area in the southeast, south and southwest with potentials between −100 and −50 mV. From a typical profile shown in Fig.28B it appears that the zero level in the southeast is locally about −100 to −150 mV lower, probably due to a zone of crushed bedrock striking northeast–southwest to east–west, roughly along the base line 0. It will be noted from the depth contours of the solid bedrock (dashed curves in Fig.28A) that the loose material above the bedrock is particularly thick in this region. A subsidiary SP-minimum due to the crushed rock is evident.

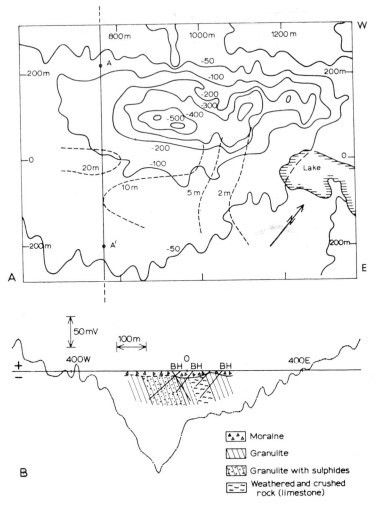

Fig. 28. A. SP map of the Gransjö orefield, central Sweden. Contours in mV. Linear scale in m. B. SP profile marked in part A showing a superimposition of SP due to a crushed zone. (Courtesy of BGAB.)

The copper deposits of Chalkidiki, northern Greece

An instance of a combination of two geophysical methods to obtain different data supplementary to each other is afforded by the geophysical measurements in the Chalkidiki area of northern Greece. The example is due to Zachos (1963) whom we shall follow closely in the description below.

Most of the rocks of the Chalkidiki peninsula are crystalline and include (precambrian?) gneisses, mica schists, sericitized schists and chlorite schists. They are strongly sheared and numerous granitic-granodioritic and ultrabasic intrusions occur in the metamorphic

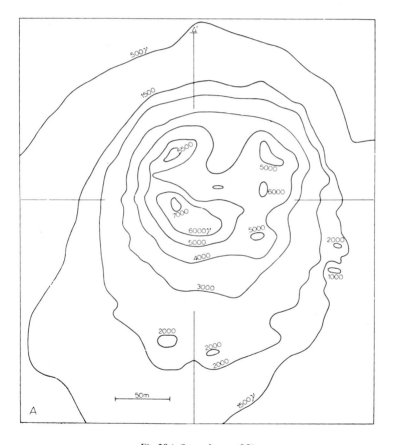

Fig.29A (legend see p.95).

rocks. The igneous rocks are all mineralized to some extent – the acid with pyrite, galena and sphalerite, and the basic with magnesite and chromite.

Tertiary volcanic activity, with flows of trachytes, andesites and porphyritic granodiorites, has caused extensive mineralization of copper minerals and pyrite. There is much faulting and fracturing in

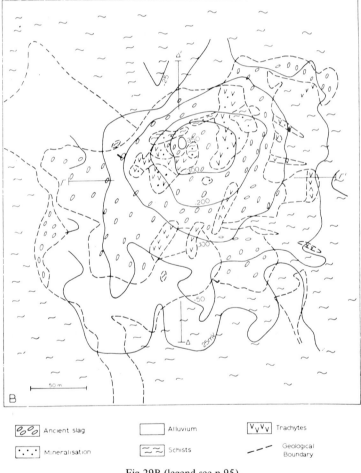

Ancient slag Alluvium Trachytes

Mineralisation Schists Geological Boundary

Fig.29B (legend see p.95).

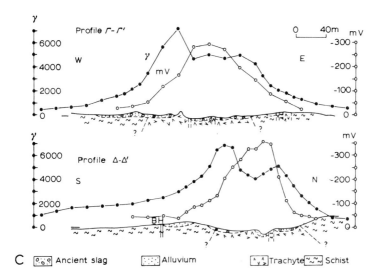

C [⚬ꞏ⚬] Ancient slag   [:::::]Alluvium   [ᐱᵥᐱ]Trachyte[~~~]Schist

Fig. 29. A. Magnetic vertical intensity map of the Chalkidiki area, northern Greece. (Adapted after Zachos, 1963.) B. Self-potential map and geology of the Chalkidiki area. Contours in mV. (Adapted after Zachos, 1963.) C. Magnetic and SP profiles in the Chalkidiki area. (After Zachos, 1963.)

all directions and consequently a dense network filled with copper minerals and quartz has arisen. There are many ancient copper workings in the area.

The copper mineralization forms three distinct zones of which the uppermost, or oxidized zone is poor (average 1% Cu) due to leaching. It passes into a zone of secondary enrichment, 2–3 m thick and rich in oxidized copper minerals (malachite, azurite, cuprite etc.) with the Cu-content occasionally exceeding 20%. This is followed by the zone of primary mineralization, with chalcopyrite, pyrite, bornite and syngenetic magnetite, commencing 20–30 m below the surface and extending to a depth of at least 300 m.

The area was surveyed by the magnetic and self-potential methods in a systematic exploration programme. The magnetic anomaly, shown in Fig. 29A, is due to the magnetite in the volcanic rocks and consequently maps the extent of these rocks, which seems to coincide approximately with the 4,500γ contour.

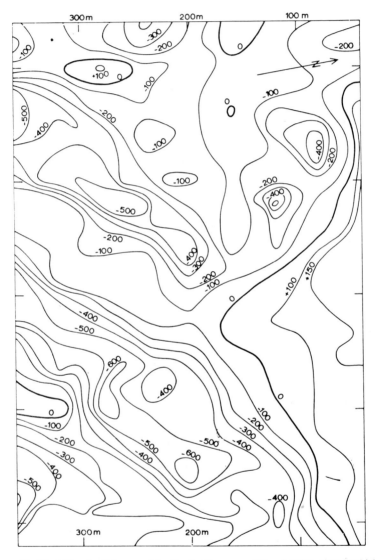

Fig.30. Self-potential map of the Gautosjö area, northern Sweden, showing high
anomalies over graphitic shales. Contours in mV. (Courtesy of BGAB.)

The existence of copper (and iron) sulphides in the area is indicated, on the other hand, by the SP anomaly (Fig.29B). Fig.29C showing two mutually perpendicular profiles is particularly instructive. Here it is clearly seen that the maxima in the magnetic and the SP anomalies are displaced with respect to each other. The magnetic maxima occur slightly inside of the edges of the trachyte dome while the SP maxima occur over concentrations of copper ore. In the lower profile in particular, the oxidized low-susceptibility zone containing copper sulphides is clearly marked by a depression in the magnetic anomaly curve.

The reader will no doubt notice many other interesting correlations of the anomalies and the geology.

The shales of Gautosjö, northern Sweden

This example (Fig.30) is included here for its intrinsic interest as an instance of large self-potentials on rocks other than sulphide orebodies.

The area is situated in a nappe of the Caledonian mountain range in northwestern Sweden. Geologically, the area is very complicated owing to intense tectonic activity which has given rise to much overthrusting, folding and faulting. But for our purpose it will be sufficient to note that the rocks within the area of Fig.30 consist of a series of alternating beds (in reality isoclinal folds) of quartzites and graphitic shales. The strike is about $50°$ east of north and the dip is gentle to steep towards the northwest.

The self-potentials are very large in magnitude, the maximum value observed being about -700 mV. These negative anomalies occur in rather well-defined straight belts and, considering the known geology, there is no doubt that they are due to graphitic shales. In fact, the correlation is so striking, where it can be directly observed, that the shale and quartzite horizons can be traced and distinguished from each other by means of the SP anomalies where outcrops are lacking.

The use of SP anomalies for mapping geology and structures in the bedrock has been a somewhat neglected aspect of geophysical prospecting but there is little doubt that a careful analysis of SP anomalies is capable of yielding considerable information about features, such as shallow fissures, faults, crushed zones etc.

CHAPTER 5

Electromagnetic Methods

INTRODUCTION

When an alternating electromagnetic field, produced by means of a cable or a coil in which an alternating current is flowing, propagates through the ground, it induces electric currents in any conductor in its path. These secondary currents flow in such a way that their electromagnetic field opposes the inducing field. Thus, if at a point on the surface of a conductor the primary flux is entering it, the secondary flux (due to the induced currents) will be emerging at that point. Conversely, if the primary flux is leaving the conductor at a point the secondary flux will be entering it at that point. When the secondary field spreads out in space the total field at any point differs from the primary field, i.e., from the field arriving at the point directly from the source.

The strength of the induced currents depends, among other factors, upon the electric resistivity of the conductor concerned and the frequency with which the primary field is alternating. Generally speaking, the currents are stronger the smaller the resistivity and the higher the frequency.

The electric resistivity of some ores, rocks and minerals is shown in Fig.56, in the next chapter. From this it will be seen that graphite, pyrrhotite, pyrite, chalcopyrite, galena and magnetite are good conductors of electricity while haematite, zinc blende, braunite and chromite are almost insulators. Ores containing the former minerals, to which we may also add some others like arsenopyrite, therefore make suitable targets for electromagnetic prospecting.

Ores of haematite, zinc blende, braunite, chromite etc., will be detectable electromagnetically only if they contain sufficient amounts of some accessory mineral having low electrical resistivity. For example, zinc-blende deposits can often be located by electromagnetic methods if they contain dissemination of pyrite or galena.

The very low, almost metallic, resistivity of graphite is, however, troublesome in general because graphite beds, which are not of economic importance as a rule absorb electromagnetic waves heavily and may screen any ores in their vicinity. On the other hand, the low resistivity of pyrrhotite, also an economically unimportant mineral, is welcome since pyrrhotite often occurs in intimate association with sulphide ores and even thin veins or moderately good impregnations of it can be of great help in tracing sulphide ore formations.

Electromagnetic disturbances are also caused by faults, fractures in the bedrock, zones of crushed rock and fissures bearing conductive water, thin conducting veins etc., all of which are in themselves worthless conductors although they may in some cases have indirect connection with ore deposits. Artificial electromagnetic indications are often encountered in the vicinity of telephone lines, pipes, power lines, railways etc. These are usually easy to recognize by their character: long, narrow and straight zones with very high values for the electromagnetic field.

GEOMETRY OF THE ELECTROMAGNETIC FIELD

At every point in an electromagnetic field there is an electric intensity (V/m) and a magnetizing force (A/m). In practice it is usually the magnetic field that is measured and we shall therefore select this field for a discussion of all electromagnetic anomalies.

In the absence of subsurface conductors the field at any point oscillates along a definite line and can be represented by a vector of proper magnitude, giving the amplitude of the field. The undisturbed direction and magnitude of the field depend upon the relative positions of the source and the observation point as well as on the nature of the source (e.g., a coil, cable etc.). For example, the field lines due to a current-carrying coil are rather like those which a magnet would produce if it were placed perpendicular to the plane of the coil, while the lines of force due to a long current-carrying cable are concentric circles with planes perpendicular to the cable (cf. Fig.32).

However, if a subsurface conductor is present the field vector at any point does not simply oscillate in one direction but describes an ellipse in a definite plane and the electromagnetic field is said to be elliptically polarized (Appendix 10). Such a field is equivalent to two oscillating vectors at right angles to each other, one along the major axis of the ellipse and the other along the minor axis.

A convenient arrangement for mapping an electromagnetic field is a "search coil" consisting of several hundred turns of copper wire wound on a suitable rectangular (or circular) frame having a side (or diameter) of, say, 50–100 cm, the ends of the coil being connected, via an amplifier, to a pair of head-phones or some other suitable indicator of alternating current. The voltage induced in a search coil is proportional to the component of the electromagnetic field perpendicular to the coil. If the normal to the coil makes an angle θ with the field, the voltage is proportional to $F \cos \theta$. Hence, when the coil is placed in the primary field of a cable or a loop and tilted, the signal becomes maximum when the plane of the coil is perpendicular to the field vector ($\theta = 0$, $\cos \theta = 1$, see Fig.31).

On the other hand, no signal is obtained in the detector when the vector lies in the plane of the coil, since no magnetic field will then thread the coil and induce a voltage in it. In the undisturbed field of a cable or a loop there are an infinity of such null positions because the vector will continue to lie in the plane of the coil as the coil is rotated around a diameter coinciding with the direction of the field. But as soon as there is a subsurface conductor the field is elliptically polarized and there is one, and only one, position of the coil in which the induced voltage in it is zero, namely that in which its plane coincides with the plane of the ellipse.

The plane of polarization can be determined in practice as follows. Rotate a search coil around a vertical axis until the signal is at a minimum; thereupon rotate the coil around its horizontal diameter until another minimum is obtained and finally, rotate it around an axis at right angles to the above two axes. When the signal is reduced to zero, which might need small adjustments in the position of the coil, the plane of the coil coincides with the plane of polarization.

A

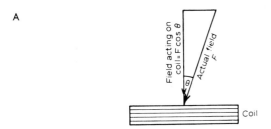

B

Fig. 31A. Effective electromagnetic field acting on a search coil. B. Search coil
mounted on a stand. (Courtesy of BGAB.)

Obviously, in order to carry out this procedure the coil must be mounted on a tripod in such a way that it can be swung round three mutually perpendicular axes.

The orientation of the plane of polarization is defined by its dip and strike. The dip is the angle made by the plane with the horizontal. The strike is the direction of the line of intersection of the plane of polarization and the horizontal plane, i.e., the direction of the horizontal line in the plane of the coil in its position of minimum signal.

However, the orientation of the ellipse itself in the plane of polarization is not known unless the inclination of the major (or the minor) axis of the ellipse is also known. To this end, the coil is held perpendicular to the plane of silence and turned until a maximum signal is obtained. The normal to the coil in this position gives the direction of the major axis of the ellipse of polarization. The inclination of the major axis with the horizontal is called the tilt of the electromagnetic field. The distinction between the dip and the tilt should be carefully noted.

THE TILT-ANGLE METHOD

One method of electromagnetic prospecting is based upon measuring only the tilt of the major axis of the ellipse of polarization. To understand how the tilt behaves when a subsurface conductor is present, we refer to Fig.32A and B.

In Fig.32A, the primary field is produced by a vertical loop and is horizontal at the observation points. This is easily understood if we imagine a magnet to be placed at the centre of the loop perpendicular to its plane. In Fig.32B the source is a long cable and the primary field is vertical at the surface of the ground. We assume the conducting orebody to have a great strike-length perpendicular to the plane of the figure and the secondary induced current in it to be concentrated along the upper edge. The current produces a magnetic field which opposes the primary field.

In both the cases shown the plane of the paper is the plane of elliptic polarization. Hence the profile of measurement itself gives the strike (or azimuth) of the plane of polarization.

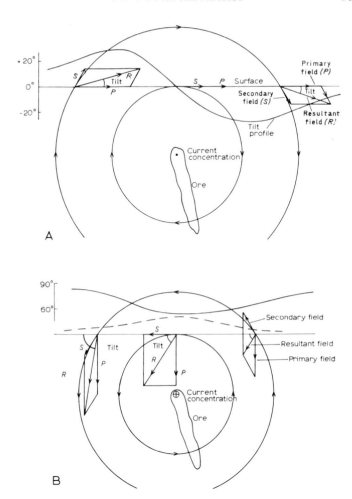

Fig. 32. Tilt of the electromagnetic field. A. Primary field horizontal. B. Primary field vertical.

The resultant field at any point is obtained by combining the primary and secondary fields by the parallelogram law of forces. Without going into the detailed theory, which is given in Appendix 10, it may be stated that provided the conductor is fairly good, as is often the case, the resultant vector is almost coincident with the major axis of the polarization ellipse. The tilt is therefore easily determined as follows. Hold a search coil at right angles to the profile and turn it around a horizontal diameter. In the position of minimum signal the resultant vector lies in the plane of the coil and the angle made by the coil with the horizontal gives the tilt.

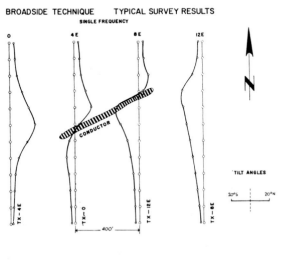

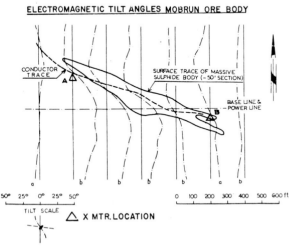

Fig.33A. Examples of tilt-angle surveys with the SE-200 outfit manufactured by Scintrex Ltd., Downsview, Canada.

In Fig.32A the resultant field dips above the horizon (positive tilt) on one side of the conductor and below the horizon (negative tilt) on the other. The conductor is located below the inflexion point, where also the tilt is zero.

In Fig.32B the field is vertical far from the conductor and inclines less steeply in its vicinity, the flattest inclination being obtained above the conductor. The dashed curve shows the angle of departure from the vertical (co-tilt) and is an alternative manner of plotting the anomaly.

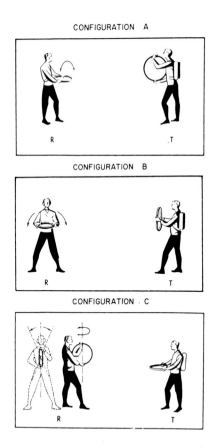

Fig.33B. Different coil configurations for the tilt-angle method. R = receiver; T = transmitter. (Courtesy of H.O. Seigel.)

Examples of tilt-angle surveys with a vertical loop as the primary source are shown in Fig.33. Tilt-angle profiles with a vertical primary field are shown in Fig.40.

The tilt-angle method was widely used in the early days of electromagnetic prospecting and, on account of the comparative simplicity of the apparatus needed, it is still a popular method, for example, in Canada. However, its precision and especially its resolution power are not very great and, apart from a rough location of the conductor, the method yields little quantitative information about the subsurface electric conductivity. Besides, the field from poor or deep-lying conductors is often so weak that the resultant field differs little in orientation from the primary field. The tilt-angle method thus has severe limitations of which the principal one is the fact that owing to the out-of-phase fields (to be discussed in the next section) the signal positions of the search coil are often very unsharp and impossible to determine accurately. It must be pointed out here that some of the modern methods such as Afmag and VLF, to which we shall turn later, are essentially tilt-angle methods.

AMPLITUDE AND PHASE

The modern methods of electromagnetic prospecting utilize certain other properties of the electromagnetic field. They depend, so to speak, upon decomposing the ellipse of polarization. It can be shown that the ellipse is a result of two oscillating magnetic fields of the same frequency – the frequency of the alternating source – but out of step with each other. The relationship of these two fields is most easily understood by fixing our attention on some definite spatial component of the total electromagnetic field at any point, say, the vertical or the horizontal component.

Any spatial component of the electromagnetic field is characterized, firstly by its amplitude and secondly by its phase with respect to the primary field.

The amplitude is an easily understood concept: it is the maximum value that the field strength attains at the observation point as it oscillates with the frequency in question. The amplitude is altered from its undisturbed magnitude as soon as there is a secondary field from a conductor.

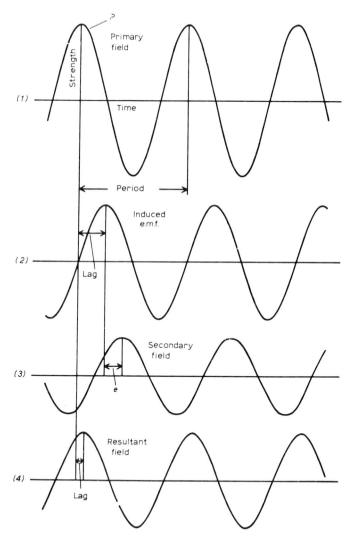

Fig. 34. Phase lags of induced voltage, secondary field and resultant field.

In order to grasp the idea of phase we refer to Fig.34. Here the sinusoidal curve P represents the primary field at an observation point on the surface. The primary field at a subsurface conductor will of course have a different amplitude but it will nevertheless be in step with P, attaining its maxima and minima at the same instant as P. The time interval between two successive maxima (or minima) is the period of the field, and its reciprocal, the number of oscillations in one second, is the frequency.

When the conductor is subjected to an alternating magnetic field, a voltage (electromotive force) of the same frequency is set up in it but this voltage lags behind the inducing field by a quarter of a period. In other words, it attains its maximum value (or, indeed, any corresponding phase) a quarter of a period later than the inducing field, as shown by the second curve in Fig.34.

Owing to the resistance of the conductor and its inductance (the tendency to oppose a change of the magnetic field linked with it), the current in the conductor lags behind the induced voltage and consequently behind the primary field. The secondary magnetic field produced by the induced current, being in phase with the current, also lags behind the primary alternating field. Curve 3 shows the secondary field at the observation point, with its extra phase lag e.

The bottom curve in Fig.34 is the sum of the first and the third curves and represents the resultant electromagnetic field at the observation point. This is the field which a detecting coil will pick up, and obviously it differs in amplitude from the primary field and lags a fraction of a period behind it.

The phase lag (fraction of a period) is, of course, a time delay, equal to lag multiplied by period, or in other words, lag divided by frequency.

THE PHASE ANGLE AND THE VECTOR DIAGRAM

There is another way of looking at phase differences. Suppose we let a complete period (whatever it may be) represent an angle of 360°. If the frequency is then, say, 1,000 c/sec, a phase difference of 1° between two fields means a time difference of $(1/360) \times (1/1,000)$ sec between the epochs at which the fields attain their respective maxima (or minima).

The phase angle enables us to represent the time relations between the primary, the secondary and the resultant fields very conveniently by means of a so-called vector diagram.

In Fig.35 the x-axis towards the right represents the epoch during one oscillation, when the primary field is maximum and the length of the vector $P(=OA)$ represents this maximum value, that is, the amplitude.

We now fix the convention that a vector making an anticlockwise angle with the sense of P is to be understood as lagging behind P. Consequently, the induced electromotive force is represented, because it lags one quarter period behind the primary field, by a vector making an anticlockwise angle of $90°$ (= 360/4) with the sense of P, that is, by a vector along the upward y-axis.

As the secondary field lags behind the electromotive force (e.m.f.) by a further fraction of a period, it is represented in Fig.35 by the arrow S drawn at the appropriate angle φ, measured anticlockwise from the e.m.f. vector. The length of S represents the amplitude of the secondary field.

If the conductor is very good, φ is almost $90°$ and the secondary field lags almost half a period ($180°$) behind the primary field. If the conductor is poor, φ is almost $0°$ and the secondary field lags a quarter of a period behind the primary field. Thus, the phase lag of the secondary field is a measure of the conductivity, the nearer the phase lag to $180°$ the better the conductor.

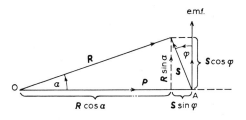

Fig.35. Vector diagram representing the phase relations between primary (P), secondary (S), and resultant (R) fields.

Note that the directions of the vectors in Fig.35 represent only the mutual time relations and not the spatial directions of the various fields. Spatially, all the fields in the diagram are supposed to be in one particular direction, say, the vertical.

REAL AND IMAGINARY COMPONENTS

The vector diagram leads to some further concepts of great importance in modern electromagnetic prospecting.

The projection of R on the x-axis is $R \cos \alpha$. As it makes an angle of zero degree with P it must be in phase with it, and attain its maxima and minima in step with the primary field. This "in-phase component" is also called the "real component".

The projection of R on the y-axis, $R \sin \alpha$, is a vector turned $90°$ anticlockwise from P. It is called the out-of-phase, quadrature or imaginary component, and attains its maxima and minima a quarter of a period later than the primary field.

Similarly, the secondary field S can be resolved into a real component of magnitude $S \sin \varphi$ and an imaginary component of magnitude $S \cos \varphi$.

Although a field which is $90°$ out of phase with a primary field is usually termed imaginary, there is nothing imaginary about it. It is as real as the real component. The adjectives real and imaginary in this connection are of historical origin and do not have their dictionary meanings.

It should be realized that any *spatial* component of the electromagnetic field, say, the northward one, the eastward one, the upward one etc., can be separated into two *electromagnetic* components, one real and one imaginary, that is, one in phase and one $90°$ (quarter period) out of phase with the primary field.

The ratio of the strength of the real (Re) and imaginary (Im) components of the secondary field is related to the phase angle φ (being its tangent), and can also be employed for characterizing the conductivity instead of the phase angle.

The larger the Re/Im anomaly ratio, the better is the conductor.

An Re/Im ratio of 1.0, corresponding to a phase lag of 45° (one-eighth period), is often arbitrarily considered as representing a "medium" conductor.

Theory and practice show, however, that matters are not always quite as straightforward as the above simplified description would suggest. For example, the Re/Im anomaly ratio varies depending upon the position of the observation point with respect to the conductor and upon the frequency of the primary field. The explanation of such effects is complicated but their existence means that care and experience are needed before one can reliably predict the conductivity of an orebody from simple rules of thumb.

MEASUREMENT OF THE REAL AND IMAGINARY COMPONENTS

The principle behind the measurement of the real and imaginary components of an unknown alternating voltage induced in a search coil is very similar to that behind the measurement of an unknown direct current voltage (Fig.25). The difference is that *two* standard adjustable voltages, which differ 90° in phase from each other must be available with which the given voltage is compared. Such voltages can be obtained by suitable circuits including electric capacitances and inductances.

Instruments for this purpose are known as alternating current compensators or bridges and they are included in the commercially available e.m. prospecting equipments. The a.c. compensators can be calibrated to read either the amplitude and phase of the field picked up by the receiver coil, or the magnitudes of the real and imaginary components of the field.

Some electromagnetic methods employ amplitude and phase readings, others employ real and imaginary components, but these are only alternative ways of describing the time relations in an electromagnetic field and are equivalent to each other.

A discussion of a.c. compensators will be found in Parasnis (1966).

CLASSIFICATION OF ELECTROMAGNETIC METHODS

A great variety of methods differing in source–receiver layouts has been employed in electromagnetic ore prospecting. The most convenient manner of classifying them is to divide them into two main categories: (*1*) methods in which the source of the field is stationary and the receiver mobile; (*2*) methods in which the source as well as the receiver is mobile. Each of these may be further subdivided according to the details of operation but only the more important subdivisions are included here for description.

(*1*) *Fixed-source methods*
    (*a*) Tilt-angle method.
    (*b*) Bieler–Watson method.
    (*c*) Two-frame method for amplitude comparison.
    (*d*) Compensator or Sundberg method for real and imaginary component measurements.
    (*e*) Turam method for amplitude-ratios and phase differences.

(*2*) *Moving source–receiver methods*
    These methods, which use portable transmitter and receiver coils, have been variously labelled as Slingram, Loop-frame, EMG, VEM, HEM etc. They differ from each other only in the transmitter–receiver configurations employed. An infinite variety of mutual coil-orientations are, of course, possible but not all are practicable. We shall here consider the three commonly used ones:
    (*a*) Coils horizontal and coplanar.
    (*b*) Coils vertical and coplanar.
    (*c*) Coils vertical and coaxial.
    Other systems in which, for example, one coil is horizontal and the other vertical are sometimes used but these will be omitted here.
    The order (*a*) to (*e*) under *1* is roughly that in which the electromagnetic methods were gradually developed between about 1920 and 1940, mainly in Sweden, America, Canada, Australia and Germany. The years between 1940 and 1950 saw the development of group *2* methods, the initial impetus for which seems to have come from Swedish prospectors.

FIXED-SOURCE METHODS

Tilt-angle

This method has already been described in a previous section. It may be added that the Mason-Slichter-Hay method and the Radiore method, which have been referred to in the literature (for example Eve and Keys, 1956) are essentially tilt-angle methods. The theory and some practical examples of the tilt-angle method have also been discussed in detail by Parasnis (1966).

Bieler–Watson

This method uses a large loop laid horizontally on the ground as the source of the primary field. The operation is based on the assumption that the major axis of the ellipse of polarization, representing the real component of the resultant field, is nearly vertical and the minor axis, representing the imaginary component, is horizontal.

The receiver system consists of two mutually perpendicular rectangular coils, each about $1' \times 2'$, of which the horizontal one, according to assumption, picks up the real component; the other coil is vertical and picks up the imaginary component. It is the latter component that is measured, in terms of the real component, by balancing it, after shifting its phase, against a part of the voltage induced in the horizontal coil.

Two readings are taken at each station, one with the vertical coil facing north and the other with it facing east. The readings are added vectorially by the parallelogram law, to obtain the direction and magnitude of the total imaginary component at the point.

The interpretation of the vectors obtained with the Bieler–Watson method is not very obvious (for field examples see Heiland, 1946, p.805; Eve and Keys, 1956, pp.173–174). The method is not used now to any great extent.

Two-frame method

Since the procedures based on the tilt of the electromagnetic field alone do not yield sufficient accuracy and are slow in operation, it becomes necessary to search for better methods. The Swedish two-frame method, a first step towards the goal, was designed in the 1920's. It measures the ratio of the vertical field amplitudes at two adjacent points along a line. It is an ingenious method requiring no compensator for the purpose.

Although the method has now been superseded by more efficient variants, we shall consider it in some detail because many of the principles involved are of importance in connection with the compensator and Turam methods to be discussed later.

The primary field is produced by a loop or a grounded cable through which an alternating current of low frequency, say 500 c/sec, is flowing. Two receiver coils, placed horizontally at A and B (normally 10 or 20 m apart) are connected through an amplifier to a pair of headphones in such a way that their currents oppose each other. If

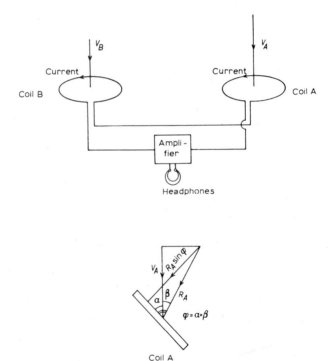

Fig. 36. Principle of the Swedish two-frame method.

the fields normal to the coils are not equal, a note will be heard in the phones. On tilting one of the coils through an appropriate angle the sound is, however, reduced to a minimum and in some cases a complete silence may be obtained.

Suppose that the coil A has to be tilted. Then (Fig.36) the effective amplitude of the field acting on the coil A is $R_A \sin \varphi$ where R_A is the amplitude of the total electromagnetic vector at A. If β is the tilt of R_A from the vertical, the vertical field at A is $R_A \cos \beta = V_A$, say, so that $R_A = V_A/\cos \beta$. Hence, when the coils are balanced against each other:

$$R_A \sin \varphi = \frac{V_A \sin \varphi}{\cos \beta} = V_B$$

or:

$$\frac{V_A}{V_B} = \frac{\cos \beta}{\sin \varphi} \tag{5.1}$$

which gives the desired ratio of the vertical field amplitudes at A and B.

The actual operation of the method is as follows. First, the polarization ellipse at A is determined by turning the coil A alone around a vertical axis, until the sound is minimum (Fig.37A). During this procedure the two coils are not connected to each other. The coil is then turned round, still in the vertical plane, through 90° (Fig. 37B). Finally, it is turned around a horizontal axis CD in this position and the tilt of the field (β) is determined from the minimum signal position. The two coils A and B (the latter being kept horizontal) are now joined in opposition and the angle φ referred to above is determined by tilting the coil A. An alternative procedure of operation is described elsewhere (Parasnis, 1966).

As the primary field varies with the distance (r) from the source, there is a normal field-ratio between two adjacent points A and B, for which the observed ratio must be corrected. In the case of a long cable as the source, the normal fields are proportional to $1/r_A$ and $1/r_B$ where r_A and r_B are the distances of A and B from the cable. The

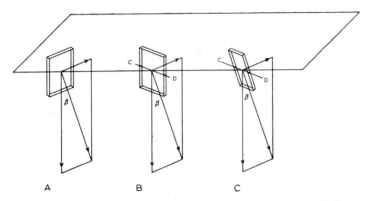

Fig.37. Operational stages of the observations in the two-frame method.

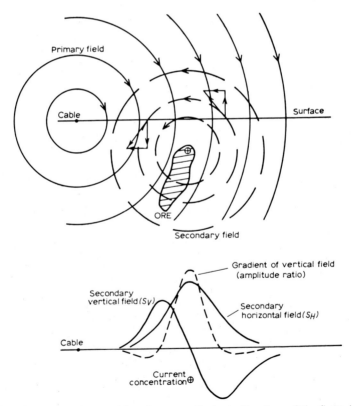

Fig.38. Long conductor with strike perpendicular to the plane of the figure in the field of a current-carrying cable.

correction is made by dividing the observed ratio V_A/V_B by the normal ratio $(1/r_A)/(1/r_B) = r_B/r_A$.

As the corrected or reduced ratio $V_A r_A/V_B r_B$ will equal 1.0 if there are no subsurface conductors, its departures from this value immediately indicate a conductor.

To gain an idea of the electromagnetic indication obtained with the two-frame method we shall consider a long sheet-like conductor in the field of a current-carrying cable (Fig.38). Both the cable and the plate are assumed to be perpendicular to the plane of the paper. If the primary current is instantaneously flowing into the paper its magnetic field lines are concentric circles in the clockwise direction. Obviously, the normal field in the horizontal plane of the cable is vertically downwards.

The secondary current may be assumed to be concentrated along the upper edge of the plate but instantaneously flowing out from the paper. Its magnetic field lines are therefore circles in the anticlockwise direction. Between the cable and the conductor this secondary field has a vertical component that is directed downwards at points on the ground surface, that is, in the same sense as the instantaneous primary field. The component is therefore reckoned positive. On the "far side" of the conductor the secondary vertical component is negative, while directly above the ore it is zero since the secondary field is here horizontal.

Fig.38 shows the secondary vertical component and its gradient, which is a measure of the normalized ratio $V_A r_A/V_B r_B$, in a schematic manner. It will be seen that the conductor is located below the maximum value of the amplitude ratio.

Fig.39 shows some laboratory two-frame curves obtained above a metal sheet having different attitudes with respect to the primary field lines, which, in this experiment, were due to a rectangular loop and not a long cable. It should be noted that the x-coordinate in this figure is the position of the rear coil, and not the position of the point midway between the coils. This is the reason for the displacement of the maximum with respect to the conductor edge.

It is most interesting to note that the electromagnetic indication above the conductor dipping as shown in 2 is practically nil because the lines of force are almost parallel to it, and consequently induce very weak currents in it. An ore sheet with such an attitude might be missed (in any fixed source method) *if the surrounding medium is non-conducting*. In case the surrounding medium (or the overburden) has appreciable conductivity the distributed currents induced in the one or the other or both will be collected by the ore conductor on

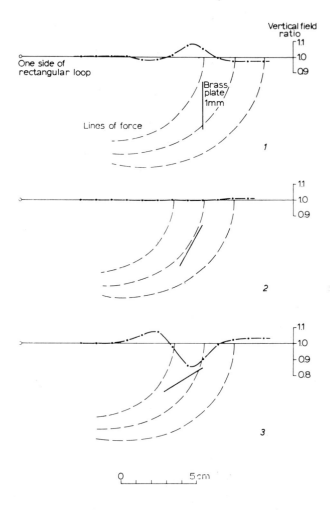

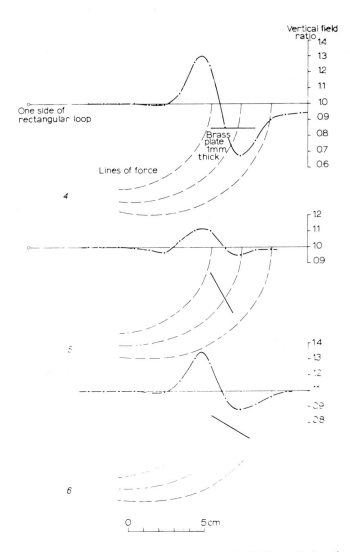

Fig. 39. Laboratory electromagnetic curves for the vertical-field amplitude ratio above a metal sheet having different attitudes. (Measurements by Öhrn, 1934.) (Courtesy of BGAB.)

120   ELECTROMAGNETIC METHODS

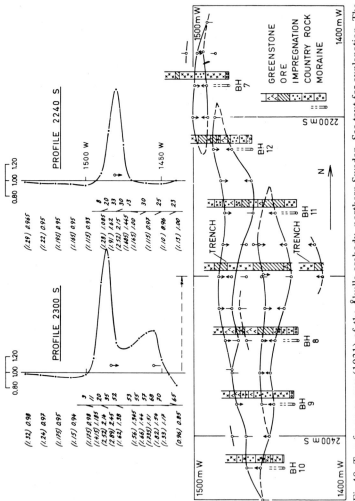

Fig. 40. Two-frame survey (1931) of the Åkulla orebody, northern Sweden. See text for explanation. The body shown was discovered and delineated by electromagnetic work. It yielded about one million tons of

account of its relatively good conductivity and an indication can still be obtained even if no magnetic flux cuts the sheet conductor and induces secondary currents in it. This is also often the reason behind the fact that buried bare wires, rails, pipes etc. produce electromagnetic indications although they present a negligible area to the primary flux lines.

Properly speaking, the ratio maximum does not indicate the conductor as such but the secondary current concentration in it. This fact has an important practical bearing because, owing to a phenomenon called the skin effect shown by alternating currents, the secondary current tends to concentrate on the side of the conductor towards the source of the primary field. Consequently, if the conductor is thick it is possible to estimate its width from the distance between the ratio-maxima obtained with the cable on either side of the conductor once this has been located.

The upper part of Fig.40 shows a couple of typical two-frame profiles. These were measured across the Åkulla orebody in the Skellefte district of northern Sweden.

The short lines along the profiles denote the azimuth of the (nearly vertical) polarization plane. The bracketed numbers are the observed ratios, the non-bracketed ones beside them are the normalized ratios. Finally, the numbers nearest the profile-axis are the co-tilt angles (β in Fig.37). Notice that the co-tilt angles vary approximately as implied in Fig.32B. For plotting convention see p.117.

In the lower part of Fig.40 are plotted the positions of the ratio maxima measured in opposite directions along a set of parallel lines. The arrows point away from the source of the primary field. The boundary of the ore lens, as inferred by joining these maxima, agrees very well with that ascertained in subsequent drillings. This survey was carried out in 1931 and the ore, which contained pyrite and chalcopyrite, was mined out between 1944 and 1950.

The two-frame method has been very extensively used in Sweden as late as 1952, and its success in locating conductors has been striking. For a further discussion of it, the reader is referred to a paper by Parasnis (1966).

The compensator or Sundberg method

In the two-frame method the balance of voltages is never perfect because there is a residual signal in the telephones due to the phase difference between the fields acting on the search coils. This drawback is overcome in the compensator method devised by Sundberg, which measures the real as well as the imaginary component of the electromagnetic field, thereby also allowing inferences to be drawn about the conductivity of a subsurface conductor (cf. section *Real and imaginary components*). As far as the author is aware, the only commercially available compensator outfit at present is manufactured by the ABEM Company of Stockholm.

The layout is shown in Fig.41. The primary field is produced by a several kilometers long, grounded, insulated cable, fed by alternating current of low frequency. The measurements consist in reading the real and imaginary components of the electric voltage induced in a search coil placed at the observation point. As the measurement of the imaginary component implies a time reference, a reference voltage is

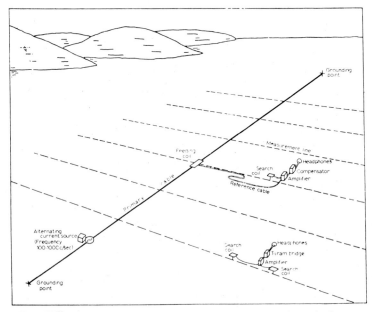

Fig.41. Layout for compensator and Turam electromagnetic methods.

needed. This is provided by means of an auxiliary or feeding coil permanently stationed near the cable and connected to the compensator by an insulated, two-conductor cable.

The voltage in the search coil is directly proportional to the amplitude of the magnetic field (flux density, Wb/m^2) acting on the coil and to the current strength (ampere, A) in the cable. Therefore, the compensator readings of the voltage in the search coil can be conveniently expressed in terms of the magnetic field per unit primary current (Wb/m^2 A or, since the flux densities involved are very weak, as nano-Wb/m^2 A, that is γ/A)* rather than in volt.

The observations in the compensator method are taken as the search coil is advanced in steps of, say, 20 m, along lines perpendicular to the primary cable. The reference cable, wound on a reel, is laid off as the search coil and the compensator are carried to successive points. In many surveys it suffices to measure the real and imaginary components of the vertical field (V) for which the search coil must be held horizontally; but a complete knowledge of the electromagnetic field involves also the measurement of the real and imaginary components of the horizontal fields parallel and perpendicular to the profiles, denoted by H_1, and H_2 respectively, to obtain which the coil must be held vertically in the appropriate azimuth. From these six determinations, three of the real and three of the imaginary component, we can construct the total real and total imaginary electromagnetic vector at each point in the same way we constructed the total magnetic vector in Fig.20.

On level ground the four horizontal components should all be normally zero. In practice they are not exactly zero owing to stray effects. Values of H_1 and H_2 differing significantly from zero are therefore the values of the secondary horizontal fields.

As for the vertical field, only its imaginary component is normally zero so that measured values of it, differing from zero, directly give the imaginary component of the secondary vertical field.

Consider now the real component of the secondary vertical field. In order to obtain this we must subtract the primary vertical field

---

* In the older literature the units microgauss and microgauss per ampere will be found to be used. 1 nano-Wb/m^2 = 1 γ = 10 μG.

from the measured real component. For a long, straight cable the primary field is given by $\mu_0 I/2\pi R$ (Wb/m^2) or, inserting the value of μ_0 (p.19), $200I/R$ (γ), that is, $200/R$ (γ/A), where the current I in the cable is in amperes and the distance R is in metres.

If the cable and the point are not on the same level the primary field strength is reduced by a factor cos θ, where θ is the "angle of sight" of the point from the cable. The true vertical field is then obtained by dividing the measured one by cos θ. In this case there is also a spurious anomaly in the horizontal field H_1 (the field *parallel* to the profile) equal to $(200I/R)$ sin θ. These various considerations tacitly assume that the cable itself is straight, or reasonably so, and not undulating because of violent topography in the direction in which it is laid. If this condition is not met with, the topographic corrections to compensator measurements become very complicated.

The secondary vertical and horizontal fields, S_v and S_h respectively due to a long subsurface concentration, are shown in Fig.38. Mathematically these fields are expressed as:

$$S_v = \text{constant} \cdot \frac{x}{x^2 + a^2} \qquad (5.2)$$

$$S_h = \text{constant} \cdot \frac{a}{x^2 + a^2} \qquad (5.3)$$

where a is the depth and x is the distance from the epicentre.

The conductor is located below the inflexion point of S_v or the maximum point of S_h. The distance between the positive maximum and the negative minimum of S_v is twice the depth of a long current concentration. Alternatively the depth is equal to the distance from the maximum at which the horizontal field falls to half the maximum value.

A word of caution is not out of place in this connection since the ideal form of anomaly curves represented by eq.(5.2) and (5.3) is not always met with in practice. Experience shows that the simple rules above tend to give conductor depths which are too large, often by a factor of 2–4. The physical reason for this is not completely understood but, in part, the effect seems to be due to the electric conductivity of the overburden.

Thus, in the example of compensator measurements in Fig.42 the simple rule would indicate a depth of 54 m to the upper surface of the conductor, or rather the current concentration in it, while the actual depth is probably only 25 m. The dashed curve in the figure is calculated from eq.(5.2) assuming the depth a = 54 m. The conductor here is a graphitic shale embedded in sericite quartzite and is a key horizon in the district.

Another example of compensator measurements is shown in Fig.43, which is a profile across the Rudtjebäcken ore (42% S, 4% Zn, 1% Cu) in the Adak area of northern Sweden. The orebody which, like all the other orebodies in the area, was discovered by geoelectrical work, is a sheet, about 900 m long in the strike direction and about 300 m along the dip (25° from the horizontal). It has a thickness varying between 1 and 8 m. The mineralization continues up-dip towards the bedrock surface but soon passes into poor impregnation of pyrite. The electrical conductivity of the orebody varies along dip, being about tenfold better in the lower parts than the upper ones.

The calculated points (open circles) shown in Fig.43 rest on the simplifying assumption that there is a system of four induced currents in the orebody. Two of these currents are in one direction and situated at 54 and 100 m, while two counter-currents, which complete the electric circuit through the body, run at a depth of 250 m and "infinity".

It is interesting to note that the inflexion point of the imaginary component indicates a point in the orebody further up-dip than the real component. This is an instance of a frequent observation that the "imaginary" current concentration, i.e., the part of the secondary current which attains its maxima and minima a quarter period after the primary field, occurs nearer the edge of a conductor than does the "real" current concentration. Fig.43 also shows the total electromagnetic vectors.

The operational range of the compensator method is determined by the length of the reference cable that can be conveniently transported in the field. Another consideration limiting the range is that if

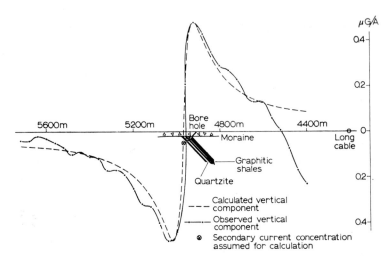

Fig.42. Electromagnetic compensator indication (microgauss per ampere) in the real component of the secondary vertical field on conductive graphite shales. Mossatjärn area, northern Sweden. (Courtesy of BGAB.)

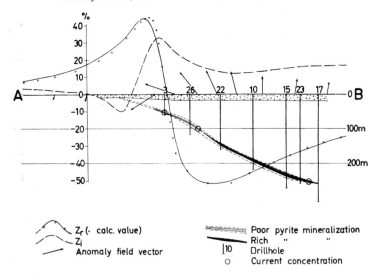

Fig.43. Electromagnetic compensator measurements across the Rudtjebäcken ore sheet, northern Sweden. Z_r = real component of vertical field. Z_i = imaginary component of vertical field. (After Werner, 1958.)

the cable length becomes excessive, its electrical resistance, inductance and capacity shift the phase of the reference voltage itself and therefore also the time reference needed to ascertain the imaginary component. The maximum distance from the primary cable to which reliable measurements can be made in the compensator method seems to be of the order of 1–2 km.

The Swedish Geological Survey has developed and successfully operated, a modification of the compensator method in which the reference voltage is transmitted to the compensator by a very high-frequency radio wave, thus avoiding the use of a cable connection. With this arrangement it is possible to measure outwards to several kilometres from the primary cable. The basic data collected are, of course, the same.

The Turam method

This method, also of Swedish origin and devised by H. Hedström, is a further development of the two-frame method on the one hand and of the compensator method on the other (Hedström, 1937). (The Swedish equivalent of "two-frame" is "två-ram". The word Turam is coined by replacing "två" by its archaic form "tu".)

Two identical search coils are held a fixed distance apart, say 10 or 20 m, and measurements are made of the ratio of the amplitudes of and the phase difference between the two electromagnetic fields, as the coils are moved to successive stations along a profile. The phase difference is expressed in degrees (cf. section *The phase angle and the vector diagram*).

Usually the coils are held horizontally and the arrangement then compares the vertical components of the electromagnetic fields.

Turam measurements are thus essentially similar to two-frame measurements, with the difference that the comparison of the electromagnetic fields is rendered complete and also much more accurate by the bridge type apparatus used for determining the ratio and the phase. The ratios can be measured with an accuracy of about 5 parts in 1,000 and phase difference to about 0.2°. From the discussion in sections *Amplitude and phase* and *The phase angle and the vector diagram*, it is clear that the latter figure is equivalent to an accuracy of about 1.11 μsec in the measurement of the time difference between the epochs at which the fields in the two coils attain their maxima (or minima), assuming a frequency of 500 c/sec for the primary field.

As in the two-frame method the measured amplitude ratios must be reduced to take account of the normal ratios existing between the fields at pairs of adjacent points. The successive reduced ratios are equal to 1.0 in the absence of subsurface conductors. No correction is needed, however, for the phase differences as these are normally zero (if the near-surface layers are poorly conducting).

The Turam method has the operational advantage that it requires no reference cable between the measuring system and the source of the electromagnetic field. However, as the voltages in the search coils become very small at large distances from the source and cannot be compared accurately there is a practical limit to the distance, out to which measurements can be made from the source. The great advantage is, of course, that the measuring crew can move over directly to a parallel profile. In the compensator method the cable must be rewound when it is exhausted before the measurements can be continued.

Like the two-frame method the Turam is especially well suited for detecting relatively shallow and steeply dipping conductors. The depth of exploration can be controlled to some extent by altering the coil distance, a larger coil separation giving a greater depth penetration.

Over a conductor, the reduced ratios in Turam attain a maximum (as in the two-frame method) while the phase differences attain a negative minimum.[1] The general shape of both anomaly curves is similar to that of the two-frame curves in Fig.39.

An example of a Turam profile is shown in Fig.44, where the coordinate plotted along the x-axis is the position of the forward search coil. The profile is one across the Kimheden orebody discussed in Chapter 4, under the heading *Examples of SP surveys*. It will be

---

[1] This implies the convention that the phase difference is expressed as the lead of the e.m. field in the *forward* frame over that in the rear frame. The dial of the Turam equipment manufactured by the ABEM Company, Stockholm is calibrated with this convention.

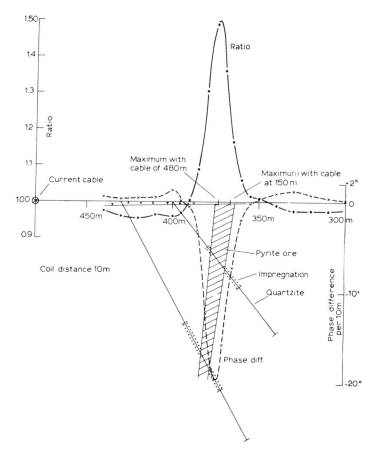

Fig.44. Electromagnetic Turam profile (ratio and phase difference per 10 m) across the Kimheden orebody in Fig.27. Profile 720E. Frequency 350 c/sec. (Courtesy of BGAB.)

noticed that the width of the ore is fairly well indicated by the distance between the maxima obtained with the primary source on each side of the conductor. The width estimates possible in Turam work are more accurate than those in the two-frame method owing to the tendency of the phase minimum to occur farther out towards the edge than the ratio maximum.

In connection with the width estimates based on electromagnetic anomalies it should be remembered that they are reliable only if the conductor in question can be looked upon as homogeneous. Grossly. erroneous results may be obtained if, for example, the conductor consists of a vein of differing resistivity cutting an impregnation zone.

Turam measurements can be used to obtain the actual real and imaginary components of the electromagnetic field. The procedure is briefly indicated in Appendix 4.

The interpretation of Turam measurements has been considered in great detail in a paper by Bosschart (1964).

LOOP LAYOUTS

In the discussion so far we have mostly assumed the source of the primary field to be a long, grounded, insulated current-carrying cable. But the primary field can also be produced by an insulated, plane, rectangular (or circular) loop laid flat on the ground, or by a suitably supported vertical loop. We shall here consider only horizontal loops, whose typical dimensions may be, say, 1,000 m X 200 m but much larger loops have also been employed.

With the grounded cable, the subsurface conductors are excited not only inductively but also galvanically in the sense that the return current from one grounded end to the other tends to concentrate preferentially within subsurface conductors instead of being distributed at large in the ground. This is often advantageous if great depth penetration is desired because the indications obtained are stronger than would otherwise be the case. However, the normal field may be disturbed because of the return current, distributing itself in the overburden, especially at large distances from the cable, and the interpretation of the anomalies becomes very difficult at times. There is no return current problem with loops as the source.

On the other hand, loops are not as convenient to lay out as cables. Moreover, the calculation of the normal field (for the compensator method) and normal ratios (for the two-frame and Turam methods) as well as the calculation of topographic corrections if the ground is not level is more complicated for loops.

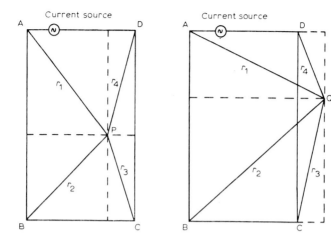

Fig.45. Rectangular loop.

One very important advantage of loop sources is, however, that they can be employed even when the overburden layers are badly conducting or insulating (e.g., in arid areas, on frozen grounds and lakes etc.). The cable source is out of the question here since no electrical connection can be secured with the ground.

All the electromagnetic methods discussed up to now can be used with a large loop instead of the cable as the primary source, and measurements may be made inside as well as outside the loop. The only change needed is to replace the normal field and normal ratios appropriately.

Consider a rectangular loop as in Fig.45. The vertical field (Wb/m^2) at an internal point P due to the current I flowing in the loop is given by (see Appendix 3):

$$V_P = 10^{-7} I \left(\frac{r_1}{A_1} + \frac{r_2}{A_2} + \frac{r_3}{A_3} + \frac{r_4}{A_4} \right) \tag{5.4}$$

where the r's denote the distances of P from the corners of the loop and the A's the areas of the sub-rectangles having the respective r's as diagonals. For an external point such as Q:

$$V_Q = 10^{-7} I \left(\frac{r_1}{A_1} + \frac{r_2}{A_2} - \frac{r_3}{A_3} - \frac{r_4}{A_4} \right) \tag{5.5}$$

The fields at neighbouring points can be found in a similar manner
and the necessary Turam ratios calculated.

MOVING SOURCE–RECEIVER METHODS

This class of methods is characterized by the fact that besides the
receiver arrangement, the source of the primary field is also mobile,
consisting of a light-weight portable coil. In principle, however, the

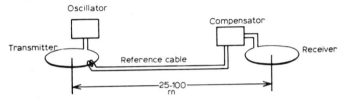

Fig.46. Layout of moving source–receiver method.

Fig.47A. Electromagnetic gun (moving source–receiver outfit) in field operation.

Fig.47B. Complete self-contained Turam outfit comprising primary-source cable, motor generator, two receiver coils (staffs), and ratio and phase meter. (Courtesy of ABEM Company, Stockholm.)

layout is the same (Fig.46) as that of the compensator method with a loop source.

The source coil (transmitter) is fed by alternating current from a portable 1−2 W oscillator and a fixed reference voltage taken from it is fed into a compensator. The voltage in the receiver is decomposed into two components, one in phase, and the other 90° (one quarter period) out of phase, with the reference voltage, and the magnitude of each is determined by comparison with the reference voltage.

The transmitter and receiver are held a fixed distance apart and moved together in the direction of their line, which may be parallel or perpendicular to the presumed strike of the conductors depending upon the orientations of the transmitter and receiver.

Moving source−receiver outfits are commercially available from a number of different firms (ABEM, Sweden; McPhar, Canada; Scintrex, Canada are some). The photograph in Fig.47A shows the ABEM electromagnetic gun (EMG) in field operation. In this outfit the conventional coils have been replaced by staffs wound on ferrite cores.

The field work with the moving source−receiver systems is relatively simple; the survey need not be rigidly bound to stake lines and the systems allow great flexibility in the detailed electromagnetic investigation of a conductor, once this has been located. Further, a crew of two or three suffices for the operations, one man carrying the oscillator on his back and the transmitter round his waist, the other carrying the receiver coil and the compensator in a similar fashion.

For these various reasons the moving source−receiver systems are the most popular electromagnetic systems. For practical reasons the systems must use relatively small coil-separations (25−100 m), with the result that stray anomalies due to near-surface conductivity variations are liable to interfere with the anomalies from deeper sources.

In general, the source and the receiver are not rigidly connected to each other. The distance between them is kept constant by using the length of the reference cable as a measuring tape.

Moving source−receiver outfits are usually constructed to read the real and imaginary components of the field at the receiver in percent of the primary field at it when the system is placed on neutral ground.

Such ground is often provided by exposures of rocks like granite, basalt, sandstone etc.

The transmitter–receiver distance having been selected, the system is placed on neutral ground and, by turning built-in potentiometer screws, the compensator dials are adjusted to read zero for no signal in the receiver coil which means that the primary field has been compensated. After this adjustment, the departures of the dial readings from zero directly yield the secondary field components. (The real-component dial markings in some commercial outfits are such that they show the actual field, in arbitrary units, rather than the anomaly. The dial will then read, for example 100, on neutral ground. The secondary field (anomaly) is given by the actual dial reading minus 100.)

The magnetic field, due to a small current-carrying coil, varies inversely as the cube of the distance from the coil so that a change of 1% in the nominal source–receiver distance produces a spurious anomaly reading of 3% in the real component of the field picked up by the receiver. Thus, if the source–receiver separation is 40 m this must be kept constant within 13 cm ($^1/_3$% of 40 m) if an overall accuracy of 1 percent in the measured field reading is aimed at. Consequently, it is essential to ensure that the reference cable is taut every time a reading is taken.

Owing to the difficulty of keeping the source–receiver distance precisely constant, it is not possible, using the reference cable as a tape, to obtain an effective accuracy of better than ½–1% of the primary field.

In an apparatus named the beam-slingram constructed at the Boliden Mining Company in Sweden, the source and receiver are mounted rigidly with respect to each other at the ends of a hollow (split) cylindrical aluminium beam. The field at the receiver is measured in parts per million of the normal primary field, instead of in percent, and a reproducibility of about 20 p.p.m. has been achieved. However, the stray anomalies are often of the order of 100–500 p.p.m. and the effective indications of orebodies above this geological noise level are of approximately the same relative strength as those with the ordinary systems.

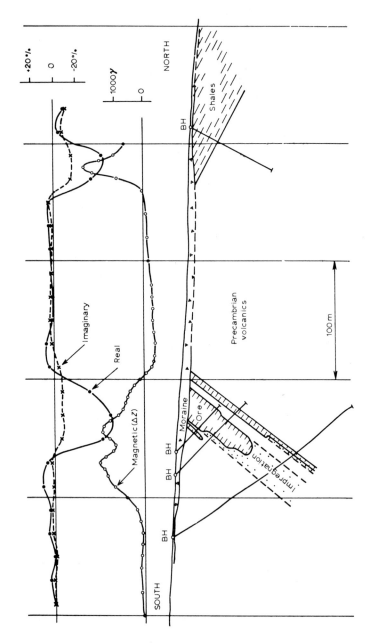

Fig.48A. Moving source–receiver profile in the Kankberg area, northern Sweden. Horizontal coplanar coils. Separation 60 m, frequency 3,600 c/sec. (Courtesy of BGAB.)

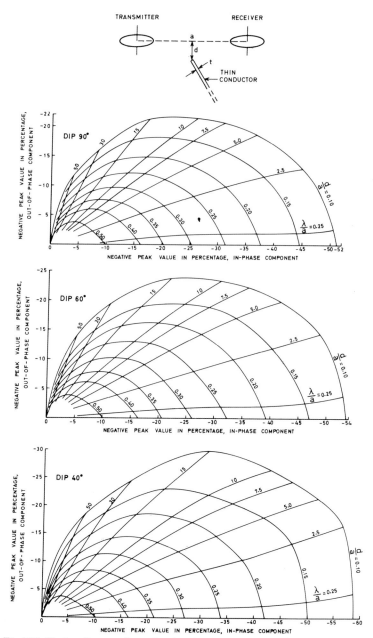

Fig.48B. Vector diagrams for estimating depth and resistivity/thickness parameter of thin conductors from anomalies obtained with the horizontal, coplanar
coil-system. (After Nair et al., 1968.)

The moving source–receiver configurations which we shall consider below are all symmetrical ones and in using them it is convenient to refer to the midpoint of the transmitter–receiver line as the observation point. This convention will be adopted throughout in what follows. It should also be noted that no matter how complicated the geometry of subsurface conductors, it is immaterial whether a symmetrical configuration is advanced with the transmitter in the rear or the receiver in the rear. Configurations are sometimes used in which one of the coils is vertical and the other horizontal but the anomalies then depend upon the direction of approach and an isoanomaly chart in such cases often shows a "herring bone" pattern if the survey is made in the normal zig-zag way. The interpretation of such patterns is unnecessarily tedious so that symmetrical configurations should in general be preferred.

We shall consider three configurations in turn.

(1) Coils horizontal and coplanar

Of all the moving source–receiver systems used in ground electromagnetic work this one is probably the most common.

The system is advanced in the direction of the transmitter–receiver line which, in turn, is perpendicular to the geological strike or to the presumed longitudinal direction of the ore. The system may be run parallel to the strike as well, which the experienced geophysicist might find desirable in detailed surveys, but the pattern of anomalies is then rather complicated.

Typical real and imaginary component curves above a sheet-like orebody are shown in Fig.48A. At a large distance from the conductor the anomalies in the field picked up by the receiver are naturally zero. As the coils approach the conductor both anomaly components increase above zero, reach a maximum and start decreasing. When the system straddles across the ore sheet the components become negative, the minima being obtained directly above the ore. The asymmetry in the curves is diagnostic of the dip of the conductor, the side-maximum being greater on the down-dip side. A vertical conductor yields a symmetrical curve. A method for estimating the dip from the asymmetry in the positive maxima has been devised by Nair et al. (1968).

The ratio of the real to the imaginary anomaly minimum is large (6.3) and indicates a very good conductor (see p.111). It is also of interest to note that the strong anomaly to the extreme north along the same profile is caused by graphite-bearing schists (phyllites).

Provided that the frequency is not too high and the overburden effects are negligible, the depth and the resistivity/thickness ratio of thin and steeply dipping sheets can be fairly accurately estimated from the anomaly directly above the ore. Diagrams for this purpose for sheet-like ores dipping at various angles are given in Fig.48B. The pair of real and imaginary component readings directly above the ore, when read into the appropriate diagram yields d/a, the ratio of the conductor depth to the coil separation and the parameter λ/a. In the latter parameter $\lambda = 10^7 \, \rho/vt$ where ρ (Ohm-m) is the resistivity, t(m) the conductor thickness and v the frequency (c/sec). Since a and v are known, the depth and the ratio ρ/t can be estimated. Under certain circumstances it is even possible to estimate ρ and t separately within certain limits, by making multifrequency measurements (Parasnis, 1971).

Fig.49A shows the effect of varying the transmitter–receiver separation in a horizontal coplanar system, in steps, from 60 to 8 m. The ore zone in question has a length of about 1.5 km (perpendicular to the plane represented by the figure) and an average width of some 45 m. The predominant conducting mineral is pyrite but the grade is fairly low across the entire width of the zone, except within a 5 m thick lens on the footwall side where the pyrite content is high.

In the first four cases shown the anomaly minima coincide with the position of the ore lens which is undoubtedly the sole cause of the electromagnetic anomalies. (Note that the imaginary component is plotted negative upwards, for convenience.) It seems as if the adjoining conducting zone produces no effect of its own. This is an interesting phenomenon which is very often observed in this area (and no doubt elsewhere in the world also). It has an obvious bearing on the interpretation of electromagnetic anomalies and the placing of drillholes.

The explanation of the phenomenon is that the secondary currents induced in the thin ore lens are so strong on account of the lens' high electrical conductivity that their counter-magnetic field completely annuls the field to which the broad zone would otherwise be subjected. Consequently, no currents are induced in the broad zone and it is not indicated by the electromagnetic measurements. In the absence of the lens, the zone would however be indicated!

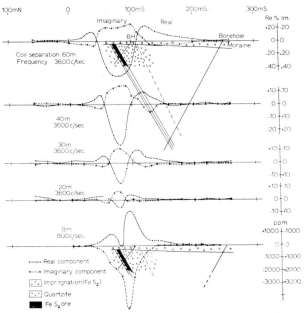

Fig.49A. Moving source–receiver measurements along a profile across the Kedträsk pyrite orebody, northern Sweden, showing variation of anomaly with coil separation. (Courtesy of BGAB.)

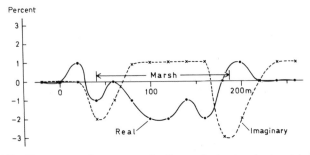

Fig.49B. Electromagnetic response of a flat conductor to a horizontal coplanar system. Coil separation 60 m, frequency 3,600 c/sec. Area: Vindfall, Sweden. (Courtesy BGAB.)

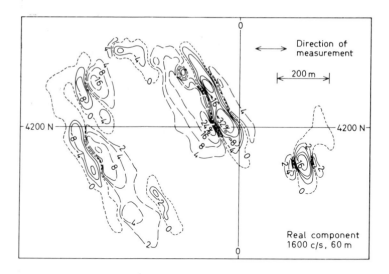

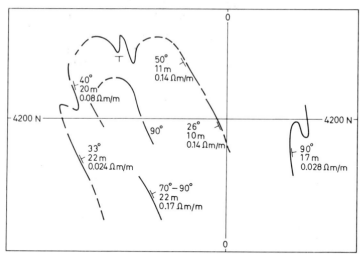

Fig.49C. Delineation of a syncline by electromagnetic measurements with a horizontal, coplanar coil system. Svartliden area, Sweden. The lower part shows the inferred depths, dips and resistivity/thickness ratios of the conducting horizon in the syncline. (Courtesy BGAB.)

The first four cases show that the anomalies decrease rapidly with the coil-separation. It follows that other conditions being the same a large coil-separation is to be preferred if the ore targets are expected to produce weak anomalies, for example, if the ores are deep-seated.

The anomalies (p.p.m.) for a coil-separation of 8 m were measured with the beam-slingram apparatus (p.135). Although the anomaly, in the absolute sense, is small it stands well above the background because of the high accuracy of measurement with the system (20 p.p.m.). It should be noted that the real as well as the imaginary component anomalies in the 8 m case are positive instead of negative as in the remaining cases. The reason seems to be that the ore zone no longer acts like a conductor that is thin compared to the coil-separation but one that is thick. Note also that in this case the poor zone as well as the rich vein are indicated.

We have only considered steeply dipping conductors owing to limitations of space. Gently dipping and horizontal conductors will be found to be treated elsewhere (Parasnis, 1972). On the whole, such conductors produce much more complicated anomaly patterns with moving source–receiver systems so that considerable experience and familiarity with model experiments are necessary for correctly interpreting the results in areas of low dips.

Fig.49B shows a profile across a flat conductor (a marsh). It is seen that the edges of the conductor are indicated by anomaly peaks while over the marsh itself the real component is in this case negative and the imaginary is positive. The signs, however, depend in a somewhat complicated manner on the conductivity, the depth and the frequency.

In Fig.49C are shown the results of another survey with the horizontal coplanar coil system and their quantitative interpretation. Here the survey indicates a horse-shoe shaped conducting sheet, the dip being towards the inside of the horse-shoe. It was inferred that the sheet represented a conducting horizon in a syncline. As there are no outcrops anywhere in this and the surrounding area (note the consistently large thickness of the overburden), the measurements were thus seen to give an entirely new information. A few holes drilled to verify the interpretation proved that the conductor is a shale with pyrrhotite impregnation. The existence of a syncline was also confirmed. Note the folding indicated at the apex of the syncline and a weaker horizon on the inside.

(2) Coils vertical and coplanar

This system is of particular interest in airborne prospecting (Chapter 11), but is sometimes used in ground work when it is desired to suppress the effect of near-surface layers as far as possible. During the operation of the method the plane of the transmitter must be orientated so that the lines of force cut *across* the plane of a presumed orebody e.g., a sheet. In general, this means that the transmitter must be held parallel to the strike.

For airborne work the coils are mounted at the tips of an aircraft wing with their axes in the flight direction which must, of course, be perpendicular to the strike if there is to be an electromagnetic coupling between the source and a vertical conductor. (A horizontal conductor will always be excited.) In ground work it is more practical, in view of trees, bushes etc., to advance the vertical coplanar coil-system along the coil-line which is then run parallel to the strike. In this case readings along the lines may be taken at relatively large intervals but the lines must be run fairly close to each other.

The shape of an anomaly curve obtained with this system is shown in Fig.121 (Chapter 11). It can be easily deduced from simple arguments of the type we have previously used in sections *The tilt-angle method* and *Fixed-source methods* (cf. also Parasnis, 1972, p.117; Parasnis, 1966, p.198). The reader is strongly advised to carry out this procedure in order to gain an insight into the induction phenomena in orebodies.

(3) Coils vertical and coaxial

This system too, like the previous one, is of interest in ground as well as airborne work. The direction of advance is along the transmitter–receiver line which is run perpendicular to the strike.

In common with the previous system the vertical, coaxial coil-system has the advantage of being less sensitive to near-surface conductivity variations than the horizontal coplanar system. The anomalies obtained with it are, however, often more difficult to interpret than those with either of the other two systems. For instance, there are two maxima in the real component above a vertical conductor but only one maximum in the imaginary component. An example of a survey with this system (on a gently dipping conductor) is discussed on p.148.

Topographic corrections

On relatively flat ground the mutual orientation of the source and the receiver in the mobile systems may be said to be reasonably constant. But under other topographic conditions the orientation may alter so that the primary field at the receiver is altered from its normal value, a change which may be misinterpreted as an anomaly due to a subsurface conductor.

Thus, the coils of the horizontal coplanar system will not be in the same plane when the system is on a slope. If h is the elevation difference (not necessarily small) between the coils whose separation is r, a false anomaly of $-300\ (h^2/r^2)\%$ results in the real component. Consequently, a topographic correction of $300\ (h^2/r^2)$ must be added to the measured real component.

Levelling is necessary if accurate topographic corrections are to be obtained but this adds considerably to the cost and labour of a survey. Therefore, an alternative procedure, which is found to be satisfactory for most purposes, is used to allow for the topographic relief. In this, each man sights the other's coil and holds his own coil in such a way that the coils are approximately in the same, although inclined, plane. The correction is then automatically eliminated.

With vertical coplanar coils elevation differences cause no spurious anomalies; however, it is essential that neither of the coils depart appreciably from the common vertical plane which is the plane through the line of advance, but this is easily ensured.

In the vertical coaxial system a correction of the amount $150\ (h^2/r^2)\%$ must be added to the observed real component anomaly when the coils cease to be coaxial as a result of the elevation difference h.

Topographic corrections are not needed for the imaginary component which is a purely secondary phenomenon representing only a time difference between the primary and resultant fields and is not dependent upon the irregularities in the strength of the primary field. Hence, imaginary component maps are found as a rule to show much less correlation with topography and therefore to be more informative than real component maps in areas with appreciable relief.

The Svansele orebody (northern Sweden)
The real and imaginary component maps obtained on this body, the discovery of which is to be credited to electromagnetic methods,

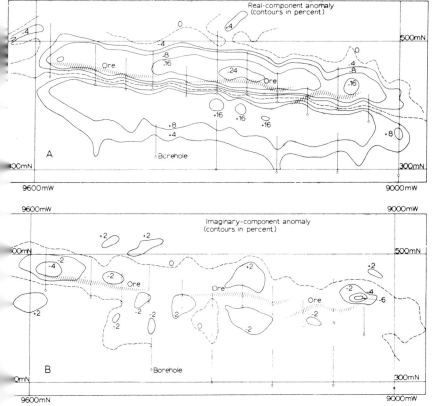

Fig.50. Moving source–receiver survey of the Svansele pyrite orebody, northern Sweden. Horizontal coplanar coils. Separation 60 m. Frequency 3,600 c/sec. A. Real component. B. Imaginary component. (Courtesy of BGAB.)

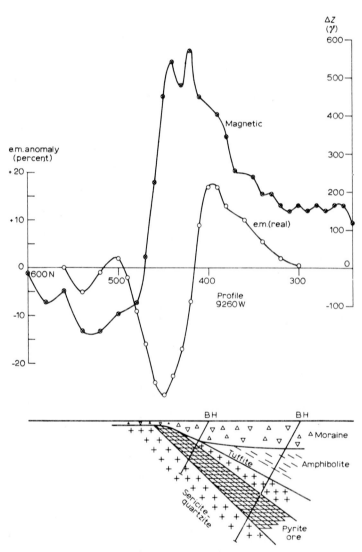

Fig.51. Profile across the Svansele orebody (Fig.50) showing e.m. real-component, magnetic vertical field anomaly, interpretation and drillhole results. (Courtesy of BGAB.)

are shown in Fig.50. This survey was carried out with the horizontal coplanar system having a coil-separation of 60 m, the frequency being 3,600 c/sec.

Firstly, we notice that the imaginary component anomaly is practically zero, while the real component anomaly is large. According to the theory explained in section *Real and imaginary components* this would indicate an excellent conductor, which checks with the facts as known from measurements on drill cores. The unusually high electrical conductivity of the Svansele orebody is due to its high pyrite and pyrrhotite content.

Fig.50 shows that the sub-outcrop of the ore, as ascertained by extensive drilling, is displaced southward with respect to the anomaly centre. The moraine cover within the area appears to be uniform at least at the sites of the 30-odd drillholes, placed south of the ore in view of its southerly dip.

One possible explanation of the displacement is that the electromagnetic anomaly is not caused by the ore at all but by the gossan above it, the latter being a very good electrical conductor on account of its high electrolyte content. But the drainage appears to be good in the area and it is difficult to believe that the upper 20 m or so contain active electrolytes.

Another interpretation is that the moraine cover is considerably thinner at the anomaly centre than at the drillhole sites so that the sub-outcrop of the ore actually occurs north of the position in which it is shown in Fig.50. This alternative interpretation is sketched in Fig.51 in which the magnetic anomaly profile has also been drawn. The very sharp gradient in the anomaly on the northern side also indicates a rather shallow depth to the cause of the anomaly.

The R-sjö sulphide occurrence (Sweden)

This small orebody (2% Cu, 2% Zn) is embedded in gneissic rock and occurs under a lake. The survey, the results of which are reproduced in Fig.52, was carried out with the vertical coaxial coil system at a frequency of 800 c/sec, using the beam-slingram apparatus (p.135), the distance between the coils being 8 m. The readings on the maps are the electromagnetic anomalies in tens of p.p.m.

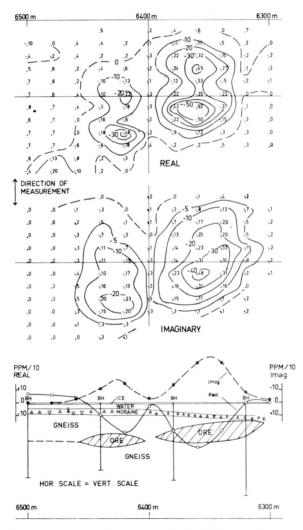

Fig.52. Moving source–receiver survey of the R-sjö sulphide occurrence, Sweden. Vertical coaxial coils. Separation 8 m. Frequency 800 c/sec. (Courtesy of BGAB.)

The real as well as the imaginary component reveals two distinct "highs" separated sharply from each other. Detailed interpretation suggests that the anomalies are probably caused by two small horizontal or gently dipping "discs", an interpretation which is also supported by the magnetic picture (not shown).

The conductivity of the eastern conductor appears to be higher (Re/Im ratio 2.0) than that of the western one (ratio = 1.5).

The results of four of the nine drillholes placed on the indication are shown in the lower part of the map. They seem to confirm the geophysical interpretation.

USE OF TWO FREQUENCIES IN ELECTROMAGNETIC PROSPECTING

One major concern in electromagnetic interpretation is to be able to tell whether an anomaly is due to overburden effects or to conductors like orebodies. In case of doubt it is sometimes possible to resolve the ambiguity by making observations at two different frequencies. The principle behind such measurements is as follows.

We start with an assumption, which is often found to be in accord with facts, that the overburden has a high electrical resistivity while conductors such as many sulphide orebodies have a much lower electrical resistivity.

Now, irrespective of the resistivity of a conductor, the ratio of the real and imaginary components of the *secondary* field, i.e., the anomaly ratio Re/Im (tan φ in Fig.35), always increases when the frequency is increased.[1]

However, the ratio of the real and imaginary components of the *resultant* field (tan α in Fig.35) shows a different behaviour. It increases with frequency if the conductor is poor but decreases if the conductor is good. For examples see Parasnis (1966).

The real and imaginary components of the resultant field are easy to obtain. The imaginary component is identical to the secondary imaginary component. To obtain the real component we merely add

[1] Strictly speaking it is the phase angle (apparent range $0-360°$) given by $\tan^{-1}$ (Re/Im) which increases with frequency but we do not need this ramification.

the secondary real component to the primary field (which, to recall, is usually designated as 100% in the moving source–receiver methods).

Thus, in case of doubt, the anomalies due to variations in a badly conducting overburden can be distinguished from the anomalies due to good conductors like some orebodies, by two-frequency measurements.

However, certain overburdens (e.g., clays) may be as good conductors as some orebodies and, conversely, certain ores (e.g., galena) may be as poor conductors as overburdens like moraine. How are we to distinguish between overburden and ore effects in such cases? The method which is sometimes found useful is to make moving source–receiver surveys with different coil-separations. The overburden anomalies, being of shallow origin, will tend to be relatively large for small separations and small for large separations while those of ores, being of deeper origin, will not change significantly with moderate variation in the coil-separation and might even increase with increasing coil-separation (cf. Fig.49A).

The reader will no doubt realize that a combination of two-frequency and multi-separation techniques can be of great help in the analysis of electromagnetic anomalies, but a judicious application of such techniques requires some experience.

Some commercial Turam outfits, as well as moving source–receiver outfits, have provision for measurements on two different frequencies e.g., 220 and 660 c/sec or 440 and 1760 c/sec.

DEPTH PENETRATION OF ELECTROMAGNETIC METHODS

An important question is how deep an orebody may lie and yet give a recognizable electromagnetic anomaly on the surface. It is not an easy question to answer since a number of factors like the shape and conductivity of the body, its size, the source–receiver distance, the masking effect of near-surface conductivity variations etc., must be considered.

When an electromagnetic wave propagates through the ground, its energy is continuously absorbed by the rocks on account of their electric conductivity. Hence less and less of it is available for the excitation of an orebody the deeper the body lies. This is only half of the story since the signals returning from the ore also lose some of their energy to the surroundings before reaching the surface.

The lower the resistivity of the country rock or the greater the frequency of the waves, the higher is the absorption of energy and the smaller the depth penetration. Hence, in normal geological surroundings frequencies higher than about 3,000–4,000 c/sec cannot be profitably employed towards ore prospecting and, in fact, the optimum in most cases lies around 500–2,000 c/sec. If the surface layers are very good electric conductors, as when they comprise shales, clays, water-logged soils etc., frequencies as low as 100 c/sec may be needed and, even with these, prospecting may be difficult or impossible as, for instance, in many equatorial regions or in parts of Australia where electrolytes in the overburden more or less completely screen the deeper conductors and themselves cause highly irregular anomalies.

In this connection it is worth noting that radio or radar frequencies are of no use in ore prospecting unless the rocks are exceptionally dry.

The question of depth penetration is discussed in more detail in Chapter 11 in connection with airborne electromagnetic surveys. Here it will be sufficient to note that the depth penetration of the usual horizontal coplanar system for steeply dipping conductors is about one-half to two-thirds the distance between the coils. For horizontal conductors the system has a greater depth penetration, of the order of twice the coil-distance. Similar orders of magnitude are obtained for the other moving source–receiver systems.

In the fixed-source systems the depth penetration is a function of the maximum distance from the source to which sufficiently accurate measurements can be made. It seems, however, from a number of theoretical considerations, that under favourable conditions these methods should be capable of detecting orebodies at as much as several hundred metres.

For example, the maximum anomaly of the conductor shown in Fig.42 would still be about twice the measuring accuracy even if the conductor were to lie at a depth of about 200 m. Similarly, the anomaly of the Rudtjebäcken ore in Fig.43 is estimated to be detectable even if the ore were to be at 500 m.

AFMAG

An interesting development in geophysical exploration was reported
some years ago. It has been termed the afmag method and utilizes the
audio-frequency (1–10,000 c/sec) magnetic fields that are constantly
reaching any point on the earth's surface. These fields originate in
thunderstorms and are very weak but they can be detected by means
of receivers very sharply tuned to a definite frequency (510 c/sec in
one version).

The fields are strongly polarized with the oscillating magnetic
vector normally parallel to the earth's surface. The vector shows a
diffuse azimuth perpendicular to the geological strike, which can be
determined by rotating a search coil, connected to a tuned amplifier
and a detector, around a vertical axis until the voltage in it is
maximum. The tilt of the vector is normally horizontal. However, in
the presence of subsurface conductors the magnetic vector tilts out of
the earth's surface since the primary field vector is compounded with
the vector of the secondary field from the conductor. By essentially
the same construction as in Fig.32A it can be seen that the resultant
vector must show the same characteristic variation. The conductor is
located below the inflection point of the tilt-angle curve. In fact, the
afmag may be considered to be a tilt-angle method with the source
(thunderstorms) removed to infinity. As such it suffers from the
disadvantages inherent in the tilt-angle method, namely an incomplete
knowledge of the e.m. field and a precision which is inferior to that of
the other prospecting methods.

A very large depth penetration (several hundred metres) has been
claimed for the afmag on the ground that the source–receiver distance
is effectively infinity (cf. close of previous section). It seems, nevertheless, that as the primary field in the afmag is homogeneous, even
small conductivity contrasts in the earth will produce large anomalies
provided they present a large total area to the field. Among such
contrasts may be mentioned those associated with vertical or steep
contacts between rock formations, faults, long water-filled fissures
etc. Also, brooks, rivers, ridges etc., or sections of them running
parallel to the geological strike, may be expected to give strong
anomalies. Hence, the background noise in afmag may be expected to

be high and the resolution and the depth penetration of the method, as far as small scale structures like orebodies are concerned, is probably very much less than that claimed.

An example of an afmag survey in a known mining district is shown in Fig.53A (Jewell and Ward, 1963).

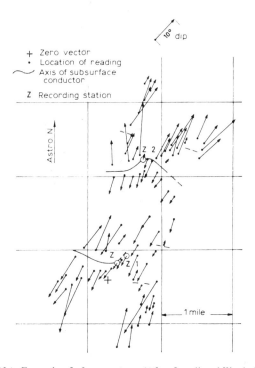

Fig.53A. Example of afmag vectors. (After Jewell and Ward, 1963.)

In this figure the direction of an arrow represents the azimuth of an afmag vector while its length represents the tilt of the vector. If an arrow pointing southwards represents, say, an upward tilt, one pointing northwards will represent a downward tilt. The conductors are found along lines where the tilt changes from upwards to downwards, that is, along the locus of the inflection points (see Fig.33).

H-MODE VLF

Powerful radio transmitters set up for the purpose of military com-
munication in different parts of the world radiate unmodulated carrier
waves, either continuously or with Morse code signals, on frequencies
in the band 15–25 kc/sec. In radio technology, the frequencies are
called Very Low Frequencies since the carrier frequency of ordinary
radio programmes is more than ten times as much. However, in the
context of geophysical methods, where frequencies down to 100 c/sec
are used, the designation VLF is a misnomer.

Some examples of VLF transmitters are: NAA, Cutler, U.S.A.,
17.8 kc/sec, 1 MW; GBR, Rugby, England, 16.0 kc/sec, 500 kW;
ROR, Gorki, U.S.S.R., 17.0 kc/sec, 315 kW; NWC, North West Cape,
Australia, 15.5 kc/sec, 1 MW.

The antenna of VLF transmitters is effectively a long vertical wire
through which an alternating current is flowing. It produces a magnetizing force in the space around it, the lines of which are concentric,
horizontal circular loops with centres at the antenna (Fig.53B).

Within a small area at a very large distance from the antenna the
magnetizing force (A/m), and the flux density (Wb/m^2) caused by it
in the air (= μ_o times magnetizing force), may be taken to be constant, so, that a conductor in the area will be subjected to a homogeneous, horizontal magnetic flux density.

Vertical sheet conductors, such as C_1, whose strike is parallel to
the local bearing of the VLF station will be threaded by a maximum
magnetic flux and an induced electric current will flow in them producing a secondary magnetic field. This field will be such as to oppose
the primary VLF flux cutting the conductor (upper part of Fig.53C).
The total magnetic field, which is horizontal far away from the conductor, will be tilted out of the horizontal plane in its vicinity. The
tilt is upwards on the side of the VLF station and downwards on the
opposite side, as the construction in Fig.53C shows. Directly above
the conductor the tilt will be zero.

Conductors such as C_2 in Fig.53B whose strike is perpendicular to
the bearing of the VLF station will not be cut by the magnetic field,
will have no induced currents and therefore produce no tilt anomalies.

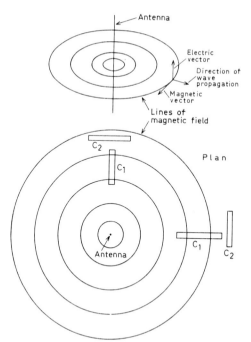

Fig.53B. The VLF field.

Hence, the choice of the VLF station must be made with due regard
to the strike of the target conductors within the area of measurement.

Measurements in the VLF method are carried out as follows. A coil
tuned to the frequency of the selected VLF station, and connected to
a signal detector, is held with its axis horizontal and turned until a
minimum signal is obtained. It is then turned through 90°, the axis
continuing to be horizontal, and finally it is tilted around its horizontal diameter until a minimum signal is obtained and the tilt of the coil
noted. In this position the vector R in Fig.53C lies in the plane of the
coil.

Fig.53C shows two VLF profiles, 1 km apart, across two several
kilometres long, parallel conductors (both sericitized, pyrrhotite-
bearing shales). For comparison the results of a moving source—
receiver survey along the same profiles are also shown. The conductors
are not continuous over their entire strike length but are, in places,

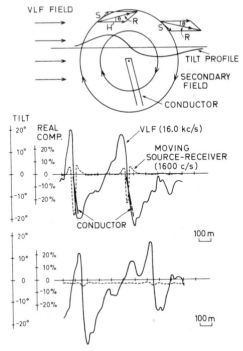

Fig.53C. Tilt of the VLF magnetic vector across a conductor. Åmliden area, northern Sweden. (Courtesy BGAB.)

interrupted by gaps some tens of metres long. One such interruption occurs (in both conductors) on the lower profile. It will be seen that while the moving source–receiver anomaly immediately indicates the break, the anomaly in the tilt of the VLF field is not diminished to any significant extent.

The effect can be understood from Fig.53D where we see a sheet conductor with a short interruption along the strike. The homogeneous VLF field induces currents which flow along the edges of either half of the sheet. If we look at the conductor from the side the situation will appear to be somewhat as in the lower part of the figure. Now, the currents *a,b* being rather near to each other and oppositely directed, the entire current system is practically equivalent to a *single*

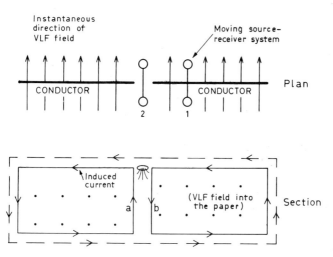

Fig.53D. Comparison of VLF and moving source–receiver fluxes.

current loop shown by the dashed line. The break in the conductor does not manifest itself.

However, the situation with the moving source-receiver system with its strongly inhomogeneous field is different. When the system is in the position *1*, virtually all the flux from the transmitter goes into the right-hand half of the conducting sheet, inducing in it a current as shown by the continuous line. In the position *2*, on the other hand, virtually all the flux goes in the gap between the two halves and no (or very weak) currents are induced in the conductor halves themselves.

Thus, the VLF method (or, in fact, any method exploiting a homogeneous primary field) is ill adapted to mapping details of conductor structures. The method has the same disadvantages as the afmag method.

For the electromagnetic exploration of small-scale structures the most rational strategy seems at present to be to use a strongly inhomogeneous electromagnetic field, such as that produced by current-carrying cables and loops, and place the source of the field at a relatively short distance from the presumed position of the structure.

158 ELECTROMAGNETIC METHODS

DISTORTION OF ANOMALIES DUE TO
MAGNETIC PERMEABILITY

We have hitherto considered the magnetic field produced by the secondary currents induced in a conductor. However, in measurements on magnetic ores, sulphide ores and on other geologic bodies containing magnetite and pyrrhotite (e.g., black shales, basic and ultrabasic rocks, etc.) there often arises an additional effect due to the magnetic permeability of these bodies, an understanding of which is essential for correctly interpreting the survey data.

An oscillating primary field induces secondary currents in an electric conductor as we have already seen, but if the conductor has a sufficiently high magnetic permeability it also induces an appreciable oscillating magnetization intensity in the conductor. The magnetic field due to this intensity is, of course, oscillating, and like any other oscillating magnetic field it induces an electromotive force in the receiving coil. The net magnetic field detected by the receiver is therefore the sum of the field due to the secondary electric current in the subsurface conductor and that due to the magnetization intensity in it.

Now, the strength of the secondary current is proportional to the frequency as well as the strength of the primary field, but the induced magnetization intensity depends simply on the magnitude of the field.

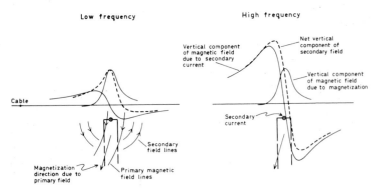

Fig.53E. Distortion of electromagnetic anomalies due to magnetic permeability.

Hence at low frequencies the field due to the magnetization may dominate over that due to the secondary current, if the body is sufficiently magnetic. As the frequency of the primary field is increased the former field remains the same but the latter increases so that at sufficiently high frequencies this will be the dominating field at the receiver. What happens to the electromagnetic anomalies observed can be understood from Fig.53E.

Suppose we have a long, vertical conducting sheet in the field due to a current-carrying cable as shown. We shall consider the vertical secondary field at the receiver. This will have the characteristic form (an inflection point flanked by a maximum and a minimum) which, by now, is familiar to us (see Fig.38). If the conductor is magnetic it will acquire a magnetization intensity in the direction of the local primary field (that is, tangential to the primary field lines), approximately as shown in the figure. The vertical magnetic field due to it is easily visualized qualitatively from Fig.12B.

The dashed curve in the left-hand part of the figure is the sum of the other two curves and represents the net field if the frequency is relatively low. We notice that the anomaly is distorted from its "standard" shape and we obtain a maximum, instead of an inflection point, above the conductor! If the frequency is increased, say, fourfold the situation will be as in the right-hand part of the figure. The magnetic field due to the current is now four times as much as that at the lower frequency and dominates the field due to the magnetization which remains unaltered. Consequently we find an inflection point above the conductor.

In a similar manner it can be shown that the effect of magnetic permeability on symmetric anomalies such as those in Fig.40, 44 and 49 will be to distort them in such a fashion that an inflection point, instead of a maximum or a minimum, is obtained above the conductor.

It is evident that inferences about conductor location should not be based upon single-frequency measurements alone if a conductor is suspected to be highly magnetic. The survey should always be carried out in such cases on at least two well-separated frequencies.

CHAPTER 6

Electrical Methods

INTRODUCTION

Under electrical prospecting methods we shall classify methods in which an electric current is sent into the ground, and the resulting distribution of potentials (voltages) is mapped on the ground by means of a pair of electrodes driven into the ground and connected to a sensitive voltmeter. Like the self-potential method, the electrical methods can be employed only if a satisfactory electrical contact with the ground can be secured. Thus, they cannot be used in regions with non-conducting surface formations like dry desert rocks, frozen ground etc.

When the positions of the points at which the current enters and leaves the ground are known, it is possible to calculate the potentials, and the paths which the current would take if the ground were homogeneous. Inhomogeneities, like electrically better or worse conducting bodies, are inferred from the fact that they deflect the current and distort the normal potentials.

The nature of these distortions will be understood by reference to Fig.54. The continuous lines in the lower part of the figure represent the paths that an electric current takes on the surface of a homogeneous ground in going from one electrode, e.g., a metal spike, connected to one pole of a battery, to another electrode connected to the other pole. Each dashed curve is such that along it the electric potential has some constant value. It is called an equipotential line and a voltmeter connected between any two points on such a curve would show no voltage difference. Every equipotential cuts a current path at right angles.

If a subsurface body is a better electric conductor than the surrounding ground, the current will tend to flow through this body rather than through the rest of the ground. The current paths and the equipotentials are then distorted in the neighbourhood of the ore, and also at some distance from it, as shown in the upper part of the figure. The result is that the voltages in an area above the orebody tend to be more uniform than in the absence of the body. On the periphery of this area, on the other hand, the voltage difference between any two points is increased above its undisturbed value, which is evident from the crowding of the equipotentials.

When the orebody is a poorer conductor than the host rock the current tends to avoid the orebody, and the voltage difference between any two points above the ore is increased, while that in the peripheral regions is decreased.

RESISTIVITY

The electric anomalies of subsurface conductors depend upon the electric resistivity contrast between the conductors and the host rock. It is therefore desirable to have an idea of the resistivities of rocks and ores within a survey area.

Formally, the electric resistivity of a homogeneous medium is defined as the ratio of the voltage gradient across a small surface element within it to the current density (A/m^2) flowing across the element at right angles to it. Numerically the resistivity is equal to the resistance (ohm) between two opposite faces of a cube of side of 1 m, but the dimensions of resistivity are ohm x metre (Ωm). Resistivity has sometimes been expressed as ohm per cm^3 or m^3, but this is both a careless and a wrong usage. Other things being equal the resistance which an electric current experiences is proportional to the length of the path (m) that it has to travel and *not* to the volume of the object whose resistivity is being measured.

It is not difficult to determine the electric resistivity of fairly homogeneous samples of ores like magnetite, pyrite, chalcopyrite, galena, pyrolusite, graphite etc., but some difficulty may be experienced in the case of sandstones, limestones, crystalline rocks etc.

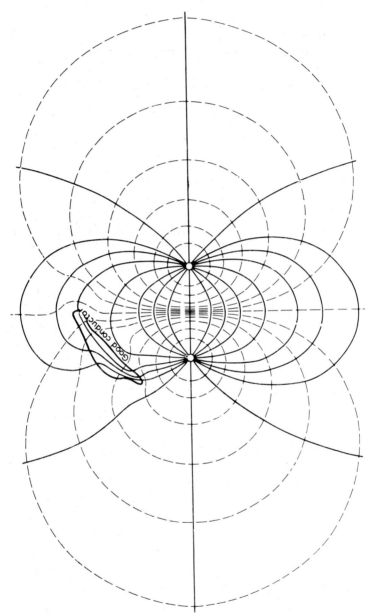

Fig.54. Lines of current flow (continuous curves) and equipotentials (dashed curves) due to a pair of point electrodes on the surface of the ground. For reasons of clarity the potential difference between adjacent equipotentials is not the same. If it were the equipotentials would be tightly crowded near the electrodes and farther apart in the centre. The lower part of the figure is diagrammatic and not merely schematic.

One method (Fig.55A) is to prepare a sample in the form of a rectangular parallelepiped and press two metal plates against a pair of opposite faces. A current is sent through the sample by joining the metal plates to a battery, and the voltage between two points M and N along a line perpendicular to the faces is read on a voltmeter. The resistivity ρ is given by:

$$\rho = \frac{A}{l} \cdot \frac{V}{I} \quad \Omega m \qquad (6.1)$$

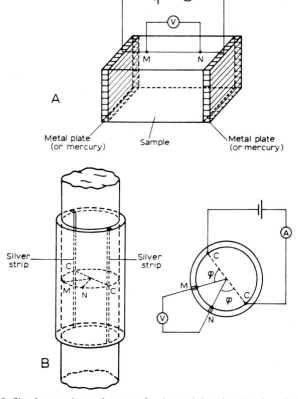

Fig.55. Simple experimental set-ups for determining the electric resistivity of a rectangular sample (A), and a drill core (B).

where A = area (m^2) of the faces across which the current is passed, V = voltage (V) between M and N, l = distance (m) between M and N, and I = current (A).

We may also use a borehole core in the form of a short right cylinder, instead of a rectangular sample, sending the current through the end faces.

For borehole cores there is another convenient method which has the advantage that the end faces need not be ground flat. A plastic tube into which the core fits snugly is taken and two narrow silver or copper strips (say 1–3 mm wide) are glued on its inside along two diametrically opposite generators. Two holes are made in the tube along a circle half-way along the tube (Fig.55B) for inserting potential electrodes M and N (stiff copper wires) through them to make contact with the core when it is inserted. The strips are joined to a battery and the voltage between M and N is measured. The resistivity is given by:

$$\rho = \frac{b}{k} \frac{V}{I} \tag{6.2}$$

where b = length of the current strips, V = voltage between M and N, I = current,

$$k = \frac{1}{\pi} \ln \frac{1 + \cos \varphi}{1 - \cos \varphi}$$

φ = angle shown in Fig.55B. (ln denotes the natural logarithm = logarithm to base 10 multiplied by 2.303). For example, if $\varphi = 60°$, $k = 0.3498$ and:

$$\rho = 2.859 \, b \, \frac{V}{I}$$

Instead of the resistivity, the concept conductivity is also used. Numerically, the conductivity is simply the reciprocal of resistivity. Its dimensions are expressed as $\Omega^{-1} m^{-1}$ (i.e., per ohm per metre) or as mho/m, the word mho being coined by spelling "ohm" backwards, or in the Système Internationale as Siemen per metre (S/m).

RESISTIVITY OF ROCKS AND MINERALS

The electrical resistivity of rocks and minerals is an extremely variable property and depends on a number of factors. The resistivity of crystalline rock formations such as granulite, granite, diorite etc., in situ is largely dependent upon the water in the fissures and fractures. Similarly, the porosity, the degree of saturation and the nature of pore-electrolytes govern the resistivity of rocks like sandstones, limestones etc. Generally speaking, hard rocks are bad conductors of electricity, but zones of crushed and badly fractured rocks may sometimes have resistivities as low as those of certain ores. Again, some clays as well as waterlogged soils and sedimentary rocks like chalk, marls etc., may possess low resistivities. In the dry state most rocks are non-conducting.

Ores and minerals can be rather sharply divided into two classes, the good conductors and the bad ones, notwithstanding the large variations in the resistivities of individual samples of one and the same type of ore. Generally, minerals having a metallic lustre and their ores are good conductors. Among such minerals are pyrite, pyrrhotite, chalcopyrite, arsenopyrite, galena, magnetite etc. Two notable exceptions to the "rule" are haematite and zinc blende. Graphite, graphitic shales and schists, pyrolusite, psilomelane etc., are also good conductors.

The resistivity of ore deposits depends, of course, upon the amount of conducting minerals in them, the mode in which these minerals are distributed etc. Thus, massive ores of pyrite, magnetite etc., have a low resistivity while impregnation ores have a high resistivity. In some impregnation ores the individual grains or flakes of the conducting mineral are sometimes not in contact with each other. The ore as a whole will then appear as an insulator or a poor conductor and will be a poor target for electrical prospecting methods. It may, however, be detectable by electromagnetic methods.

Crystalline bedrock may sometimes be impregnated by conducting minerals like magnetite, pyrrhotite, and graphite and therefore acquire a considerably lower resistivity than would otherwise be the case. Thus granulite rock in Sweden, when unimpregnated, has resistivities

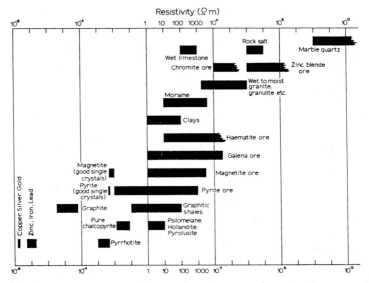

Fig.56. Approximate resistivity ranges of some rocks, minerals, ores and common metals. The resistivity scale (horizontal) is logarithmic.

of the order of 20,000–50,000 Ωm (in situ) but moderate impregnation of conducting minerals brings its resistivity down to 3,000–5,000 Ωm in many areas.

Fig.56 shows the approximate resistivity ranges of various ores and rocks. A fuller discussion of the resistivity of ores will be found in Parasnis (1956).

APPARATUS

The apparatus required for electrical prospecting need not be complicated and is therefore easily rigged up, unless a number of refinements like automatic controls are desired. In fact, very satisfactory electric surveys can often be carried out with the simple equipment consisting of high-tension dry batteries as the source of electric current, four metal stakes — two as current electrodes and two as voltage probes — a milliammeter, a voltmeter and a sufficient length of well insulated cable.

Suitable batteries for the work are the so-called anode batteries giving 45 or 90 V per battery. Two or three such batteries are connected in series so as to give a total voltage of some 135–180 V. Also included in the circuit are a mA-meter, a switch and an adjustable resistance to regulate the current (Fig.57), the whole assembly being neatly mounted in a small box.

Anode batteries do not have a very great current capacity and they need frequent replacement. Hence, for large scale surveys it is found more convenient to use a petrol-driven direct-current generator supplying, say, 200 W–1 kW power. Such a generator cannot, of course, be carried along like a battery box but must be kept stationary and connected to the current electrodes by long cables.

The mA-meter should be capable of reading, say, 100 mA full scale but suitable shunts should be provided so that its measuring range can be extended if necessary. Usually, manufacturers will supply the necessary shunts for a mA- or a μA-meter. Universal type instruments such as the AVO-meter, Simpson, Philips, Unigor etc., which have several current ranges, can also be employed for the measurement of current.

The current electrodes may be round stainless-steel rods, about 70 cm long, with a provision (like a clip) for fastening the uncovered end of the cable leading to the battery. A satisfactory electrical contact will usually be obtained on reasonably moist ground if the rods are

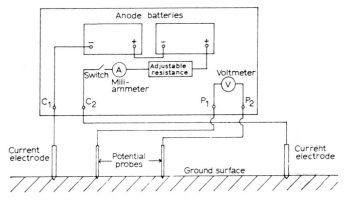

Fig.57. Scheme of simple field apparatus for resistivity measurements.

driven about 10–20 cm in the ground. On dry ground an unsatisfactory contact can sometimes be improved by watering the electrodes.

The potential electrodes, usually called probes, can also be made of
stainless-steel rods but non-polarizable electrodes of the type used in
SP measurements (Fig.24B) are preferable. As in SP work a shallow
hole is first scooped out in the ground and the electrodes pushed into
it for contact. The voltage arising between the probes when a current
flows through the earth can be measured as in the self-potential
method by means of a voltmeter or a d.c. compensator (Fig.25). This
voltage, however, must be corrected for any self-potential difference
that may be present between the probes due to natural electric currents.

Corrections for SP voltages may be made in two ways. The direct
way is to note the SP voltage, which is simply the reading of the
voltmeter when the battery is not switched on, and subtract it from
the voltage read when a current is introduced into the ground. Another, more convenient way, is to have an auxiliary circuit from which
a voltage equal and opposite to the self-potential is taken to bring the
voltmeter reading to zero before introducing the current into the
ground. A couple of ordinary flash-light cells (1.5 V each) are quite
sufficient in the auxiliary circuit since the maximum self-potentials
encountered are only of the order of 1 V in magnitude.

COMMUTATION OF CURRENT

If the current in the ground is always sent in one particular direction,
electrolytic polarization effects can arise. To avoid these the direction
of the current is periodically reversed, say, between observations at
successive points. A convenient arrangement for this purpose, when a
battery box is carried as the current source, is to replace the switch in
Fig.57 by a reversing key.

If the current source is a stationary d.c. generator, a mechanical
device, such as a rotating wheel attached to an electric motor, can be
used for automatic current reversals at suitable intervals, say 5–15

sec. A period of no-current must, of course, intervene between the reversals so that self-potentials in the ground can be compensated.

In order to avoid a commutator arrangement, some workers use very low-frequency alternating current instead of a direct current, the frequency being of the order of 10–20 c/sec or less. The ammeter and voltmeter must then be replaced by suitable a.c. instruments. Alternating current has one advantage that small voltages, such as those obtained on highly conductive ground or ores, can easily be amplified by means of electronic amplifiers. Moreover, self-potentials need not be compensated since they are steady potentials which will not be picked up by the a.c. instrument.

However, if the current leads are long, electromagnetic induction

Fig.58. The ABEM terrameter for resistivity measurements. (Courtesy of ABEM Company, Stockholm.)

effects can be troublesome even if the a.c. frequency be very low. Besides, the leakage of current from the wire insulation, especially on moist ground, also affects the readings.

Ready-made resistivity outfits are available on the market. A photograph of one such outfit is shown in Fig.58. This is a low-frequency a.c. outfit.

Some of the commercially available outfits are highly sophisticated instruments allowing a very wide range of ground resistances to be measured and conform only in principle to the simple scheme of Fig.57. For work in arid or desert areas very special high-voltage sources and current electrodes have to be devised to get a significant current in the ground. On the contrary in areas of extremely low surface resistivity, the voltage developed between the potential probes is frequently so low that highly sensitive voltmeters are needed. Sometimes even these may not be adequate and it may be necessary to increase the current injected in the ground to very high magnitudes (several to several tens of amperes) calling again for specially constructed current sources.

CLASSIFICATION OF ELECTRIC METHODS

Electric ore prospecting methods fall broadly into two classes according to whether they measure the electric potential of the observation points with respect to a fixed point or the gradient of the potential at each point.

The potential methods include the equipotential and the "mise-à-la-masse" methods while the gradient ones include the earth resistivity (E.R.) and the potential-drop ratio (P.D.R.) methods. Of these the various E.R. procedures are the most commonly used methods at present.

EQUIPOTENTIAL METHOD

The tracing of equipotential lines (cf. Fig.54) has been the basis of an ore prospecting method used as far back as 1912 by Schlumberger and 1918 by Lundberg. Its principle (but not the actual operation followed by Lundberg) is as follows (Lundberg, 1922).

Two potential electrodes are connected to a voltmeter and one of them is kept fixed at some selected point. With the other electrode a second point is located such that when the electrode is placed at it, the voltmeter reads zero. The point is marked by a peg in the ground or on a map. Then, by the definition of an equipotential line (see *Introduction* of this chapter) the two points lie on one and the same equipotential. The second electrode is then moved to another similar point and so on, until a series of points defining the particular equipotential line are obtained. After this the fixed electrode is moved to some point not on this line and the whole procedure is repeated to obtain another equipotential line.

The equipotentials thus obtained are not those due purely to the impressed current but include also the effect of the self-potentials in

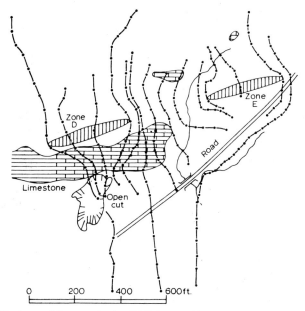

Fig.59. Equipotential survey in the Griffith area, Queensland, Australia. (After Edge and Laby, 1931.)

the ground. In Lundberg's original version, however, this uncertainty did not arise since he employed an alternating current and a pair of headphones instead of a voltmeter. The self-potentials, being d.c. potentials, do not influence the "readings".

The tracing of equipotential lines in the field is a dilatory procedure. Besides, the interpretation of an equipotential map obtained in the above fashion is often difficult even with considerable experience on the part of the interpreter. The more rational method of obtaining equipotential lines, which is used in modern work, is to measure the electric voltage at each observation point with respect to a fixed point in the same manner as an ordinary SP survey, plot the results on a map and draw isoanomaly lines as usual.

An example of an equipotential survey after the manner of Lundberg, carried out in Australia, is shown in Fig.59. It should be noticed that the equipotentials tend to be pushed away from well conducting zones such as D and E (shaded areas) and become crowded at the extremities of such zones.

EARTH-RESISTIVITY METHODS

We shall leave the "mise-à-la-masse" potential method for a later section and discuss here the earth-resistivity methods, which are undoubtedly the most highly developed modern electrical methods, from the operational as well as the theoretical standpoint.

For a proper understanding of the earth-resistivity methods it is necessary to have an idea of the potential produced by a given current-electrode system on a homogeneous earth. The simplest form of an electrode is a single point electrode which is realized in practice by a metal stake of small diameter. Star-like, hexagonal, or rectangular patterns of bare copper wire, pegged to the ground by means of long nails, may be considered to be point electrodes if observations of the potential are made at distances which are large compared to the linear dimensions of such patterns.

In Appendix 4 it is shown that if I is the current passing through a point electrode, placed on a flat "semi-infinite" earth of resistivity ρ, the electric potential at a point P, distant r from the electrode, is:

$$V = \frac{I\rho}{2\pi} \frac{1}{r} \tag{6.3}$$

This actually means that if a voltmeter is connected between P and a point very far from the electrode it will show a reading of V volt. For instance if I = 50 mA, ρ = 5,000 Ωm and r = 100 m the voltage will be 398 mV as substitution in eq. (6.3) will readily show.

In practice, there are always two current electrodes – a positive one through which the current enters the ground and a negative one to which it returns. Further, we do not measure a potential as such but always a potential difference, that is, a voltage difference.

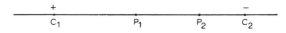

Fig.60. Array of four electrodes.

Suppose that the two current and the two potential electrodes C_1, C_2 and P_1, P_2 respectively are in one line as in Fig.60, C_1 being the positive and C_2 the negative current electrode, then the total potential at P_1 is:

$$V_1 = \frac{I\rho}{2\pi} \left(\frac{1}{C_1 P_1} - \frac{1}{C_2 P_1} \right) \tag{6.4}$$

and that at P_2 is:

$$V_2 = \frac{I\rho}{2\pi} \left(\frac{1}{C_1 P_2} - \frac{1}{C_2 P_2} \right) \tag{6.5}$$

When the probes are between the current electrodes, the potential at the probe nearest to the positive current electrode (C_1) is always greater than that at the probe nearest the negative electrode. The voltage difference $V_1 - V_2$ between P_1 and P_2 is therefore positive and given by:

$$\Delta V = V_1 - V_2 = \frac{I\rho}{2\pi} \left(\frac{1}{C_1 P_1} - \frac{1}{C_2 P_1} - \frac{1}{C_1 P_2} + \frac{1}{C_2 P_2} \right) = \frac{I\rho}{2\pi} G \tag{6.6}$$

In eq. (6.6) G is an abbreviation for the expression in the brackets. As

G depends upon the positions of the electrodes it is called the geometric factor of an electrode configuration. Some writers put $1/G$ instead of G for the bracketed expression.

From eq. (6.6) we have:

$$\rho = 2\pi \cdot \frac{1}{G} \cdot \frac{\Delta V}{I} \qquad (6.7)$$

The ratio $\Delta V/I$, of the voltage between the probes and the current in the ground, is frequently denoted by R. It has the nature of an electrical resistance and is expressed in Ω. We must be careful, however, *not* to think of it as the resistance of a volume of the earth between the potential probes.

Now G can be calculated when the distances of the four electrodes from each other are known. Therefore, the resistivity of a homogeneous ground is obtained by reading ΔV on a voltmeter connected between P_1 and P_2 and the current I on an ammeter placed in series with the battery.

Commercial instruments, like the terrameter in Fig.58, read the ratio $\Delta V/I$ directly.

APPARENT RESISTIVITY

If the electrode configuration is altered so that G becomes different the ratio $\Delta V/I$ will alter on homogeneous ground in such a way that the calculated resistivity ρ will always be the same. But on inhomogeneous ground the value obtained for ρ from eq. (6.7) does not remain the same on altering the mutual geometrical relationships of the electrodes, for example if one or two electrodes are moved while the others are kept fixed. Similarly, if a given configuration is moved *as a whole*, so that G, the geometrical factor, is not altered but the electrodes occupy new positions, eq. (6.7) will again yield a different value for ρ for each position of the array, if lateral variations of resistivity exist within the ground.

On inhomogeneous ground, therefore, the value of ρ obtained from eq. (6.7), on inserting in it the appropriate value of G and the observed magnitudes of ΔV and I, is known as the *apparent resistivity*. It is denoted usually by ρ_a.

What is the physical interpretation of apparent resistivity? Before going into this question we shall take a look at some typical apparent resistivity curves.

Fig.61 shows the variation of apparent resistivity on the surface of an earth consisting simply of two extensive outcropping rock formations in contact with each other along a vertical plane. The formations strike perpendicular to the plane of the figure and the left hand formation is electrically four times as resistive as the right hand one. A method of calculating the curves in Fig.61 is indicated in Appendix 6. In general, however, the calculation of apparent resistivity curves is a complicated mathematical problem.

Curve (a) shows the apparent resistivity when a pair of potential probes very close to each other are moved along a line perpendicular

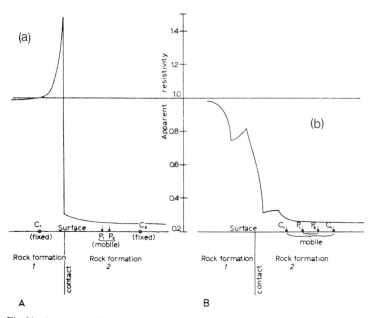

Fig.61. Apparent resistivity across a vertical contact between two rock formations using different electrode configurations. Formation *1* is four times as resistive as formation *2*.

to the strike, while the current electrodes are fixed on the line in the positions shown by the circles. The apparent resistivity is plotted against the point midway between the potential probes. In the present case the geometrical factor G alters each time the probes are moved.

Curve (b) shows the apparent resistivity over the same earth when a configuration of four collinear, uniformly spaced electrodes is moved as a whole along a direction perpendicular to the strike so that G is constant in this case. The apparent resistivity is again plotted against the point midway between the potential electrodes which, incidentally, is the centre of the whole configuration in this case.

Obviously, these curves are not simple but it is evident that the apparent resistivity is intimately connected with the geometry of the electrode system and is not a property or magnitude that can be uniquely assigned to a point on the surface of an inhomogeneous earth.

The concept of apparent resistivity is a central feature of the earth resistivity method of prospecting. The choice of the name "apparent resistivity" is, however, unfortunate for it has led many authors into making the erroneous statement that the apparent resistivity is a mean of the resistivities within some suitable volume around the electrodes. The matter is not so simple, a fact which needs some emphasis because the statement is frequently repeated in geophysical text books, popular accounts of resistivity methods, and in pamphlets and brochures on resistivity equipment.

For instance, at a very large distance towards the left in Fig.61A, the potential electrodes are surrounded essentially by the formation of resistivity 1 but the apparent resistivity here is 0.7 and *not* 1. Similarly, the apparent resistivity at a very large distance towards the right is 0.175 and not 0.25. Such examples can be multiplied and show that it is incorrect to interpret the apparent resistivity as volume average of resistivities.

The apparent resistivity is a formal concept and, in terms of measurable quantities, it represents a standardized voltage difference. Formally, it is the resistivity that a semi-infinite *homogeneous* earth must have, if a potential difference equal to that actually observed between the probes of an electrode configuration is to be obtained, on

placing the configuration on the surface of the imaginary homogeneous earth, and keeping the current unaltered. In a general sort of
way, of course, low values of the apparent resistivity do suggest the
occurrence of relatively good electrical conductors and high values
that of relatively poor ones, but a measured value of the apparent
resistivity at a point must not be directly associated with the electric
resistivity of the ground immediately below the point.

ELECTRODE CONFIGURATIONS IN RESISTIVITY METHODS

A large number of different electrode configurations have been
proposed and used in electrical prospecting of which some are shown

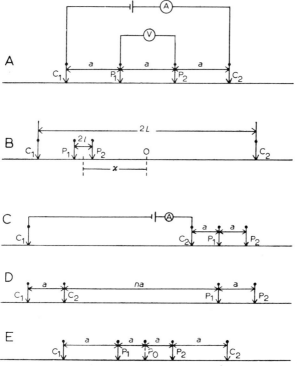

Fig.62. A few commonly used electrode configurations in resistivity work. A.
Wenner. B. Schlumberger. C. Three-point. D. Dipole–dipole. E. Lee.

in Fig.62. All the electrodes are assumed here to be point electrodes such as are furnished by metal spikes or polygonal patterns of small dimensions fashioned out of bare copper wire pegged to the ground. From the viewpoint of routine field work, only collinear arrays like those shown here are of importance but we could also use, say, square or rectangular configurations with the electrodes at the four corners. However, the field routine will be cumbersome with such configurations.

The special features of the various configurations shown are briefly as follows.

In the *Wenner array*, one of the first to be proposed, the separations between adjacent electrodes, are equal to each other and the apparent resistivity is given by:

$$\rho_a = 2\pi a \, \frac{\Delta V}{I} \qquad (6.8)$$

where a is the uniform separation. The factor $1/G$ in eq. (6.7) is thus equal to a for the Wenner array.

In the (generalized) *Schlumberger array* the distance $(2l)$ between the potentials probes is small compared with the distance $(2L)$ between the current electrodes. If the probes are sufficiently far from either current electrode, say at least 10 times the distance $2l$, the apparent resistivity may be calculated from the formula:

$$\rho_a = \frac{\pi}{2l} \cdot \frac{(L^2 - x^2)^2}{L^2 + x^2} \cdot \frac{\Delta V}{I} \qquad (6.9)$$

where a is the distance of the observation point (the point midway between the probes), from the centre O of the line $C_1 C_2$.

In the *three-point system* one of the current electrodes is kept fixed at a very large distance from the remaining three, which have a uniform separation a. As the potential due to the fixed electrode is practically zero at the probes, the configuration is essentially a three-electrode system. It is often used for drillhole measurements. The apparent resistivity is given by:

$$\rho_a = 4\pi a \, \frac{\Delta V}{I} \qquad (6.10)$$

the geometrical factor $(1/2a)$ here being exactly half that in the Wenner array.

In the so-called *dipole–dipole system* the potential probes are outside the current electrodes, each pair having a constant mutual separation (a). If the distance between the two pairs is relatively large, the current source may be treated as an electric dipole which, by definition, consists of a positive and a negative electric pole having a separation that is small compared with the distance from the observation point. For the apparent resistivity we have:

$$\rho_a = \pi n(n + 1)(n + 2)a \cdot \frac{\Delta V}{I} \qquad (6.11)$$

where na is the distance between the two innermost electrodes, one current and the other potential. The voltage difference ΔV is considered positive when P_2 is at a higher potential.

The *Lee configuration* employs five electrodes, the outer two being the current and the inner three the potential electrodes. Two of the potential electrodes are located as in the Wenner array so that they divide the line $C_1 C_2$ into three equal segments, each of length a, while the third potential electrode is placed at the centre of the configuration. From the voltage differences ΔV_1 and ΔV_2 between the central electrode and each of the other two potential electrodes we obtain two apparent resistivities given by:

$$\rho_{a_1} = 4\pi a \, \frac{\Delta V_1}{I} \qquad (6.12a)$$

$$\rho_{a_2} = 4\pi a \, \frac{\Delta V_2}{I} \qquad (6.12b)$$

These are said to "belong" to the respective halves of space on either side of the partitioning plane, a somewhat loose usage that has little theoretical justification.

Of these various configurations the Wenner and the Schlumberger are by far the two most commonly employed ones. The present tendency, moreover, favours the Schlumberger configuration rather than the Wenner. The Schlumberger configuration has decided advantages in the theoretical computation of apparent resistivity curves. Besides, it is also more convenient from the operational point of view.

ELECTRIC SOUNDING

Resistivity surveys are carried out using one or both of two distinct procedures known, by analogy, as electrical sounding and electrical mapping (or trenching). These are more or less complementary to each other but electrical mapping is the more important in ore prospecting.

The object of electrical sounding is to deduce the variation of electric resistivity with depth below a given point on the earth's surface, and correlate it with the available geological knowledge in order to infer the substructure in further detail. The procedure is based on the fact that the fraction of the electric current, injected into the ground, penetrating below a given depth, increases with the separation of the current electrodes. This will be appreciated from Fig.63. Here, the current fraction penetrating below a depth z in a homogeneous earth is plotted against the ratio "current-electrode separation/depth".

We see, for example, that if the electrode separation is equal to z, not more than 29.5% of the total current will penetrate below this depth but it increases to 50% if the separation is twice the depth and to 70.6% if it is four times the depth. Again, if we wish, say, 90% of the current to penetrate below a particular depth so that only 10% is confined above it, the current-electrode separation must be 12.6 times the depth in question.

Thus, as the current-electrode separation is increased, the electric potential distribution on the surface will be affected relatively more by deep-lying inhomogeneities within the earth.

In sounding with the Wenner configuration (Fig.62A) the separation a is increased in steps by moving each of the four electrodes outwards from the centre ("the sounding point") and a series of readings are taken with different separations. A typical set of separations is $a = 2, 6, 18, 54. . .$ m etc., trebling the separation each time so that the potential electrodes occupy the positions of the current electrodes in the previous set-up. Usually, however, intermediate separations will be found necessary to get a satisfactory apparent resistivity curve.

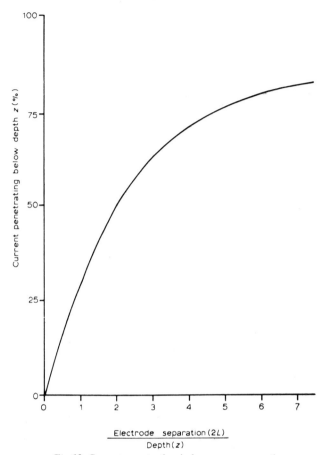

Fig.63. Current penetration in homogeneous earth.

In using the Schlumberger sounding method the potential probes are kept fixed at the centre of the line $C_1 C_2$ (Fig.62B), while the current electrodes are moved symmetrically outwards in steps. Since only two electrodes are moved, the field routine with the Schlumberger procedure is much more convenient than that with the Wenner one. Furthermore, as the potential electrodes are kept fixed, the effect of local shallow resistivity inhomogeneities in their vicinity (due to soil, weathering etc.) is constant for all observations.

A typical scheme of current-electrode separation (2L) in the Schlumberger sounding procedure is to start with a probe separation of, say 2 m and, keeping this constant, take observations with 2L = 10, 20, 30, 50,70, 100, 200, 300, 500, 700. . . m. If at any stage the voltage between the probes is deemed to be too small for accurate measurement, the probe separation is increased to, say, 10 m and the observations continued with the next current electrode separation in the series. The apparent resistivity is given by:

$$\rho_a = \frac{\pi L^2}{2l} \cdot \frac{\Delta V}{I} \qquad (6.13)$$

a formula obtained by putting $x = 0$ in eq. (6.9).

The first step in the interpretation of sounding observations is to prepare a graph in which the calculated apparent resistivities (eq. (6.8) and (6.13) respectively) are plotted as ordinates. In Wenner measurements it is customary to plot the electrode interval a as the abscissa, while in Schlumberger measurements half the current-electrode separation (L) is chosen for this purpose.

Some insight may be gained into the nature of electric sounding curves by studying a few simple cases.

In Fig.64 we consider a single layer of a certain thickness overlying a bedrock which extends downwards to "infinity". Suppose first that the top layer is a better electric conductor than the bedrock. Such a case may arise, for example, when conducting soil or moraine overlies a poorly conducting substratum. If the current-electrode separation is very small the apparent resistivity will not differ greatly from the resistivity of the top layer because the current will be largely confined near the surface. As the electrode separation increases, more and more current penetrates into the bedrock and the apparent resistivity increases.

For very large electrode separations practically all the current flows through the bedrock so that the curve approaches the resistivity of the bedrock. The complete resistivity curve has the smooth appearance shown in Fig.64A in which there is no sharp change in the curve indicative of the depth to the bedrock.

On the other hand, if the top layer is a poorer conductor than the

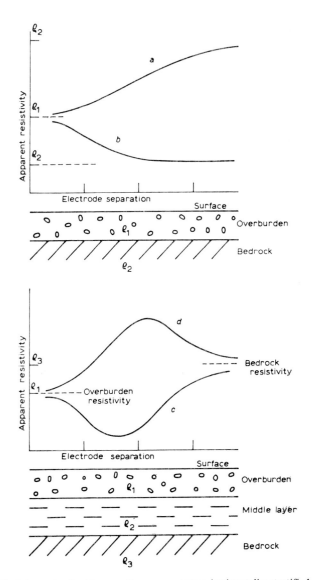

Fig.64. Schematic electric sounding curves over a horizontally stratified earth.

bedrock, as may very well happen if, for example, the bedrock is impregnated with conducting sulphides like pyrite, magnetite etc., the apparent resistivity will decrease with increasing electrode separation. A curve of another type will then be obtained (Fig.64B).

If a third layer is sandwiched between the top layer and the bedrock, a variety of apparent-resistivity curves result. An exhaustive discussion of these curves is beyond the scope of this book and we shall here consider only two principal cases. A more detailed discussion will be found in Parasnis (1972).

In Fig.64C the middle layer is a better conductor than both the top layer and the bedrock. The bedrock is supposed to be the most resistive of the three layers. Again, the apparent resistivity for very small electrode separations approaches the resistivity of the top layer but, as the separation increases, a significant part of the current enters the second layer and the apparent resistivity falls. For some electrode separation the apparent resistivity reaches a minimum value. On increasing the electrode separation further, more and more current enters the poorly conducting bedrock and the apparent resistivity starts rising again. For very large electrode separations the apparent resistivity approaches the resistivity of the bedrock.

If the middle layer is a poorer conductor than the top layer and the bedrock, the apparent-resistivity curve may follow the pattern in Fig.64D.

Detailed theoretical analysis shows that the electrode separation at which the turning point in apparent resistivity is attained in cases such as these, bears, unfortunately, no simple or obvious relation to the depth of the middle layer. Similarly, the minimum or the maximum value of the apparent resistivity by itself gives no indication of the resistivity of the middle layer.

The problem of interpreting electric sounding curves is one of the most intricate ones in the whole of applied geophysics and the reader should constantly guard against any simple rules of thumb in this respect. Unless one has considerable experience in the interpretation of these curves, all that can reasonably be inferred from a cursory study of them is the existence or otherwise of a good or bad conductor at *some* depth.

In relatively simple cases involving only two or three layers, a fairly satisfactory picture of the stratification can often be deduced by means of standard curves published in several places (e.g., Rijkswaterstaat, 1969; Orellana and Mooney, 1966).

ELECTRIC MAPPING

A distribution of resistivity consisting of a succession of horizontal, electrically conducting, layers is generally not one of immediate interest in ore prospecting, unless the problem is one of determining the depth to the bedrock or that to some key-horizon in a horizontal or gently dipping stratification.

In ore prospecting, the more pertinent type of resistivity distribution is a single mass of relatively small dimensions (an orebody) whose electrical resistivity differs from that of the surrounding rock. Although electric sounding may be used in the search for such bodies in the manner indicated above, it is obviously a questionable method since we must, to start with, decide where to sound. The role of electric sounding in ore prospecting is, therefore, rather limited although it is one of the principal methods in other branches of geophysics, for example, water prospecting.

In ore prospecting the procedure of electric mapping which we shall now consider is of incomparably greater importance.

The object of electrical mapping is to detect lateral variations in the resistivity of the ground. The procedure can be carried out using any of the electrode configurations shown in Fig.62 but, as before, we shall here confine attention to the Wenner and Schlumberger arrays only.

In Wenner mapping the configuration of four electrodes with a definite interval, say, 20 m (or 50 ft.), is moved as a whole in suitable steps (5 or 10 m) along a line of measurement. Each electrode is then advanced through the same distance. At the end of the line the array is transferred on the adjacent line and so on, until the area to be investigated has been covered in this zig-zag fashion.

The apparent resistivity value in each position of the array is supposed to "belong" to the centre of the configuration and is plotted against its coordinate in preparing a map of apparent resistivities. Lines of equal resistivity are then drawn on this map at suitable intervals.

An advantage of the Wenner mapping method is that all the observed voltage-current ratios — $\Delta V/I$ in eq. (6.8) — need be multiplied by one and the same factor, namely, $2\pi \times$ electrode interval, in order to obtain the apparent resistivities.

In the (modified) Schlumberger mapping procedure (or the gradient mapping method), the current electrodes are kept fixed at a relatively large distance from each other, say a few hundred metres, and the potential probes with a small mutual separation (5–50 m) are moved between them. The apparent resistivity is calculated from eq. (6.9) and a map is prepared by plotting it against the position of the point midway between the potential probes.

There is another mapping procedure which is also called the Schlumberger procedure. In this, the current electrodes are kept at a moderately large distance from each other, say 50 m, and the probes are situated midway between them at a small distance from each other, say 5 m. The entire assembly is moved along a line, as in the Wenner method, from "point-to-point" by advancing each of the electrodes through the same distance. In this case the geometrical factor for calculating the apparent resistivities remains constant (cf. eq. 6.13). We shall not, however, consider this mapping procedure in what follows. An example of a survey with it in connection with uranium prospecting has been given by Collin et al. (1958).

It should be remembered that the proper choice of electrode configuration is very important for the success of an electrical mapping survey. On the balance it seems, from theoretical as well as practical work, that the gradient array, the dipole—dipole array and the three-electrode array are the three most efficient configurations in this respect when operated perpendicular to the strike (Bloh, 1962). There is little to recommend in the Wenner configuration although this configuration is still widely used in some parts of the world.

It will be realized that the two curves in Fig.61 are really Wenner and Schlumberger mapping profiles across a vertical contact between two rock formations. In this figure the Schlumberger profile has a single discontinuity corresponding to the contact; that on the Wenner profile has four cusps. The cusps are not observed in practice, however, unless the measurements are taken at very close intervals (cf. Fig.82 below and also fig.35 in Parasnis, 1972).

The interpretation of resistivity maps for delineating lateral variations in the subsurface must be largely qualitative as the theoretical problem is very complicated. Broadly speaking, areas with low apparent-resistivity values may be associated with the occurrence of relatively good conductors, while those with high values would indicate bad conductors. However, low resistivity areas will be usually found to be flanked by high values and conversely, and it may be at times very difficult to infer the probable cause of the resistivity anomaly. It should also be noted that an asymmetry in an apparent-resistivity profile cannot be directly associated with the dip of the causative body because the relative distances of the two current electrodes from the body greatly influence the shape of the resistivity profile.

MAPPING BY LINEAR CURRENT ELECTRODES (THEORY)

In areas with a well defined strike that is approximately straight over great distances, it is generally advantageous to use a modification of the Schlumberger mapping procedure, in which the current is supplied to the earth by line electrodes instead of point ones. A line electrode consists simply of a very long, bare copper wire that makes an electrical contact with the ground along its entire length.

The lay-out in a line-electrode survey is shown schematically in Fig.65. Two equally long bare copper wires are laid parallel to the geological strike.[1] Every 5–10 m each wire is looped tightly round an iron nail and pegged to the ground to secure a proper electrical contact. The potential probes are, of course, point electrodes as usual

---

[1] Under certain circumstances the use of linear current electrodes *perpendicular* to the strike may be found to be more advantageous.

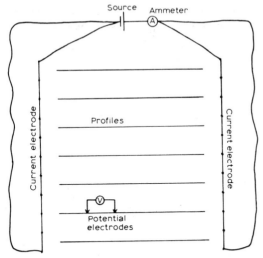

Fig.65. Layout for resistivity mapping using linear current electrodes.

(metal stakes or non-polarizable electrodes). In a typical lay-out the length of each line electrode may be from a couple of 100 m to 1 or 2 km, the spacing between them being usually of the same order as their length.

The advantage of using line electrodes is as follows. The normal electrical field is geometrically almost the same everywhere within the rectangle ABCD (Fig.66A). Thus, all the current lines on the surface of a homogeneous ground will be perpendicular to the electrodes, except at the ends of the lay-out where they start bulging. Hence, an orebody lying anywhere along a particular line such as EF within the rectangle will produce the same effect and therefore have the same chance of being discovered. With a point-electrode source (Fig.66B) this is not so because the electric field along EF becomes continuously weaker away from the line $C_1 C_2$. Therefore, it is necessary to move the point current electrodes from one line of measurement to another.

In the line-electrode system the electrodes need not be moved once they are laid out until the area ABCD has been mapped.

Line electrodes cannot be used successfully, except under special terrain conditions. In particular, the electrode-ground contact must be

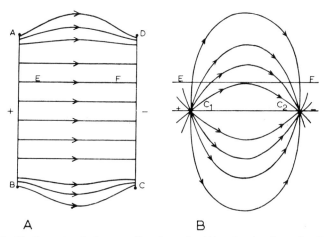

A   B

Fig.66. Current paths between line electrodes (A) and point electrodes (B).

of the same quality along the entire electrode length. This can be ensured sometimes by grounding the electrode along a more or less straight brook or the shore of a lake or marsh. Extensive marshes, shallow lakes and areas with a fairly uniform overburden are examples of terrain well suited for line electrode surveys.

We consider now a pair of parallel electrodes, each having a mathematically infinite length, laid on the earth's surface at a distance $2L$ from each other. In Fig.67 the electrodes are supposed to strike perpendicular to the plane of the paper.

It is shown in Appendix 4 that at a point P, distant x from the centre O of the line $C_1 C_2$, the electric voltage with respect to a very distant point, is given by:

$$V = \frac{J\rho}{\pi} \ln \frac{L - x}{L + x} \qquad (6.14)$$

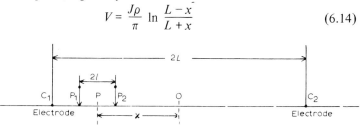

Fig.67. Configuration illustrating two line electrodes striking perpendicular to the plane of figure.

Here J is the current entering the ground *per unit length* of the electrodes and ρ is the resistivity of the ground.

If the potential probes have a *small* mutual separation $2l$ and are placed symmetrically on each side of the observation point P, the formula for the apparent resistivity at P is:

$$\rho_a = \frac{\pi}{2l} \cdot \frac{L^2 - x^2}{2L} \cdot \frac{\Delta V}{J} \qquad (6.15)$$

where ΔV is the measured voltage difference between the probes. This formula corresponds to eq. (6.9) for point electrodes.

A line electrode in reality always has a finite length and not an infinite one implied by the formula (6.15), which is, therefore, found to be satisfactory only when the distance between the current electrodes is small compared with their length, say not more than one fourth of it. Operationally, this condition restricts the area to be mapped to unreasonably narrow strips unless the electrodes are very long, which may be impractical. If a fairly wide rectangular area is to be mapped using linear current electrodes which are not too long, the apparent resistivities must be calculated from an exact formula that is reproduced in Appendix 5. If the simpler eq. (6.15) is used for short line electrodes the apparent resistivities will show a systematic tendency to increase as the electrodes are approached.

FIELD EXAMPLES OF LINE-ELECTRODE MAPPING

The general features of apparent resistivity curves obtained with linear current sources are similar to those of the curves obtained with point sources. For example, in passing across a contact between two formations of different resistivities, the apparent resistivity shows a jump as in Fig.61. In practice the jump is not as sharp as in the theoretical curve but manifests itself as a more or less steep gradient in the measured curve.

If, instead of a contact between two formations, we imagine a zone of low resistivity (like a pyrite vein, for instance) cutting through the surrounding rock, there will be two discontinuities, one corresponding to each wall.

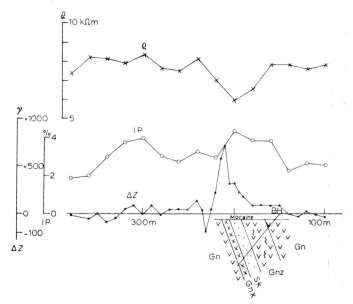

Fig.68. Apparent resistivity (ρ), magnetic vertical intensity anomalies (ΔZ), and induced polarization (IP) along a profile across the Harmsarvet silver-bearing zone, central Sweden. The mineralized zone being a good electric conductor shows up in low values of apparent resistivity. Gn = granulite rock. GnX = granulite rock with magnetite crystals. GnZ = granulite rock with Zn, Ag. Sk = Skarn. (Courtesy of BGAB.)

Fig.68 shows magnetic and resistivity (as well as induced polarization) profiles across a zone of granulite rock mineralized with zinc, silver, magnetite and very small quantities of pyrite. The magnetite mineralization shows up very clearly on the ΔZ curve but it is the resistivity profile that indicates the mineralized zone in its entirety between the coordinates 165 and 210 m. The area is covered with glacial moraine and geological observations are sparse but the direction of dip is known. Note how the combination of the geophysical information with borehole data helps to reconstruct the geological section shown. It appears that there is a more or less distinct stratification within the mineralized zone.

We shall revert to the induced polarization profile in the next chapter.

Another interesting example of resistivity mapping is shown in Fig.69 to illustrate a pitfall in resistivity interpretation. This is a profile across the Kimheden orebody discussed in Chapters 4 and 5, pp.89 and 128, respectively. Here the apparent resistivity (lower curve) shows two very sharp gradients at the coordinates 200 m and 365 m. It would be tempting to associate the very low resistivity values between these points with a good electrical conductor like pyrite mineralization. Actually, highly weathered sericite quartzite is encountered below the shallow moraine cover, not only in the two boreholes on this profile but also those on several other parallel profiles, and there is little doubt that it is the weathered zone which, being a better conductor than the fresh sericite quartzite, is causing the resistivity low. It almost, but not entirely, masks the ore anomaly

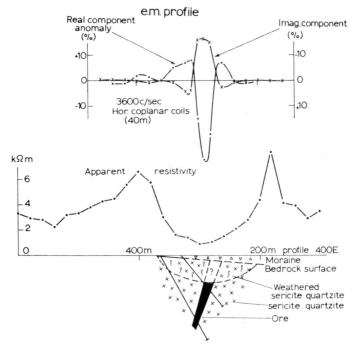

Fig.69. Apparent resistivity and e.m. profiles across the Kimheden orebody in Fig.27. Profile 400E. (Courtesy of BGAB.)

The latter is apparent only as a small kick near the minimum of the curve.

It has been possible to map the right-hand sub-outcrop of the weathered basin because of the resistivity measurements, in itself a valuable piece of information for further planning in the area.

The electromagnetic profile (moving source—receiver) is also shown for comparison (upper curve). The low values in the real and imaginary components succeed in indicating the ore plate (which, incidentally, is not compact) or possibly an electrically highly-conducting gossan above it (question mark in Fig.69). The interpretation of these electromagnetic measurements, as well as that of the Turam and self-potential measurements along the profile, points to a shallow depth to the upper surface of the conductor responsible for the anomalies and hence it seems necessary to invoke a conducting gossan formation sub-outcropping under the moraine, practically the only inference that can fit in well with the observed weathering.

The reason why the weathered zone does not show up on the electromagnetic curve is that the electromagnetic methods are not as sensitive as the resistivity methods to small differences in the electrical resistivity of rock formation (here the difference between weathered and fresh sericite quartzite). This characteristic of the resistivity methods makes them very attractive for mapping the details in ore formations and for mapping geological details like shear zones, faults, local changes in strike etc., provided these are associated with variations in electrical resistivity.

An impressive example is afforded by the resistivity and electromagnetic surveys in the Aitik orefield in northern Sweden. This ore formation is a very broad, more than 6 km long zone of poor pyrite and chalcopyrite impregnation in Precambrian, gneissic, micaceous schists. In Fig.70A, which is a resistivity map of a part of the area, the conducting impregnation zone (now well-known through extensive drilling) is indicated by the low values in apparent resistivity below 3 kΩm. On its western margin the ore formation makes a sharp contact with barren granulite rocks. This contact dips about $30°-45°$ to the *west* and shows up as the very high resistivity gradient approximately along the line 400 W.

A

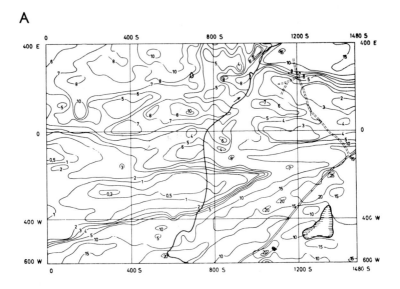

B

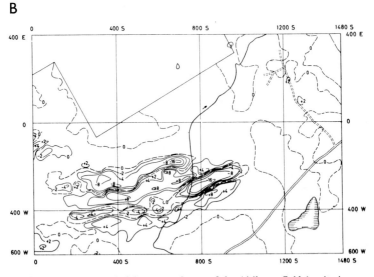

Fig.70.A. Apparent resistivity map of part of the Aitik ore field (pyrite impregnation), northern Sweden. Contours in kΩm. Coordinates on the map are in m.
B. Electromagnetic imaginary component map of part of the Aitik ore field.
Moving source–receiver system. Horizontal coils. Separation 40 m. Frequency
3,600 c/sec. Contours in percent normal field. (Courtesy of BGAB.)

The resistivity map in Fig.70A was obtained using current electrodes 800 m long and 2,000 m apart. The electrodes were laid parallel to the strike and the potential gradient was mapped by means of probes, 40 m apart, by moving them along lines perpendicular to the current electrodes.

Comparing the resistivity map with the electromagnetic (moving source—receiver) map in Fig.70B, one is at once struck with the relative paucity of details on the latter. In fact, careful scrutiny shows that the electromagnetic indication (minimum in the field, that is, negative values) by and large proves only the hanging-wall and foot-wall contacts of the ore formation with barren rock. The broad ore formation as such is not indicated! This, incidentally, is another instance of a phenomenon discussed on p.140. Extensive areas where there is no electromagnetic relief whatsoever but where the resistivity shows great detail in the impregnation (confirmed through drilling) will also be readily recognized.

In the extreme south of the area shown the sharp resistivity gradient is displaced eastwards. It is possible that the resistivity map is here evincing a geological fault or flexure.

THE "MISE-À-LA-MASSE" METHOD

This technique of electrical mapping was suggested by Schlumberger (1920). The name, which is of later origin, may be translated as "excitation of the mass". The idea is to use a subsurface conductive mass itself as one current electrode of a pair by connecting it directly to one pole of a voltage source, the second current electrode being as usual a metal one but placed on the ground surface at a great distance and connected to the other pole. A current is passed and the voltages at points on the surface are mapped by means of a voltmeter with respect to some base station. It will be noticed that the operation is exactly the same as in the measurement of self-potentials (see p.87).

The distribution of potentials will to some extent reflect the geometry of the mass and would be expected to yield some information concerning the shape of the body, its extent, dip, pitch and other

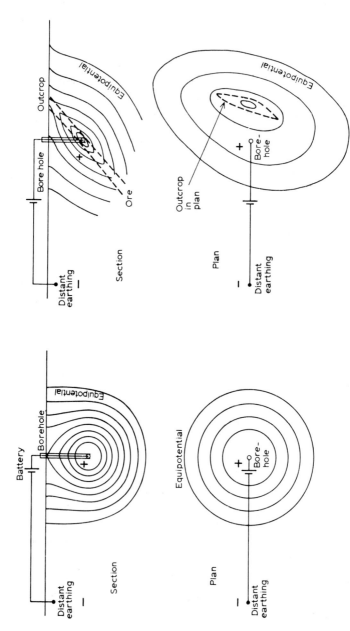

Fig.71A. Principle of the mise-à-la-masse method. Right-hand part of the figure shows the distortion of the equipotential lines due to an ore.

geometrical parameters. In Fig.71A the left-hand part shows the equipotentials around a subsurface point electrode in a homogeneous isotropic earth. These are constructed exactly from elementary formulas. The equipotential surfaces approach spherical form in the immediate neighbourhood of the electrode but strictly speaking they are everywhere surfaces of revolution of the 4th degree. The right-hand part of Fig.71A shows (schematically) the distribution of potentials such as might be expected when the point electrode is placed in a conducting body situated in an otherwise homogeneous earth of smaller conductivity.

Here, the equipotentials tend to follow the orebody and on the ground surface the centroid of the equipotential picture will be far away from the electrode epicentre (point on the ground vertically above the electrode in the borehole).

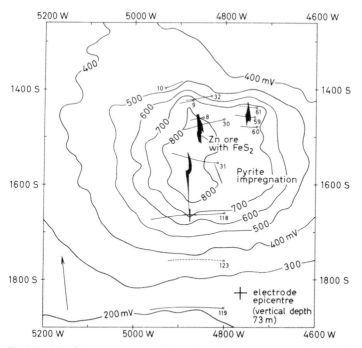

Fig.71B. Mise-à-la-masse survey of the Bastuliden ore zone, northern Sweden. (Courtesy BGAB.)

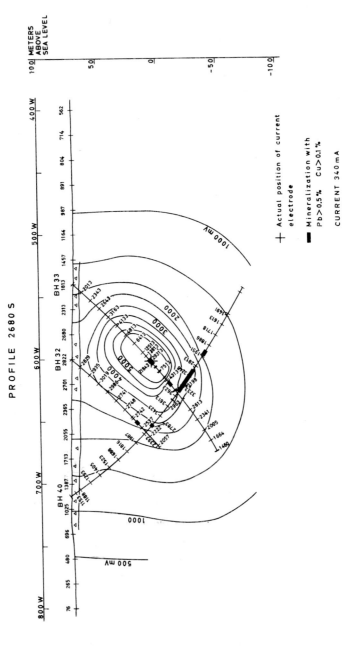

Fig. 71C. Mise-à-la-masse measurements in boreholes. Vindfall area, central Sweden. (After Parasnis, 1967.)

It is obvious, of course, that at least part of the mass concerned must be accessible so that an electrical earthing can be made in it. The mise-à-la-masse technique is of great help in testing whether a small conducting mineral show (in outcrop or in borehole) is an isolated occurrence or whether it is part of a large electrically continuous mass.

Fig.71B shows an example of a survey in a pyrite-impregnated area. The electrode was earthed in a pyrite section in Bh 118 but we see from the equipotentials that this section is only part of a very large impregnation mass, the centroid of which lies about 125 m from the hole. It is also seen that the impregnation zone is very well delineated by the measurements. The more or less sharp gradient near the holes 123 and 32 mark the edges of the zone, as is confirmed by the results of the drillings. Now, if a conducting ore mass is an extremely good conductor of electricity it will assume almost the same potential throughout and the equipotential picture should be independent of the exact location of the electrode. In the present instance the mise-à-la-masse survey was repeated with the current electrode in the ore in Bh 30. The picture obtained was so similar to the one shown, even in minute details, that it is unnecessary to reproduce it! This experiment proved that the whole pyrite zone was an excellent electric conductor. Embedded in the zone are lenses of sphalerite ore.

Mise-à-la-masse measurements can be used for correlating different parts of an orebody, for isolating different ore lenses, for determining the dip and plunge of an orebody etc. Fig.71C shows potentials in a vertical section through three boreholes cutting a lead–zinc–copper ore. In this particular case there was considerable uncertainty about the dip of the ore, despite boreholes from either direction, but the trend of the equipotentials in the mise-à-la-masse measurements clearly establishes the westerly dip of the ore.

Examples of three-dimensional mise-à-la-masse surveys for obtaining detailed structural information about complicated ores have been discussed elsewhere (Parasnis, 1967; Ketola, 1972).

POTENTIAL-DROP RATIO AND A.C. POTENTIAL METHODS

(*a*) In the early days of electric prospecting, a method known as the potential-drop ratio (P.D.R.) method was much used, particularly for investigating shallow vertical discontinuities like veins and contacts. It employed three collinear potential electrodes A, B, C and measured the ratio of the voltage drops V_{AB} and V_{BC} between the pairs of electrodes (A,B) and (B,C) respectively. An apparatus of the Wheatstone bridge type was used to read the ratio directly without having to measure the voltage drops separately.

The ratio V_{AB}/V_{AC} must be corrected for the normal ratio of the potential drops. If one point electrode is collinear with the potential electrodes and the second current electrode is at a very great distance, the normal P.D.R. (if AB = BC) is easily shown with the help of eq. (6.3) to be r_C/r_A where r_A, r_C are the distances of A and C from the current electrode. The corrected P.D.R. is obtained by dividing the measured one by r_C/r_A, so that:

$$\text{P.D.R.} = \frac{V_{AB}}{V_{BC}} \times \frac{r_A}{r_C} \qquad (6.16)$$

The P.D.R. is equal to 1.0 in the absence of subsurface conductors but departs from this value when conductors are present.

The advantage of the P.D.R. method is that eq. (6.16) is independent of variations in the current passing through the ground. This is not true of the resistivity methods in which only one potential difference, say V_{AB}, between two electrodes is measured. The apparatus in resistivity methods must therefore be constructed so that the ground current remains reasonably constant, or else the current must be noted for each observation of the voltage. However, modern technical devices allow constant-current generators to be constructed with no great difficulty. As the theory of resistivity methods is moreover very highly developed, the P.D.R. method is now out of fashion.

(*b*) A number of techniques which may be classified under a.c. potential methods were used extensively in the 1930's. An alternating electric current was sent into the ground by means of a pair of current electrodes connected to an a.c. source of fairly high frequency (a few hundred c/sec) and the voltages between two pairs of electrodes A, B and B,C were compared in magnitude and phase. The a.c. potential ratio, racom and Turam transformer are a few names encountered in the older literature. All these methods worked essentially on the same principle.

The theory of these methods has never been systematically developed, although attempts were apparently made (Edge and Laby, 1931). With the development of the modern resistivity methods the a.c. potential methods have fallen into disuse but a perusal of the literature leaves the impression that they have been abandoned rather hastily.

RESISTIVITY MEASUREMENTS IN BOREHOLES

The measurement of resistivity in boreholes has been undertaken from time to time in ore prospecting partly with the object of determining

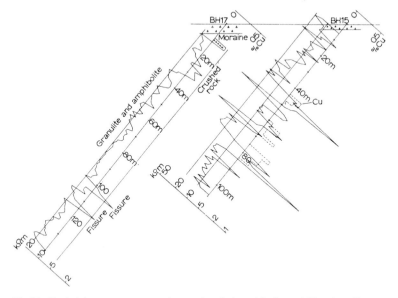

Fig.72. Resistivity measurements in two boreholes with Cu and Pb mineralization. (Courtesy of BGAB.)

the resistivity of rocks and ores in situ, partly with the object of correlating ore veins, fissures and other features in the boreholes from one hole to another, and partly with the object of checking whether surface resistivity indications can be accounted for by zones of appropriate resistivity in the holes.

In an arrangement which the author has used extensively in Swedish ore fields, a system of three electrodes (one current and two potential, Fig.62C) with a separation of 50 cm between adjacent electrodes is mounted on a plastic support, at the end of a three-conductor cable, and lowered in the borehole. If the hole is water-filled the contact between the electrodes and the earth is quite satisfactory. It can be shown that if the hole has a small diameter, the water has no effect on the measured in-situ-resistivity values.

Fig.72 is an example of borehole resistivity measurements.

CHAPTER 7

Induced Polarization Methods

INTRODUCTION

We have seen that if the current electrodes of an electrode configuration placed on the earth's surface are connected to a battery, a voltage appears between two potential probes. It is found, however, that on disconnecting the battery the voltage does not, in general, drop to zero immediately but persists for some time with a continuously decreasing magnitude. Conversely, the voltage between the probes does not attain its maximum value immediately after the current is

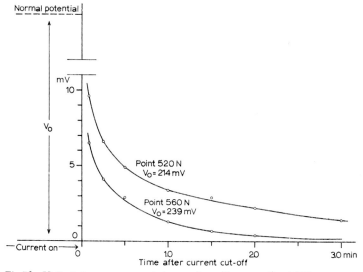

Fig.73. Voltage-decay curves at two points along profile 280E across the Kimheden orebody in Fig.27. Probe separation 40 m. Current-electrode separation 1,000 m. Current-on time 2 min. (Courtesy of BGAB.)

switched on but increases steadily towards it for several seconds or minutes.

Two voltage-decay curves obtained in the field are shown in Fig.73. It will be noticed that even a couple of minutes after the cessation of the current, the residual voltage between the probes is as much as 0.5—1% of that existing when the current was flowing. This phenomenon is termed in geophysical literature as induced polarization or IP and seems to have been first studied in geophysical investigations by Schlumberger (1920, chapter 8). Some inconclusive experiments on the IP effect in sedimentary rocks were made by Müller in 1937 (Müller, 1940) but interest in the phenomenon appears to have dwindled until about 1948 when Newmont Exploration Ltd., U.S.A. revived it.

The question arises whether the IP effect can be used to obtain information about the electric properties of the subsurface. The answer to this question is naturally linked with the origin of induced polarization, which we shall now briefly study.

ORIGIN OF INDUCED POLARIZATION

Although the phenomenon of induced polarization is extremely complex, certain insight has been gained into its mechanism as a result of recent researches. It now seems well established that we must distinguish between two principal effects: an electrode polarization and a membrane polarization.

Electrode polarization

The electric current in the ground is normally carried by ions in the electrolytes present in the pores of rocks. If the passage of these ions is obstructed by certain mineral particles which, like common metals, transport the current by electrons, ionic charges pile up at particle-electrolyte interface, positive ones where the current enters the particle and negative ones where it leaves (Fig.74A). The piled-up charges create a voltage that tends to oppose the flow of electric current across the interface and the particle is said to be polarized.

When the current is interrupted a residual voltage continues to exist across the particle, due to the bound ionic charges, but it decreases continuously as the ions slowly diffuse back into the pore-electrolytes, which process gives the induced polarization effect.

This type of polarization is called electrode polarization because it is also observed during ordinary electrolysis, at the surface of the metal electrodes dipped in an electrolyte. Physical chemists have been familiar with the phenomenon for a long time and have referred to it as *overvoltage*.

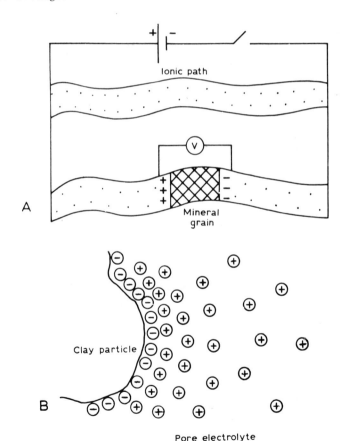

Fig.74.A. Electrode polarization phenomenon at mineral-electrolyte interfaces.
B. Membrane polarization phenomenon in clays.

Foremost among the ore minerals having an electronic mode of conduction and therefore exhibiting strong IP are pyrite, pyrrhotite, chalcopyrite, graphite, galena, bornite, magnetite and pyrolusite.

Membrane polarization

This type of polarization must be evoked for explaining the IP effects which are observed even when no metallic-type minerals are present in the ground. It owes its origin to the presence of clay particles.

The surface of a clay particle is negatively charged and thus attracts positive ions from the electrolytes present in the capillaries of a clay aggregate. An electrical double-layer is therefore formed at the surface of the particle somewhat as sketched in Fig.74B, the concentration of positive ions being greatest at the surface of the clay particle. If the positively charged zone persists far enough into the capillaries, it effectively repels other positively charged ions and so acts like an impervious membrane impeding their movement through the capillaries. When an electric current is forced through the clay, the positive ions are displaced (in fact, their displacement constitutes part of the current) and on the interruption of the current the positive charges redistribute themselves in their former equilibrium pattern. The process of redistribution manifests itself as a decaying voltage between two electrodes in contact with the clay, that is, as an IP effect.

The existence of membrane polarization complicates the interpretation of IP observations because the IP effects cannot be interpreted as unambiguous evidence of the presence of minerals having an electronic conduction (sulphides or magnetite) in contact with the electrolytes in the rock.

The above account of electrode and membrane polarization is a simplified description of what actually happens at the interface between an ore or a clay particle and an electrolyte but it qualitatively explains many features of observed IP effects. It is noteworthy that in either case, it is necessary that the movement of *ions* be impeded, the IP effect appearing as the diffusion of ions.

Polarization is essentially a surface phenomenon. Hence the greater the surface presented by sulphides or clays to an electric current the stronger are the polarization effects. A number of laboratory experiments support this view. For example, Henkel and Van Nostrand (1957) reported that the polarization voltage measured across copper plates immersed in an electrolyte was proportional to the number of plates between the potential probes. For clays they found that the polarization increased with the total clay thickness between the probes.

From the nature of the IP effect it follows that impregnation-type ores or, for example, deposits of the "porphyry" copper type, which have a large effective surface of mineral particles are particularly suitable targets for exploration with the IP method.

THE CONDENSER MODEL

There is a simple but far-reaching and useful analogy to the polarization phenomena in rocks. Consider an electric circuit consisting of a condenser and a high resistance in parallel, with a battery across them (Fig.75). When the switch S is closed, the plates of the condenser acquire electrical charges from the battery and a voltage equal to the battery voltage develops across them. A small current passes through the high resistance and the external circuit and this can be read on the ammeter A. When the current is interrupted by opening the switch, the charges stored on the condenser plates leak through the resistance and a transient current persists in the circuit ABCD in the direction of the arrows. The voltage across the condenser, initially equal to the battery voltage, steadily decreases in magnitude as the positive and negative charges leak and mix with each other.

Now, each electrolyte-mineral grain interface in the ground may be likened to a tiny condenser storing ionic charges whose rediffusion in the electrolytes, after the cessation of the current, corresponds to the leakage through the resistance in Fig.75, giving rise to a steadily decreasing voltage between two potential probes on the surface. This is the IP effect.

EFFECT OF ALTERNATING CURRENT

The circuit in Fig.75 has the property that if the battery is replaced by a source of alternating electromotive force, the magnitude of the alternating current in the circuit increases with the frequency (for constant amplitude of the voltage). In other words, the effective electrical resistance of the circuit decreases as the frequency of the applied voltage increases. The reason for the decrease is that, although a condenser presents an infinite resistance to a direct current, it allows alternating current to pass across it, so that when the current alternates an extra path becomes available to it.

However, with an alternating voltage, the current and the voltage are not in phase with each other, that is, they do not attain their maxima and minima simultaneously. In the circuit of Fig.75 the current shown by the ammeter attains its maxima and minima ahead of the voltage. Another way of looking at the phenomenon is to consider the resistance of the circuit ABCD to be itself an alternating magnitude which is out of phase with the voltage and which, moreover, varies with the frequency. Such a resistance is called a complex impedance.

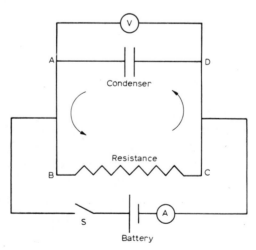

Fig.75. Electric circuit analogy to IP phenomenon.

If the polarization phenomenon in the ground were due to the ore-electrolyte interfaces acting as condensers, we should expect the resistivity of rocks to decrease as the frequency of the current passing through them increases. This is indeed found to be the case (Fig.76).

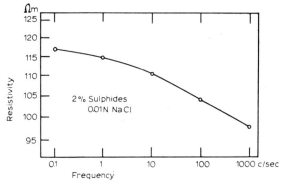

Fig.76. Decrease of the electric resistivity of rocks with the frequency of the current through them. Curve rescaled from Keevil and Ward (1962).

We see then that the transient decay of the residual voltage when a direct current is cut off, and the variation of resistivity with the frequency of an alternating current, are two different aspects of one and the same phenomenon. In fact, it can be proved mathematically that if a (linear) system's electrical response after a sudden current cut-off is known, its response to steady alternating current can be deduced and vice versa. Thus, if the curve, such as that in Fig.73, is measured the curve corresponding to Fig.76 can be deduced without further measurements. The mathematical apparatus needed for the purpose is known as the Laplace transform but a discussion of it lies outside the scope of this book.

TIME-DOMAIN AND FREQUENCY-DOMAIN IP METHODS

From the foregoing it is evident that IP measurements can be carried out in two different ways. In one we send a direct current into the ground, and observe the decay of voltage between a pair of potential probes after the current is turned off. In the second we determine the variation of apparent resistivity of the ground with the frequency of the injected current or, otherwise, the phase difference between the probe voltage and the current. These two procedures are known respectively as the time-domain and frequency-domain methods and it will be realized that they are entirely equivalent.

Any of the electrode configurations used in ordinary resistivity work (Fig.62) can be employed for IP measurements, whether in the time-domain or in the frequency-domain.

In the time-domain methods, a current is sent into the ground for a definite period, say 15 sec, turned off and the voltage between the potential probes is observed or recorded for 15–20 sec. The recording instrument is moved to the next point and the current pulse is now sent in the reverse direction for 15 sec. The scheme of current pulses is shown in Fig.77. Pulse durations of 3, 4 or 5 sec are also commonly used to effect a reduction in the survey time.

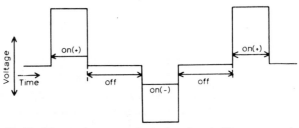

Fig.77. Scheme of current pulse in time-domain IP measurements.

An advantage of the time-domain method is the comparative simplicity of the apparatus needed. In fact, quite satisfactory observations can be made manually (for long pulse durations) using ordinary resistivity equipment described in Chapter 6 under the heading *Apparatus*. But to obtain the greatest efficiency in field work it is advisable to use one of the commercially available time-domain IP equipments providing for automatic read-out. One such equipment (manufactured by Scintrex, Downsview, Ont., Canada) is shown in Fig.78.

In time-domain methods, special attention has to be paid to the

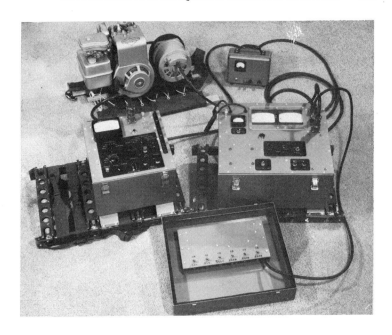

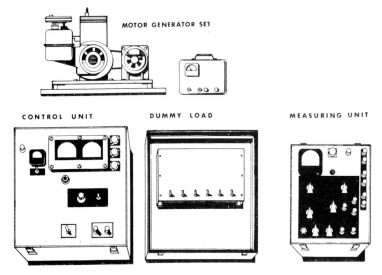

Fig.78. The Seigel mark V IP unit for time-domain measurements. (Courtesy of Scintrex Ltd., Downsview, Canada.)

cable lay-outs since the switching on and off of the current can induce an electromagnetic transient signal in the cables which lead to the probes and this signal may vitiate the IP readings.

The practice in frequency-domain methods is to determine the apparent resistivity of the ground at two frequencies, one a very low one (0.1 c/sec) and the other a higher one (10 c/sec). A full spectrum of apparent resistivity from very low to very high frequencies would give more complete information but such a spectrum is rarely taken.

In another type of frequency-domain method (called the complex impedance method) a current at a low frequency such as 1 c/sec is injected in the ground and the amplitude of the probe voltage as well as its phase with respect to the current is measured. Normally this requires a reference cable between the current source and the observation point (to obtain the reference phase, see p.122). However, it is also possible to use high-precision quartz-controlled clock standards. One of these monitors the current while the other shows the instant in the current cycle at which the probe voltage reaches its maximum. The clocks are synchronized at the start of the measurements (and subsequently at suitable intervals).

The frequency-domain measurements must be made at fairly low frequencies in order to avoid the purely electromagnetic effects which may otherwise arise due to the conductors in the ground. On the other hand, certain instrumental considerations preclude the use of too low frequencies. The region 0.1–10 c/sec appears to be the optimum for most field conditions.

MEASURES OF THE IP EFFECT

For a proper application of the induced-polarization method in geophysical prospecting, we must have suitable quantitative measures. Several different IP measures have been proposed in the time domain as well as in the frequency domain. A few of them are discussed below.

Time-domain measures

(*1*) Millivolt per volt and percent IP: the simplest measure of IP would seem to be the residual voltage at a definite time after the current cut-off, but it would be incorrect to use this because it is found to vary in proportion to the voltage existing between the probes while the current is flowing, i.e., the "normal potential". The appropriate measure must therefore be the ratio of the residual voltage $V(t)$ at a selected instant t after the current cut-off to the normal voltage V_0 while the current is flowing. The residual voltage, being small, is generally expressed in mV while the normal voltage is expressed in V. Consequently, the IP effect is then expressed as millivolt per volt (mV/V).

If both $V(t)$ and V_0 are expressed in mV and their ratio is multiplied by 100, we obtain the polarization in percent. In Fig.73, for example, IP(30 sec) = 3.5/214 = 1.54% (at point 520N).

Owing to the nature of the effect sought, it is impossible to measure the maximum residual voltage, namely the voltage at the very instant of current cut-off, and some time must necessarily elapse before the voltage is "sampled". The sampling instant must be late enough for the effects due to secondary electromagnetic currents induced in the ground to have disappeared but early enough for the residual voltage not to fall below the sensitivity of the apparatus.

Some workers sample the decay curve at 0.1 sec, others at 1, 2, 3, 5 or 10 sec.

(*2*) Normalized time-integral: this parameter has been devised to preserve some of the information that is inherent in the shape of the voltage-decay curve but is necessarily lost in measuring the residual voltage at a single instant only. Towards this purpose, the decay curve is registered over a length of time and the area under it between two time limits is determined (Fig.79). The result is expressed in the unit millivolt × second. On dividing it by the normal potential V_0 (by convention usually expressed in volt) we obtain the time-integral measure of IP (mVsec/V).

Commercial IP outfits automatically measure and read the integral between preselected time limits.

If the integration time is very short, say 0.1 sec, the area under the voltage-time curve is proportional to the average voltage during the interval. Therefore, if the integral is sampled within a number of short intervals, like 1 and 1.1, 2 and 2.1,...10 and 10.1 sec etc., it is possible to reconstruct the approximate shape of the decay curve.

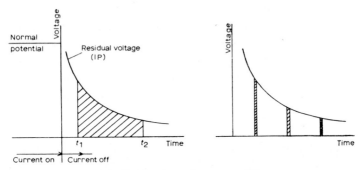

Fig.79. Time-integral measure of IP.

(*3*) Chargeability: the concept of chargeability as a measure of IP was introduced by Seigel (1959). He postulated that all the polarization phenomena occurring in a medium and impeding a current flow through it, can be represented by a volume distribution of electric-current dipoles (miniature battery cells) with a strength proportional to the current density (current per unit area) at the centre of the volume element. The factor of proportionality he called the chargeability m. It can be shown that:

$$m = \frac{V_0 - V_i}{V_0} \tag{7.1}$$

where V_i is the polarization voltage at the cut-off instant and V_0 is the voltage that existed when the current was flowing.

In practice, it is not possible to determine V_i but only the residual voltage $V(t)$ a very short time after cut-off. Hence, for practical purposes we may write:

$$m = \frac{V_0 - V(t)}{V_0} \tag{7.2}$$

It is obvious that:

$$m = 1 - \frac{V(t)}{V_0} = 1 - \frac{1}{100} \text{ I.P. } (\%)$$

Frequency-domain measures

(*1*) Frequency effect: in section *Effect of alternating current* we saw that the resistivity of rocks decreases as the frequency is increased. Let ρ_{dc} be the resistivity of a rock for direct current and ρ_{ac} that for an alternating current. Then the frequency-effect measure of IP is defined as:

$$\text{f.e.} = \frac{\rho_{dc} - \rho_{ac}}{\rho_{ac}} \tag{7.3}$$

In practice, the d.c. resistivity (i.e., resistivity at zero frequency) in the formula is usually replaced by that at the low frequency 0.1 c/sec and the resistivity at high frequency by that at 10 c/sec in which case:

$$\text{f.e.} = \frac{\rho_{0\cdot1} - \rho_{10}}{\rho_{10}} \tag{7.4}$$

In field work, the resistivities in eq.(7.3) and (7.4) are to be understood as the apparent resistivities calculated according to eq. (6.7) for the relevant electrode configuration.

(*2*) Metal factor: the theory of electrode-polarization effects shows that IP is greatly influenced by the resistivity of the electrolytes in the country rock and hence by electrolyte activity, type and temperature. The parameter known as metal factor (M.F.) was devised by Madden to correct (partially) for the resistivity of the country rock (Marshall and Madden, 1959). In principle, it is defined simply as the frequency-effect divided by the d.c.- or very low-frequency apparent resistivity. However, as the number thus obtained is inconveniently small, it is multiplied arbitrarily by $2\pi \times 100,000$ so that the practical definition of the metal factor becomes:

$$\text{M.F.} = \frac{\rho_{0\cdot1} - \rho_{10}}{\rho_{0\cdot1} \times \rho_{10}} \times 2\pi \times 10^5 \tag{7.5}$$

If the resistivities are expressed in Ωm, the dimensions of the metal factor are $\Omega^{-1}m^{-1}$, that is, those of the electric conductivity.

As the resistivity of massive sulphides is normally smaller than that of disseminated zones, the metal factors measured above them are expected to be greater since the resistivity occurs in eq. (7.5) in the denominator.

It should be realized that a knowledge of the normal potential V_0 between the probes is indispensable for obtaining time-domain IP measures. Now, V_0 is the very quantity measured in the resistivity methods and yields the apparent resistivity (cf. eq. (6.7) where it is denoted by ΔV). In frequency-domain measures, a direct knowledge of the apparent resistivity is required. Hence it follows that an IP survey always implies a simultaneous resistivity survey.

(3) Phase difference: It will be realized from the discussion on p.109 that, if the frequency is 1 c/sec, a time difference of 100 μsec between probe voltage and current corresponds to a phase difference of $0.036°$ or 0.628 milliradian (since $360° = 2\pi = 6.28$ radian) between them. Maximum phase differences normally obtained in field work are of the order of 100 milliradian if conducting mineralization is present. Background effects vary with the geological setting but typical values would be, say, 10–20 milliradian.

POLARIZABILITY OF MINERALS AND ROCKS

A great deal of research has been done in the laboratory on the polarizability of rocks and on the influence of electrolyte activity, temperature, pressure etc., particular attention being paid to the possibility of distinguishing different minerals through their IP effects.

A set of laboratory decay curves obtained on various minerals contained in an andesite matrix with 5 percent 0.01 N NaCl as electrolyte is shown in Fig.80. The shapes of such curves have been the subject of much scrutiny (Wait, 1959; Malmqvist, 1960).

If the IP effect were purely due to a single-condenser action envisaged in section *The condenser model*, the residual voltage at a

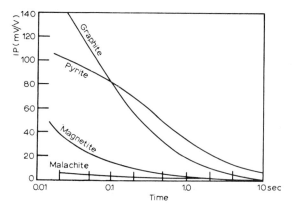

Fig.80. Some laboratory IP decay curves of minerals in andesite matrix. (After Collet, 1959.)

time t after current cut-off would be expressible by a formula of the type:

$$V = V_i e^{-\lambda t} \qquad (7.6)$$

where V_i is the residual voltage immediately after current cut-off. In this case, a decay curve and hence eventually the mineral–electrolyte system could perhaps be characterized by the decay constant $1/\lambda$ which is the time after which the residual voltage drops to $1/e(\approx 1/3)$ of its initial value.

Experiments show that the simple exponential formula or other similar formulas do not in general fit IP curves exactly, and further that the decay curves of various mineral-electrolyte systems are very alike. Moreover, in practical field work we are measuring a bulk-polarization effect of a very large volume of rock and such a volume will usually contain many different metallic minerals in contact with the rock electrolytes, whose polarization effects will be superimposed on each other.

Consequently, it does not seem practically possible to distinguish minerals from their IP decay curves. However, Fraser, Keevil and Ward have claimed that they can distinguish minerals (in laboratory experiments) by a combination of the IP magnitude and the frequency spectrum, i.e., the curve showing the variation of resistivity with frequency (Fraser et al., 1964). Great progress has also been made by

Bhattacharyya and Morrison in explaining the shapes of IP decay curves (Bhattacharyya and Morrison, 1963).

The metal factors of rocks and ore samples have also been the subject of considerable studies. Fig.81, after Marshall and Madden (1959), shows the metal factors of different rocks in a schematic way. High M.F. values are associated with well-mineralized rocks such as porphyry coppers, rich magnetite, heavy sulphides etc., and low ones with barren rocks. However, in poorly mineralized rocks the metal factors alone cannot tell whether the rocks are barren or mineralized or whether the IP response is due to clays, because in these regions there is considerable overlap in the M.F. values.

An interesting investigation was also reported by Keller (1959) who analyzed a large number of laboratory decay curves and determined a parameter which he called the static capacity (piled-up charge per metre and per volt normal potential). The parameter, ranging from 10^{-6} to 10^{-2} (coulombs per metre per volt), was not found to be diagnostic of rock type. Keller therefore formed the product of the static capacity with the resistivity of the rock in question, obtaining a ·new measure which he denoted by $\rho\epsilon$. The average $\rho\epsilon$ values were fairly constant for a large variety of rock formations (sandstones,

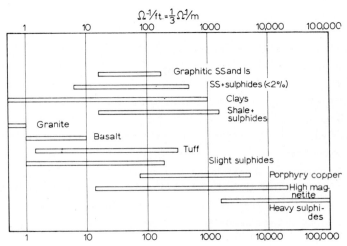

Fig.81. Metal factors in IP. (Adapted from Marshall and Madden, 1959.)

shales, limestones, dolomites, andesite, diorite, basalt, granulite, glacial till etc.), although they appeared to be significantly different for haematite, pyrite, monzonite etc. These investigations have been ramified in further work (Anderson and Keller, 1964).

EXAMPLES OF IP SURVEYS

Kankberg orebody, northern Sweden

The I.P. profile shown in Fig.82 was measured in the time domain in a simple manner by moving a Wenner configuration (cf. Fig.62) having an electrode separation of 40 m.

A direct current (about 50–100 mA) was passed in the ground for 2 min and then switched off. The residual voltage between the potential probes was read 5 sec after the cut-off.

The continuous curve shows the % IP, the midpoint of the Wenner array being, as usual, reckoned as the observation point. Above the ore and the mineralized rocks the IP values are high, as much as 10–25% while the unmineralized volcanics show low values. Around 440S, the IP reaches a high value (30%) which is due to pyrrhotite-bearing graphite shales.

The dashed curve shows the apparent resistivity. It attains low values over the ore and on the shales in the north. It will be noticed that there is a close correspondence between the IP and the resistivity curves. High values of IP are associated with low resistivities and low ones with high resistivities.

Broken Hill area, Australia

This example in the frequency domain is due to Hallof (1963). The IP data in Fig.83 are in terms of metal factors, the resistivity in terms of the apparent resistivity in arbitrary units. The survey was carried out using the dipole–dipole configuration (cf. Fig.62) with separations of 100 ft. between the two current electrodes and 100 ft. between the two potential ones.

Normally, readings in resistivity or IP are plotted at the coordinate of the midpoint of the potential electrodes or the centre of the elec-

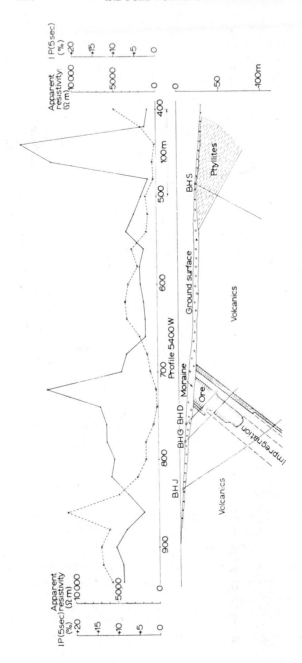

Fig. 82. Time-domain IP (continuous curve) and Wenner apparent resistivity (dashed curve) across the Kankberg sulphide orebody, northern Sweden. (After Malmqvist, 1960.)

trode configuration as a whole. Hallof's procedure for plotting requires some explanation.

With a fixed distance between the two electrode pairs, the configuration was moved as a rigid system along the survey line. The reading obtained for each position of the configuration was plotted at the intersection of two 45° lines drawn from the centre of each pair, as shown in the inset in Fig.83A. Thus, for instance, the reading 455 in the metal factor and 11 in ρ_a was obtained when the current electrodes were at the coordinate 11W and 10W and the potential ones at 7W and 6W.

The first line (n = 1) represents the readings obtained with a distance of 1 X 100 = 100 ft. between the two innermost electrodes, one current and the other potential electrode respectively, the second (n = 2) those obtained with the distance 2 X 100 = 200 ft. and so on. Contours of equal anomaly are then drawn through the readings plotted in this way.

The distance between the current and the potential pairs determines, in a general sort of way, the depth at which a resistivity inhomogeneity may lie to give a maximum effect on the ground. The greater this distance, the greater the depth sounded. Hence, the plots in Fig.83A may be looked upon very schematically as vertical sections of the ground, but the picture should not be taken too literally.

Evidently the metal factors are high above the mineralized zone and low outside it. The conducting mineralization is very clearly indicated by the low apparent resistivity values and from the point of view of detecting this mineralization, a resistivity survey would have been sufficient. In this connection, the general correspondence between high M.F. values and low ρ_a values and vice versa is again worth noting.

S—et area, northern Sweden

An example of the phase-measuring or the complex impedance type of IP work (p.212) is shown in Fig.83B. The area lies on the margin of a precambrian granite. Basic intrusions occur here and there in the granite and from the ore-genetic point of view the area is a potentially porphyry-copper area. The apparent resistivity values

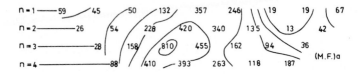

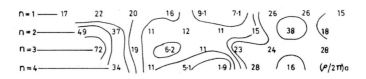

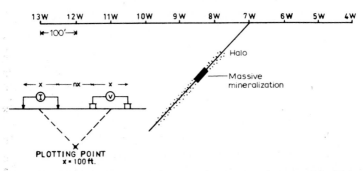

Fig.83A. Frequency-domain IP measurements (upper part) and dipole–dipole apparent resistivity (lower part) at Broken Hill, Australia. (Redrawn after Hallof, 1963.)

shown in Fig.83B are normalized gradients of the electric field between fixed current electrodes (configuration B in Fig.62) 2,600 m apart.

It will be noticed that on the lower profile the phase differences are relatively large between coordinates 8400 and 9200. The apparent resistivity values are relatively low between 8400 and 8700 on both the profiles. From the magnetic intensity profile it is evident that the area has a magnetite impregnation between about 8700 and 9300 on the lower profile and between about 8600 and 9400 on the upper one. There are a few drillholes in the area and it appears that the

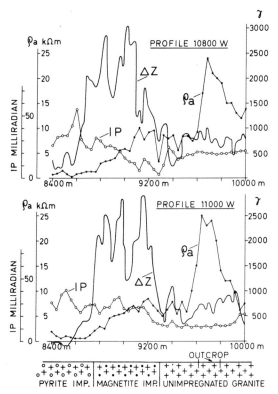

Fig.83B. Profiles of complex impedance IP (milliradian), ρ_a (kΩm) and $\Delta Z(\gamma)$ in the S-et area, northern Sweden. (Courtesy BGAB.)

resistivity low is primarily due to pyrite mineralization (about 1–3% S) between 8400 and 8700 on either profile, while the IP is equally high on pyrite as well as magnetite impregnation which may or may not be an advantage depending upon the purpose of the survey.

Between about 9400 and 9800 on either profile the phase differences amount to 10–15 milliradian, which may be taken to be the background. The apparent resistivity attains high values around the coordinate 9700 on both profiles. These are caused by almost outcropping bedrock at this point. The geologic interpretation of the combined magnetic, resistivity and IP survey is sketched at the bottom of the figure.

INTERPRETATION OF IP RESULTS

From the foregoing examples it will be apparent that high IP values, whether as percent-IP (time-domain), frequency effect or metal factor (frequency-domain) or phase differences (complex-impedance domain) are particularly interesting from the point of view of the possible occurrence of electronically conducting mineral impregnation. Quantitative estimates of depth, dip etc. are extremely difficult to make from IP anomalies since the chargeability of the medium depends upon the mode of distribution of the mineral particles.

The interpretation of IP measurements is often relatively straightforward but in the large majority of cases there exist several pitfalls.

For example, one of the serious pitfalls is the spurious anomaly that may be caused by the clogging of pores in the plugs of the non-polarizable electrodes used for the measurements. Furthermore, high conductivity overburden produces purely electromagnetic effects (current decay, variation of apparent resistivity with frequency, or phase differences, in the respective methods) which are superimposed on the true IP effects. To assess the electromagnetic effects one must know the conductivity and thickness of the overburden as well as the exact lay-out and the relative positions of source and receiver. It is usually difficult and time-consuming to make these corrections.

It should also be remembered that crushed rock containing neither clay minerals nor electronically conducting minerals can produce high IP anomalies. Similarly, fine fissures and pores in bedrock can give rise to IP anomalies due to a "mechanical" impedance to the passage of ions. Both these effects are more common than may be imagined from the beginning.

Finally, the background IP variations arising (for example) from the variations in the properties of a conductive overburden may mask significant IP anomalies (Parasnis, 1970).

CONCLUDING REMARKS CONCERNING THE IP METHOD

In the two examples of IP measurements in Fig.82 and 83 the IP anomalies were found to be closely associated with the apparent resistivity. In fact, the IP indications coincided with the resistivity ones. The same trend is evident in Fig.68.

A scrutiny of published IP and resistivity curves (as well as much unpublished material) reveals that the two types of curves resemble mirror images of each other. Moreover, it appears that strong IP indications, such as those at points 720S and 440S in Fig.82, are often spurious rather than real, arising somewhat in the following manner.

Above zones of excellent electric conductivity, the normal potentials are very small, sometimes only $1-2$ mV or fractions thereof. The polarization voltages on such zones will also be very small, since IP is proportional to the normal potential. When the current is cut off, a stray potential difference of a fraction of a millivolt to 1 mV can easily arise between the potential probes due to natural earth currents, concentration potentials etc. The voltmeter cannot, of course, distinguish this stray effect from a genuine polarization voltage. Obviously, if we divide the stray potential by the normal potential, a very large (apparent or spurious) percentage IP indication will be obtained.

Similar arguments can be advanced to explain the very high metal factor values or frequency-effect values observed at those places where the apparent resistivity is low.

Conversely, if the resistivity is high the normal potentials are large and, although the residual polarization voltages are large in this case, they are divided by a large number, so that the IP will be small.

Thus, from the point of view of ascertaining the existence of a zone of *conducting* mineralization the resistivity method is sufficient and IP could be superfluous. In this connection the reader's attention must be drawn to the circumstance that many accounts of IP surveys neglect the results of the concomitant resistivity surveys leaving a reader to infer that the resistivity survey was ineffective. Actually, a combination of the two surveys results leads to an optimal selection of drillhole sites rather than routine reliance on only one of them.

Of course, the correspondence between IP or metal factor values and apparent resistivities is only of a general nature. There are discrepancies in the sense that a given IP or M.F. value within an area is not always associated with a constant ρ_a value. This is to be expected since the origins of the two indications, although intimately related, are not identical. The question arises whether these discrepancies represent a geologic noise or whether they can be employed towards diagnostic purposes. Here recent work seems to show (see, for example, Bhattacharyya and Morrison, 1963) that IP values are greatly influenced by variations in the resistivity of ground electrolytes and, therefore, it is difficult to conceive how the discrepancies can be used for diagnostic purposes.

However, the phenomenon of IP is very complex and the future may reveal better data-interpretation possibilities, thereby extending the scope of the method. To the physicist and the physical chemist IP still provides a challenging phenomenon.

CHAPTER 8

Gravity Methods

INTRODUCTION

If we let a body, initially at rest, fall freely on the earth, it acquires a velocity of about 9.80 m/sec (32 ft./sec) in the vertical direction at the end of one second. After a further period of 1 sec the velocity is 9.80 + 9.80 = 19.60 m/sec, and so on. The increase, during each second of fall, of 9.80 m/sec in the vertical velocity of a freely falling body is called the gravitational acceleration or simply the gravity. It is written as 9.80 m per second per second or 9.80 m/sec^2. The first "per second" reminds us that the velocity is being measured as the distance travelled during one second, the other "per second" tells us that the velocity change of 9.80 m/sec occurs in an interval of one second.

The gravitational acceleration (g) is due to the force of attraction that the earth exerts on any body minus the centrifugal force experienced by the body, in a direction away from the earth, because of the earth's rotation. The net force on the body is then equal to its mass multiplied by g. Thus, numerically, the gravitational acceleration at any place is equal to the force of attraction that a unit mass experiences at the place.

If a velocity increases by 1 cm/sec in an interval of 1 sec, the acceleration, 1 cm/sec^2, is called 1 gal. The unit is named after Galileo Galilei who was the first to surmise that the gravitational acceleration is the same for all bodies irrespective of their mass, shape, size or material although one physicist, Thomas Young (cited by Browne, 1959) mentions that Lucretius was aware of this fact before Galileo. The Système Internationale (SI) unit of acceleration which we shall use is m/sec^2.

The value of g on the earth's surface is about 9.80 m/sec^2 (= 980 gal) but it varies in a systematic manner from about 9.78 m/sec^2 (= 978 gal) at the equator to about 9.83 m/sec^2 (= 983 gal) at the poles. It is greater at the poles because the earth is slightly flattened there, approximating an ellipsoid of revolution rather than a sphere, so that the poles are nearer to the earth's centre than points on the equator. A body falling freely at the poles gains velocity somewhat quicker than one falling at the equator, and a mass of 1 g weighs about 5 mg more at the poles than at the equator.

The variation of gravity, at sea level, with the latitude Φ very closely fits the formula:

$$g = 9.78049(1 + 0.00528838 \sin^2\Phi - 0.0000059 \sin^2 2\Phi) \text{ m/sec}^2 \quad (8.1)$$

which has been adopted internationally as representing the "normal" gravity on the earth's surface. As the earth is not homogeneous and its surface is not perfectly level, the actual gravity at any place differs from that calculated from eq. (8.1).

The difference is partly accounted for by the height of the observation point above (or below) sea level, since the earth's attraction depends on the distance of a point from its centre. Again, the remaining difference is partly accounted for by the extra attraction of the rock mass lying between the sea level and the level of the observation point. But even after these corrections, the differences between the observed and calculated gravity values within an area neither vanish nor are equal to each other. These differences, called gravity anomalies, indicate that the earth cannot be homogeneous, i.e., equal volumes of it cannot have equal mass.

In other words, the variations in gravity anomalies are indicative of subsurface variations in the density of rocks. Roughly speaking, if the measured gravity, after appropriate corrections, is greater at A than at B, we conclude that the vicinity of A must have heavier subsurface masses than the vicinity of B. The use of gravity methods in ore prospecting is based on the fact that orebodies sometimes differ greatly in density from their host rocks and produce distortions in the earth's normal gravity field.

Generally speaking, the gravity anomalies within a restricted area are relatively small. Therefore, it is found convenient to express them in terms of a sub-unit. For example this is the milligal (mgal) or a thousandth of a gal. As the normal gravity is everywhere about 980 gal on the earth's surface, a milligal is roughly one millionth of the normal gravity field. Thus if the gravity is 1 mgal greater at A than at B, a mass of 1 g weighs about 1 μg more at A than at B. In the SI, one millionth of 1 m/sec^2 is called the gravity unit (g.u.). The normal gravity field of the earth is therefore about $9.80 \cdot 10^6$ g.u. We see also that 1 mgal = 10 g.u.

SCOPE OF THE GRAVITY METHOD IN ORE PROSPECTING

In contrast to the methods in earlier chapters, the gravitational method is seldom employed in ore prospecting for reconnaissance purposes. It is employed on the contrary as an auxiliary method, usually on well-defined specific target areas, for "screening" the geophysical indications obtained by other methods.

Thus, electromagnetic indications on isolated thin sulphide veins, or on graphite zones and on zones of weak impregnation are often as strong as the indications due to massive orebodies. Gravity anomalies are sometimes of help in deciding between the various alternatives, because the gravity indications above a massive body will be stronger while those above an isolated thin vein or above graphite zones will be almost non-existent, in the first case because of the very small mass and in the second case because graphitic zones differ but little in density from the surrounding rock.

For example, the Kimheden orebody (Fig.27) gives long self-potential as well as electromagnetic indications. These would be attributed, on the basis of the general experience in that ore field, to graphite-bearing shales. The gravity survey on the electromagnetic indication showed a distinct, although a very slight, excess of gravity as illustrated by a few profiles in Fig.84A. An anomalous mass with significantly greater density than that of the country rock (sericite quartzite) was therefore suspected. Drilling undertaken after this screening led to the discovery of the ore.

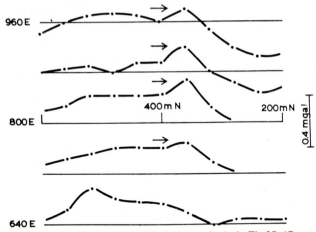

Fig.84A. Gravity profiles across the Kimheden orebody in Fig.27. (Courtesy of BGAB.)

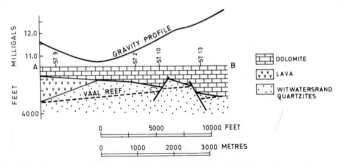

Fig.84B. Discovery of the Stilfontein gold mine, S.Africa, by gravity measurements. (After Roux, 1967.)

In prospecting for iron ores we encounter the problem that the magnetometer will only respond to magnetite ores but not to pure haematite ones, since the latter are not magnetic. Below (p.273) we will discuss an example where a gravity survey on an iron orebody provided information not obtained with magnetic measurements. Gravity methods are likely to play an important role in the future in prospecting work for haematite ores.

Similarly, gravity surveys are sometimes of assistance in prospecting for chromite bodies whose frequently strong but capricious magnetism makes the magnetometer an unreliable aid in their search.

Examples of such surveys, which, as a rule, require very flat topography, have been discussed by Hammer et al. (1945) and Davis et al.(1957).

Some deposits like zinc blende, bauxite or barite, are also poor targets for magnetic or electrical prospecting on account of their very low magnetic susceptibility and electric conductivity. These should be detectable by the gravity method, provided they have a sufficient density contrast with the surrounding rock and provided that stray anomalies, due to topography etc., do not mask the ore anomalies. It should be noted that bauxite deposits will be indicated by lower-than-normal values of gravity since their density is likely to be much smaller than the density of the surrounding rocks. An example of a gravity survey on barite deposits has been discussed by Uhley and Scharon (1954). Similarly, kimberlite pipes are known to give negative gravity anomalies (Gerryts 1967).

Gravity measurements can be employed as an indirect method of prospecting, that is, for locating not the ore itself but its host rock. Roux (1967) has described several instances in which the gold-bearing upper Witwatersrand quartzites and conglomerates in South Africa were located by gravity anomalies and led to the discovery of important mines. Fig.84B shows an example of measurements in which the light gold-bearing quartzites were discovered underneath the heavier dolomite, by the gravity low they produced.

With all the comments in mind, it must be said, however, that the most important use to which gravity measurements can be put at present is neither in screening nor in confirming other geophysical indications, but in making estimates of the total mass of the orebodies already indicated (and usually more easily) by other methods. The basis of such estimates will be considered in the section *Mass estimates* of this chapter.

SOME DIFFICULTIES

Although the gravity method may thus appear to be a fairly versatile method, it is beset with certain disadvantages which make it unsuitable as a reconnaissance method of ore prospecting in the same sense as the magnetic, electromagnetic or electric methods.

In the first place, gravity surveys are expensive on account of the rather detailed knowledge that is required of topographic heights. Further, the reduction of raw gravity data to standard conditions, which is needed for bringing forth the effect of anomalous masses, also costs time and money. More serious, however, is the fact that gravity anomalies produced by even sizeable ore masses are small and often easily masked by the effects of topographic irregularities, by moderate variations in the thickness and composition of the overburden, by regional anomaly trends due to relatively deep-seated masses and so on.

The small magnitude of gravity anomalies obtained even on compact masses will be appreciated from Fig.85, after Yüngül (1956), showing the maximum gravity anomaly produced by spherical orebodies of different tonnages, all having a density of 4.0 g/cm^3 and embedded in a host rock of density 2.5 g/cm^3. This density combination is typical of compact chromite ores and serpentine respectively but the curves are nearly, although not exactly, true of any other density combination having the same ratio, namely 4.0/2.5 = 1.6.

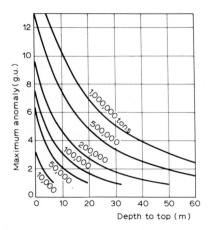

Fig.85. Maximum gravity anomaly due to spherical masses at different depths.
(After Yüngul, 1956.)

Now, assuming favourable conditions, the differences of gravity can be ascertained by modern instruments with an accuracy of about 0.5 g.u. Consequently, if we regard an anomaly of 2 X 0.5 = 1 g.u. as significant, it follows from Fig.85 that a spherical mass of, say, 200,000 tons will not be detectable if its top surface lies below a depth of 45 m. The threshold of detectability will be even shallower if the ore grade is poorer than the one for which the diagram is constructed.

There is, however, one further factor to be considered. It is found that quite moderate variations, of the order of 2–3 m, in overburden thickness can provide a background of unwanted anomalies as high as 1–1.5 g.u. In such a case an anomaly must be about 3 g.u. to be significant, and an ore mass of 200,000 tons will have to lie at a depth of not more than about 20 m to be detectable, while a poor grade ore of the same total mass will be missed even at this shallow depth. Even then there is no guarantee that the anomalous mass is an orebody because faults, anticlines, synclines, dikes, folds and other geological features also produce strong gravity anomalies.

It is clear, therefore, that the sifting of significant and non-significant gravity anomalies constitutes a very difficult problem. Further, the demands on the accuracy of gravity measurements in ore prospecting are very exacting. An accuracy of 0.1–0.2 g.u. is usually aimed at and may actually be achieved in special circumstances but the accuracy of most carefully carried out surveys is between 0.5–1 g.u. It should be noted that even the latter accuracy is equivalent to weighing one gramme of mass to better than a tenth of a microgramme.

ABSOLUTE AND RELATIVE GRAVITY MEASUREMENTS

The gravitational acceleration can be determined by means of a swinging pendulum which in reality is a falling body. If a pendulum is swinging to and fro through the arc ABC shown in Fig.86, then obviously it falls through the height h in going from A to B. If we measure the time T of one complete oscillation from A to C and back again from C to A, the gravitational acceleration can be computed from the formula:

$$g = \frac{4\pi^2 l}{T^2}$$

(8.2)

where l is the length of the pendulum. A pendulum having a length of 25 cm will oscillate with a period of about 1 sec. Despite its apparent simplicity, however, the experiment requires a great many ramifications before accurate values of the gravity can be obtained.

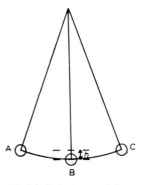

Fig.86. Swinging pendulum.

The swinging pendulum yields the *absolute* value of gravity at any place and this, by careful design of the experiment, can be determined within about 10 g.u. In geophysical prospecting we are not concerned so much with the absolute gravity as with its variations within a relatively small area. Therefore it is more convenient to measure the *difference* of gravity between an observation point and some fixed base station within the area. Such measurements are called *relative* gravity measurements.

The difference of gravity between two stations can be determined much more accurately than the absolute gravity at either of them. For example, while the swinging pendulum measures the absolute gravity to about 10 g.u., it can measure gravity differences to about 1 g.u. It will be clear from the discussion in the previous section, however, that this accuracy is barely adequate in ore prospecting. Moreover, a pendulum measurement takes a long time to make and is cumbersome as a routine operation. Hence, other instruments, known as gravimeters, which are quicker and more accurate, are used for relative gravity measurements.

GRAVIMETERS

Although the earth exerts a pull on every mass we do not find masses in our neighbourhood, except falling bodies, constantly gaining a downward velocity. This is because the gravitational force is counterbalanced by various opposing reactions. For example, if a mass is suspended at the end of a wire or a helical spring, the force of gravity is balanced by the tensional force in the wire or the recoiling force in the spring so that the mass comes to rest in an equilibrium position.

On taking a mass-and-spring in equilibrium at one place to another place where the gravity is, say, greater, there will be an extra gravitational force on the mass owing to which it will accelerate downwards. The spring will therefore extend and the restoring force in it will increase. The mass comes into equilibrium again when the increase in the restoring force brought about by the extension of the spring equals the excess gravitational force.

The downward displacement of the mass will be a measure of the amount by which the gravity at the second place exceeds that at the first. Conversely, if the mass-and-spring are taken to a place where the gravity is less, the spring will contract and the mass will rise.

A gravimeter may be considered to be an extremely sensitive spring balance working on the above principle. Although the principle is simple, the construction of a gravimeter calls for the highest ingenuity and mechanical workmanship. The main reason is that the variations of gravity on the earth's surface being small, the displacements of the mass are very minute, of the order of a few hundredmillionth (10^{-8}) of a centimetre, and must be suitably magnified before they can be detected.

One of the most well known and widely used gravimeters is the Worden which is manufactured by a number of different firms (Texas

Instruments Inc., Houston; World-Wide Instruments Inc., Houston; Beard Instruments Inc., Houston).

This instrument is available in a number of different models. It is a particularly suitable instrument for ore prospecting purposes on account of its portability (weight about 6–9 kg) and high precision. (about 0.1 g.u.).

The Worden is a development of the Atlas gravity meter. Another, and a separate outgrowth of the Atlas, is the Canadian gravimeter

Fig.87A. Exterior view of the CG-2 gravimeter. (Height about 35 cm.)

CG-2, an exterior view of which is shown in Fig.87A. This gravimeter also has a sensitivity of about 0.1 g.u. but it is claimed to have better temperature and drift characteristics. The internal system of the CG-2 is shown in Fig.87B.

A large variety of other gravimeter designs have been proposed and operated successfully during the last thirty years. Brief descriptions of some of them will be found in Heiskanen and Vening Meinesz (1958), Jung (1961), and Parasnis (1972).

The readings of a gravimeter are essentially measures of the displacements of a mass and must be multiplied by a calibration constant to obtain the gravity differences in gravity unit. The value of the calibration constant is supplied by the makers, but since it can change with time due to elastic creep in the springs and other reasons, intermittent checks on it are usually necessary. Two general methods are

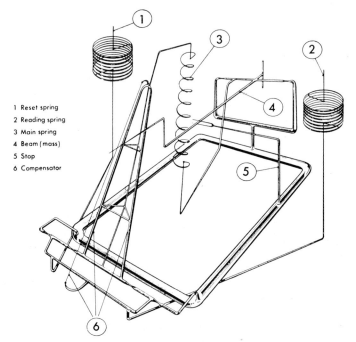

1 Reset spring
2 Reading spring
3 Main spring
4 Beam (mass)
5 Stop
6 Compensator

Fig.87B. Internal quartz system of the CG-2 gravimeter. (Courtesy of H.O. Seigel, Scintrex Ltd., Downsview, Canada.)

available for the purpose. One method is to read the gravimeter at two stations the gravity difference between which is accurately known from previous gravity measurements. The other method is to read the instrument at the top and the bottom of a tower or a building. In this case it can be shown that the difference of gravity will be 3.086 g.u. per metre of elevation (or 0.9406 g.u./ft.). The elevation difference must be known very accurately. However, it is not possible to calibrate a gravimeter over its entire range by this method since there is no sufficiently high building anywhere in the world to allow this. Therefore only the first procedure is of practical value. In most parts of the world there now exist "base lines" of gravity stations and it is usually possible to select two stations with a sufficiently large gravity difference between them.

If S_2, S_1 are the scale readings corresponding to a known gravity difference Δg, the calibration constant is $\Delta g/(S_2 - S_1)$ g.u. per scale division.

FIELD PROCEDURE

As most orebodies are relatively small-scale structures, the network of gravimeter observations in prospecting for ores must be rather dense. In confirmatory surveys, such as are carried out over indications already obtained with other methods, the grid side should not be greater than 40 m or, say, 100 ft. and this should be decreased to half or one fourth depending upon the detail desired. Usually, the smallest grid will be fixed by economic considerations since halving the grid side of a square area will approximately quadruple the survey costs.

Auxiliary gravimeter surveys are sometimes needed in ore prospecting for determining large-scale regional trends of anomalies which, if present, have to be removed from the data to obtain the anomalies of orebodies. The grid spacing for these necessary extensions of the original area may often be somewhat larger, say 200 m to 1 km (500 ft. to 1 mile), depending upon the nature of the regional trends.

Since prospecting surveys are made as relative gravity measurements, a base station has to be selected from which the gravity differences are measured. The base must be at a place where the movements of the ground due to wind, trees, settling of the ground, traffic etc., are negligible and therefore not likely to affect the gravimeter readings appreciably.

The elevations of gravity stations with respect to the base must be known accurately for calculating the corrections described in the next section. To obtain the requisite accuracy the elevations must in general be determined by spirit-levelling, although in some cases portable aneroid barometers of high precision or similar instruments (Siikarla, 1966), may be found adequate.

The readings of all gravimeters drift more or less with time, due to elastic creep in the springs, so that a gravimeter will indicate an apparent change in the gravity when placed at a station all the time and read at intervals. It should be noted that, even for gravimeters of the

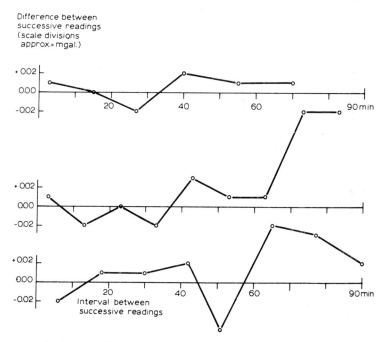

Fig.88. Typical drift curves of a gravimeter (0.01 mgal = 0.1 g.u.).

same type and manufacture, the drift differs from one instrument to the other.

The usual method of correcting for the drift is to reoccupy the base station at intervals of 1−2 h and reread the gravimeter. The series of readings are plotted on a graph paper against time and a smooth curve is drawn through them from which one obtains the reading that the gravimeter would have at the base at the time a particular station was occupied. This is the base reading to be subtracted from the reading at the station to obtain the gravity difference. A typical set of drift curves is shown in Fig.88.

CORRECTIONS TO GRAVIMETER OBSERVATIONS

Besides the drift correction, which is a purely instrumental correction, gravimeter observations require certain corrections for the normal difference of gravity which exists between any two points. These corrections, discussed below, are applied after converting the measured scale-division differences (corrected for the drift) to gravity units by means of the calibration constant of the instrument.

Latitude

Since, in each hemisphere, the gravity increases as we go towards the respective pole, there is a normal gravity difference between a station and a base, due to the latitude difference between them. The correction is:

$$\Delta g_\Phi = 0.081 \quad \sin 2\Phi \text{ g.u. per } 10 \text{ m north−south distance}$$
$$= 0.0247 \sin 2\Phi \text{ g.u. per } 10 \text{ ft. north−south distance} \qquad (8.3)$$

where Φ is the latitude of the base. If the station is on a higher latitude (that is north of the base if both are in the northern hemisphere and south of it if they are in the southern hemisphere) the latitude correction must be subtracted from the measured difference. In the opposite case it must be added to it.

Eq. (8.3) should not be used to calculate the latitude correction beyond north-south distances of about 2 km on either side of the base, because the gravity difference from the base is then not strictly proportional to the distance within the accuracy required. The exact correction in that case is given by $51723(\sin^2\Phi_1 - \sin^2\Phi_0)$ g.u. where Φ_1 and Φ_0 are the latitudes of the station and the base respectively. When the area is large a second base should be chosen and its gravity difference from the first base determined by the more accurate formula just quoted.

For the latitude correction to be accurate within 0.1 g.u. — an accuracy which must be aimed at in ore prospecting — it is sufficient that the north—south distance between the base and the station be known to within 10 m.

Elevation or free-air correction

The earth's gravitational force decreases with the height of a station above the earth's surface. If the station and the base are not on the same level, as will be the case in general, there will be a gravity difference between the two even if their north-south distance be zero. The correction for the elevation is called the "free-air" correction and amounts to:

$$3.086\, h \text{ g.u.} \qquad (h \text{ in m})$$
$$= 0.9406\, h \text{ g.u.} \qquad (h \text{ in ft.}) \qquad (8.4)$$

where h is the elevation difference.

The correction must be added to the measured gravity difference between the station and the base if the station is higher up than the base, and subtracted from it if it is lower down.

If the correction is not to exceed 0.1 g.u., the elevation differences within an area must be known to better than 4 cm or about 1½ inch. It is, above all, this condition that makes an accurate gravity survey an expensive prospecting method.

Bouguer correction

The free-air or elevation correction only takes account of the fact that the station and the base are not at the same distance from the earth's centre. Now, the rock material between the level of the station and the base (Fig.89) exerts an extra gravitational attraction at a station situated higher up than the base and therefore tends to increase the gravity difference between them. Similarly, the rock material lying above the station level also exerts an attraction at the station but it is the general practice to consider this effect separately and not to include it in the term Bouguer correction, which only takes account of the rock material between the station and the base.

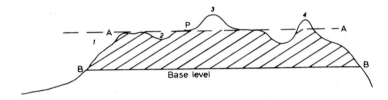

Fig.89. Bouguer correction.

If this material is considered to be a slab of very great lateral extent and of thickness h equal to the elevation difference, its attraction at the station can be shown to be:

$$0.4191 \ \rho h \ \text{g.u.} \quad (h \text{ in m})$$
$$= 0.1277 \ \rho h \ \text{g.u.} \quad (h \text{ in ft.})$$

(8.5)

where ρ is the density of the slab in $Mg/m^3 (= g/cm^3)$.

The correction represented by eq. (8.5) was first pointed out by Bouguer about 1745 in connection with his measurements of the deflection of the plumb line in the Chimborazo mountains of Peru.

It must be subtracted from the measured gravity difference if the station is above the level of the base and added if it is below. Note that the free-air and the Bouguer corrections are of opposite sign.

The magnitude of the Bouguer correction depends on the density of the postulated slab and this, of course, may not be uniform. Suppose, for example, that the material below the station, down to the level of the base, is composed of a number of horizontal strata of thickness $h_1, h_2 \ldots$ etc., having respectively the densities $\rho_1, \rho_2 \ldots$

etc., then the Bouguer correction will be $0.4191(\rho_1 h_1 + \rho_2 h_2 + \ldots)$ g.u. This extension of eq (8.5) is often required in sedimentary areas of gentle dip.

In a similar manner, account must be taken of any known lateral variations of density in the slab of rock between the station and the base, a situation often arising when the dip of the strata is steep or vertical. This topic has been considered in detail by Domzalski (1954) and by Vajk (1956). Evidently, it is essential to have some idea of the geological structure below a gravity station for calculating a reasonably valid Bouguer correction.

Terrain correction

If we refer to Fig.89, which shows the case of a station situated above the base level, it will be clear, that in applying the Bouguer correction for the infinite slab between AA and the base level, we tacitly assumed that the depressions in the topography such as (*1*), (*2*) etc., were filled with rock material. At the same time we assumed the hills like (*3*), (*4*) etc., to produce no gravity effect. The object of terrain corrections is to compensate for both these assumptions.

In a wider sense, the Bouguer correction is also a terrain correction. The division of corrections into a Bouguer correction and a terrain correction is a traditional and arbitrary division. This distinction is also somewhat unfortunate as it often leads to serious misunderstandings and mistakes in the application of these corrections. Lest the reader believe this to be a minor matter, reference must be made here to an excellent article by Vajk (1956) on this subject.

To return to the terrain correction in the conventional sense it is first clear that a hill like (*3*) will exert an upward pull at the station and tend to reduce the gravity value at it, so that a correction representing the hill's attraction must be added to the measured gravity at the station. As regards the depressions, we have, in applying the Bouguer correction, which represents the effect of the slab AA–BB, subtracted the attraction of the rock material needed to fill the depressions but actually this material does not exist. Hence, to obtain the correct value of gravity at the station, this attraction must again be added as a terrain correction to the measured gravity.

Thus, the terrain correction is always positive, irrespective of whether there is a hill beside a station, or a depression. Hills and valleys in the vicinity of a station do not tend to cancel each other's gravity effects. Further, it should be noted that a terrain correction (T.C.) must be calculated at the base also, and it is the difference $(T.C.)_{sta.} - (T.C.)_{base.}$ that is to be added to the measured gravity difference.

The calculation of terrain corrections is laborious since there are no general formulas and every area must be treated separately. Fortunately, the correction decreases rapidly as the distance between a topographic irregularity and the station increases, and generally only stations very near or on hills, knolls, valleys, mineshafts, cliffs, steep slopes etc., will need a terrain correction.

For calculating terrain corrections we must have recourse to a detailed elevation map of the area. Such a map must be prepared if it is not already available. Since the elevations of gravity stations have to be determined anyway (for calculating the free-air and Bouguer corrections), some data are automatically available for constructing the elevation map, but in regions of rough topography it may be necessary to supplement them by intermediate observations, as well as observations outside the area of measurement.

The principle of any method of calculating terrain corrections is to divide the area around a station in suitable compartments, and estimate the gravitational effect of the topography within each such compartment at the site of the station. The effects of the various compartments are then added. Tables and diagrams exist for estimating the terrain effects (Hammer, 1939; Haalck, 1953, p.73).

Usually the division of the area is effected by means of a set of concentric rings and a number of radii drawn at suitable angular intervals. In Fig.90, for example, each annular ring is divided into 8 compartments. A terrain correction diagram for this "1/8th ring system", with radii 3, 5, 10, 20, 30, 50, 70 and 100 m for the various rings, is reproduced in Fig.91 after Schleusener. The procedure for using it is very simple and is as follows (Schleusener, 1940).

A transparent template is prepared on which the rings and the radii are drawn in the appropriate scale, i.e., the scale of the elevation map.

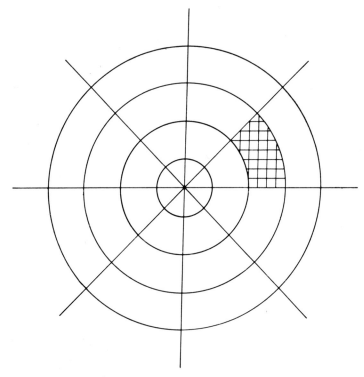

Fig.90. Template for terrain corrections to gravity observations.

The template is then placed on the elevation map so that its centre coincides with the station at which the terrain correction is to be calculated. After this, the average elevation within each compartment (shaded area in Fig.90) is estimated by treating the elevations below the station level as well as those above it as *positive* elevations, in view of the fact that the topographic correction always has the same sign. Thus, if the elevations at a number of points within a compartment, measured from the station level, are +1, −7, −10, +12, +1, +20, −2, and −3 m, then, for the purposes of gravitational corrections, the mean elevation difference in the compartment from the station level is the arithmetic mean of these numbers without regard to signs, that is 7 m (and not + 1.25 m, the mean obtained *with* regard to the signs).

Having estimated the mean elevation difference within the 1/8-ring, the corresponding terrain correction is directly read off the chart in Fig.91. The terrain correction is proportional to the density (ρ) of the feature causing it and we may write it as $T\dot\rho$ where T is the factor that depends on the size and shape of the terrain irregularity. The diagram in Fig.91 gives $T\rho$ for an assumed density of 2.0 Mg/m^3 (= g/cm^3) so that the correction read off it must be augmented or reduced in the

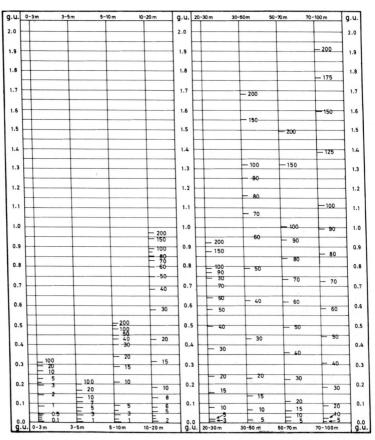

Fig.91. Terrain correction diagram. Terrain corrections for 1/8 ring and density 2.0; ΔH in ± m. Correction always positive. Example: 1/8 ring 20–30 m; ΔH = + 18 m; density 2.0; correction = + 0.21 g.u. (= 0.021 mgal). (After Schleusener, 1940.)

appropriate proportion depending upon the actual density of the terrain in the compartment in question.

The terrain corrections read off the diagram for the different compartments are added to obtain the total correction at the station and the template is transferred to the next station.

THE BOUGUER ANOMALY

If S_1 is the scale reading of the gravimeter at a station and S_0 that at the base, the observed difference of gravity is $k(S_1 - S_0)$ where k is the calibration constant (g.u. per scale division). We shall denote this difference as Δg_{obs}. We suppose further that the scale reading has been appropriately corrected for the drift. With the latitude, free-air, Bouguer and terrain corrections applied, the gravity difference now becomes:

$$\Delta g = \Delta g_{obs.} \pm \Delta g_\Phi + (3.086 - 0.4191\rho)h + T\rho \text{ g.u.} \tag{8.6}$$

TABLE IV

TYPICAL SET OF RELATIVE GRAVITY CALCULATIONS

Station	Δg_{obs} (g.u.)	Δg (g.u.)	Δh m	Free-air corr. (g.u.)	Bouguer corr. $\rho = 2.3$ (g.u.)	$T\rho$ (g.u.)	(T.C.) $-(T.C.)$ at base (g.u.)	Δg Bouguer anomaly (g.u.)
North								
1	0.00	0.0	0.0	0.0	0.0	0.0	0.0	0.0
(base)								
2	−106.2	+ 5.0	+ 48.6	+150.0	46.8	3.5	1.3	+ 3.3
3	−186.2	+ 8.0	+ 82.2	253.7	79.2	4.8	2.6	− 1.1
4	−204.2	+ 9.2	+ 88.92	274.4	85.7	3.5	1.3	− 5.0
5	−262.4	+14.0	+120.65	372.3	116.3	4.0	1.8	+ 9.4
6	−373.8	+15.3	+161.7	498.9	155.9	4.8	2.6	+12.9
7	−285.4	+34.0	+119.55	368.9	115.2	2.3	0.1	+ 2.4
8	−322.6	+31.0	+136.42	421.0	131.5	3.8	1.6	− 0.5
South								

The plus or minus sign for the latitude correction Δg_ϕ is taken as explained earlier. In the bracketed term, h is in metres and plus when the station is situated higher up than the base, minus when it is situated lower down. If h is in feet the numbers in the bracketed term become 0.9406 and 0.1277 respectively.

Table IV reproduces a typical set of calculations in a gravimeter survey.

The corrected difference Δg is termed the relative Bouguer anomaly at the station but the adjective "relative" is usually omitted.

Provided the Bouguer correction term (0.4191 ρh g.u.) and the terrain correction $(T\rho)$ adequately account for the attraction of the rock material lying between each station and the base, the variations of the Bouguer anomaly within an area will represent the density changes below the base level. If this is not the case, at least some of the variations may be due to anomalous masses, which could even be orebodies, lying *above* the base level. The variations in Δg should not, therefore, be indiscriminately attributed to anomalous masses below the base level.

DENSITY DETERMINATION

The accuracy of the Bouguer anomalies, and even more, their interpretation depends greatly on the assumed densities of rocks or rather on the differences of densities between rocks. As these differences are generally small, it is important to determine the densities within the survey area as accurately as possible.

For example, consider the gravity profile shown in Fig.92 indicative of a "step" such as is often the result of a flexure or a geological fault. Depending upon whether the density (ρ_1) of the overlying rock is less or greater than the density (ρ_2) of the underlying one, the step will have the form (a) or (b) and the ambiguity cannot be resolved unless the densities are reliably known.

It is not always easy to obtain good density values because of the difficulty of finding fresh, unweathered rock and ore samples, but when they are available (e.g., from quarries or boreholes) the density

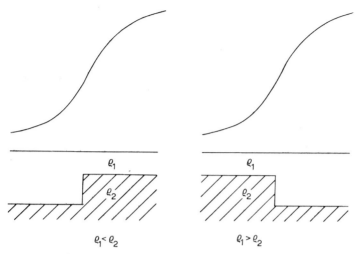

Fig.92. Alternative inferences from the same gravity profile in the absence of a knowledge of the density contrast.

may be easily determined by weighing a sample in air and water. The weight in air divided by the loss of weight in water gives the density.

For igneous and metamorphic rocks, the experiment usually presents no serious difficulty as the porosity of these rocks is very low, but for sedimentary rocks (like marls, limestones, sandstones etc.) the density depends entirely on the degree to which their pores are filled with water. It is advisable, in general, to determine two densities: one after oven-drying the sample, the other after saturating it with water. The density of the rock in situ may be assumed to lie between these two extremes, nearer to one or the other value depending upon local conditions.

Where possible the laboratory determinations should be supplemented by field determinations of density, specifically for obtaining the in-situ density estimates. Two principal methods have been suggested towards the purpose.

In the profile method, the Bouguer anomaly along a line is calculated for a series of hypothetical values of density and the shape of the anomaly curve is compared with the topography along the profile.

The density corresponding to that curve which shows the least correlation with topography is adopted as the density of the slab.

In the straight-line method the approach is somewhat different and more objective. Suppose that the Bouguer anomaly at the stations along a line is exactly zero. Then eq. (8.6) can be written, with a little rearrangement of terms, as:

$$\Delta g_{obs.} \pm \Delta g_{\Phi} = + (0.4191\,h - T)\rho - 3.086\,h \qquad (8.7)$$

If we denote the left-hand side by y and the term $+(0.4191\,h - T)$ by x we see that the equation is of the form:

$$y = \rho x + c$$

which is the equation of a straight line whose slope is ρ. Thus, if we plot the measured quantity $\Delta g_{obs.} \pm \Delta g_{\Phi}$ along a profile against x, and draw a straight line through the points, the slope of this line will yield the density of the slab. In practice, the points will not all lie exactly on a straight line because the Bouguer anomaly will not in general be zero. The statistical expedient of least squares can be used in this case for drawing the best straight line.

The subject of field determinations of density is more complicated than the above description would indicate and the interested reader should refer to the extensive literature on this subject (Nettleton, 1939; Hammer, 1950; Cook and Thirlaway, 1952; Parasnis, 1952; Domzalski, 1955; Vajk, 1956; Whetton et al., 1957; Jung, 1959; Grant and Elsaharty, 1962).

Table V summarizes the density data on some of the important rocks and ores, but the values indicated should not, of course, be looked upon as substitutes for rock density measurements within the survey area.

In the Système Internationale (SI) the unit of density is kg/m^3 which is a thousand times larger than the unit g/cm^3. It is recommended in the SI that additional units may be created by multiplication of any basic units by powers of ten. If then we multiply the SI unit by 1000 we get the unit megagramme/m^3 (=tonne/m^3) and this

TABLE V

DENSITIES[1] OF ROCKS AND ORE MINERALS IN PURE FORM

	Density (g/cm^3)
Sand, dry	1.40–1.65
Sand, wet	1.95–2.05
Coal	1.20–1.50
English chalk	1.94
Rock salt	2.10–2.40
Serpentinite	2.50–2.55
Limestone	2.60–2.70
Quartzite	2.60–2.70
Gneiss	2.70
Granite	2.50–2.70
Anhydrite	2.96
Diabase	2.50–3.20
Basalt	2.70–3.30
Gabbro	2.70–3.50
Zinc blende	4.0
Chalcopyrite	4.2
Chromite	4.5–4.8
Pyrrhotite	4.6
Pyrite	5.0
Haematite	5.1
Magnetite	5.2
Galena	7.5

[1] The density of an ore will depend upon the relative amounts of gangue and ore minerals.

is exactly the same as g/cm^3. Where rock and ore masses are concerned it is far more appropriate and realistic to talk of the density as Mg/m^3 than as g/cm^3. On account of the convenient size of the numbers obtained when density is expressed as Mg/m^3 (g/cm^3) all the formulas appearing in this book in connection with gravity work imply that the density is expressed as Mg/m^3.

INTERPRETATION OF GRAVITY ANOMALIES

Towards the end of section *The Bouguer anomaly* we noted that the variations of the Bouguer anomaly suggest the subsurface variations in the density of rocks. Unfortunately, however, the problem of interpreting gravity anomalies in terms of the size, shape, depth, density etc., of the anomalous masses has the same ambiguity as the magnetic problem, namely that a variety of distributions of the anomalous masses can be found, all of which exactly explain a given set of gravity data, however accurate and dense these data may be. In other words, gravity measurements alone do not suffice to uniquely determine the distribution of anomalous masses.

Now, there is one sort of ambiguity in interpretation which is readily appreciated. Suppose, for example, that a spherical mass having a certain volume and density contrast explains a set of anomalies within the accuracy of measurement; then a sphere of larger volume but proportionately smaller density contrast (or vice versa) is also capable of explaining the given set of anomalies equally well. Obviously, there are any number of such spheres. However, the ambiguity in gravity (and magnetic) interpretation is not of this trivial kind but is more fundamental, in that quite different geometrical types of mass distributions can explain a set of data.

Fig.93 shows an example of an anomaly which is exactly explained by three different mass distributions, each striking perpendicular to the plane of the figure. These are: (*a*) a thin surface layer of rock material with a variable density, (*b*) a horst or ridge of rock heavier than the overburden, and (*c*) a horst or ridge flanked by two troughs filled with the lighter material of the overburden. Further, these three alternatives do not exhaust the possibilities.

Clearly, in order to arrive at a working hypothesis concerning the subsurface mass distribution, it is necessary to obtain information that will enable us to assume plausible forms, sizes, depth etc., for the presumed masses. Geological data, as well as inferences drawn from the results of other geophysical surveys, usually help towards adopting a particular model, such as a sphere, a plate, a step etc., as a working hypothesis. Once a model has been selected we calculate its anomalies,

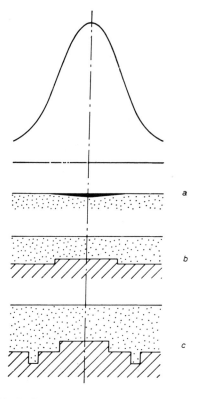

Fig.93. Ambiguity in gravity interpretation. (After Jung, 1961.)

compare them with the observed anomalies and adjust the parameters like depth, density, size of a mass, throw of a fault etc., until a reasonably satisfactory fit is obtained between observation and calculation. These calculations may often be tedious, and facility with them can only be acquired by practice, but they are mathematically straightforward once the relevant formulas are available. Some formulas for the purpose appear in Appendix 7. The labour of calculating gravity anomalies is considerably reduced by the use of an electronic computer which is therefore often used in this connection. A computer program for the purpose will be found in Appendix 11.

KEY VARIABLES OF GRAVITY INTERPRETATION

The practitioner of gravity methods, whether a geophysicist or a geologist, must remember that although detailed computations have their proper place, there is an aspect of gravity interpretation which is more important than making subtle adjustments of various parameters for obtaining the best agreement between observed and calculated anomalies. This is to develop a "feel" for gravity anomalies so that one can, on the one hand, deduce the salient features of the disturbing masses without excessive labour and, on the other, estimate the effect of deliberate variations in the assumed parameters of the masses on the calculated anomaly values without having to go through the whole procedure of complicated computations.

Some help in this task can be had by focussing attention on the "key variables" of gravity anomalies, a phrase due to Romberg (1958). We now consider the bearing of these on the interpretation.

Magnitude

The magnitude or size (g.u. or mgal) of a gravity anomaly is its most fundamental attribute. It is important because the size of an anomaly is proportional to the size (volume) of the structure, for example, an orebody, producing it. This applies not only to the maximum anomaly but to every observed or calculated value. The magnitude is proportional to the density contrast between a structure and its host rock and not to the absolute density of any one of them.

The magnitudes of gravity anomalies are important also in that the excess or deficit mass that a gravity survey indicates can be determined merely from the magnitudes, even if the density contrast and the geometry of the mass is unknown. We shall return to this topic in the section *Mass estimates* (p.270).

In trying to fit the calculated anomalies to the observed ones it is helpful to remember that the magnitude of an anomaly due to a concentrated mass such as a small orebody decreases approximately as the square of the depth to the mass, while the anomaly due to a very long body decreases roughly in inverse proportion to the depth. For structures which are both long and wide, e.g., horizontal or gently dipping sedimentary strata or gently dipping ore sheets, the anomaly magnitude varies little or not at all with the assumed depth to the structure and is therefore of little help for obtaining information about the probable depth.

Sharpness

The sharpness of an anomaly manifests itself most clearly in profile curves. Sharp anomalies are easy to identify whereas broad ones tend to merge in the general background. The sharper the anomaly the more rapidly does it fall from the maximum. The anomalies of shallow masses fall quickly with distance from the maximum while those of deep masses are perceptible out to considerable distances. Thus the sharper the anomaly the shallower is the mass (Fig.94).

The two observed parameters, the maximum value of an anomaly and the maximum rate of its fall, can be employed in certain simple cases for estimating the depth of a body or structure believed to resemble the relevant form (Appendix 8). In general, however, when the form is unknown the two parameters can only yield estimates of the *maximum* possible depth to the body. Fortunately some simple rules exist for obtaining such estimates. Two of these, due to Smith (1959, 1960), can be quoted here but a fuller discussion of the topic will be found in Parasnis (1972).

(*1*) If $\Delta g_{max.}$ and $\Delta g'_{max.}$ are respectively the maximum values of the gravity anomaly and its horizontal gradient, g.u. and g.u./m (or ft.), the depth to the top of the body must be less than or at most equal to:

$$0.86 \; \frac{\Delta g_{max.}}{\Delta g'_{max.}} \qquad (8.8)$$

(*2*) If neither the maximum anomaly nor the maximum gradient is known an estimate of the maximum possible depth is still possible if we use the gravity value at any point whatever, and its gradient at that point. These two quantities we shall denote by $\Delta g(x)$ and $\Delta g'(x)$ respectively. Then the depth to the top must be less than or at most equal to:

$$1.50 \; \frac{\Delta g(x)}{\Delta g'(x)} \qquad (8.9)$$

Obviously, a number of such estimates are possible, one at each of the observation points, and from among them we can choose the minimum value of the maximum possible depth. Whatever the nature and geometry of the anomalous structure, its upper surface cannot lie at a greater depth than this "minimax" estimate.

It remains to be added that the two formulas just quoted are applicable with the restriction that the body or structure whose depth is sought must be everywhere denser or everywhere lighter than the host rock in which it is embedded, but otherwise its density may be non-uniform.

Resolution

Two or more anomalies are resolved if they can be recognized as belonging to separate but adjacent structures. An obvious criterion of resolution is that a profile curve should show two or more distinguishable characteristics, like maxima or inflexion points, corresponding to each of the bodies. If only one characteristic is present, detailed quantitative calculations can sometimes tell whether the anomaly requires more than one structure for its explanation.

The resolution depends upon the distance between the bodies and their depth. For example, if the distance between two ore masses, lying at the same depth, is less than the depth, the observed gravity anomaly will usually show only one maximum and give the impression of being produced by a single mass.

Elongation of contours

As with all other geophysical anomalies, the direction of elongation of the isoanomaly contours of gravity suggests the direction of the length of the structure causing them. Short, concentrated masses produce approximately circular anomaly patterns. The terms short and long are to be understood in relation to the depth. One body may yield an elongate anomaly while another one of the same length, but situated at a greater depth, will produce a more circular anomaly pattern.

Shape

The shape of an anomaly profile or an isoanomaly contour is not a measurable magnitude but, as Romberg says, "a set of attributes". It might be imagined that the shape would be particularly indicative of the dip and depth-extent of a body. Actually, the shape of a gravity anomaly is remarkably insensitive to these two parameters and estimates of them based on gravitational calculations are usually not very reliable. For example, the gravity anomaly of a mass like a vertical cylinder of very great length is, in practice, indistinguishable from that of a concentrated mass of small depth-extent, like a sphere, placed at a suitable depth.

By way of contrast, it should be noted that the shape of a magnetic profile is highly diagnostic of the attitude and depth-extent of a (magnetic) ore mass (cf. p.44).

GRAVITY PROFILES ACROSS SIMPLE STRUCTURES

To recognize a gravity profile as being due to a mass of this or that probable type of geometry requires considerable experience and familiarity with theoretical gravity profiles. Since an exhaustive

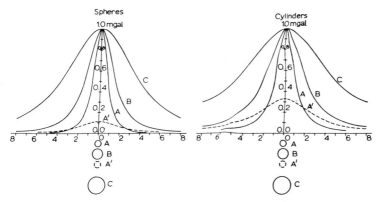

Fig.94. Gravity anomalies of a sphere and of a cylinder striking perpendicular to the plane of the figure. Sizes and depths to scale. (1 mgal = 10 g.u.).

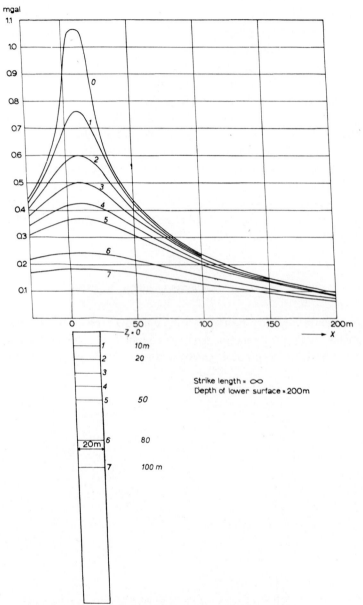

Fig.95. Gravity anomalies of sheet-like orebodies. (1 mgal = 10 g.u.) (After Lindblad and Malmqvist, 1938.)

discussion of this topic cannot be taken up here, we shall merely deal with profiles across a few idealized simple shapes.

It is convenient to start with the gravity anomaly of a spherical mass as it is one of the simplest to calculate. Fig.94 shows the profiles above such masses through the epicentre. The ordinates represent the anomaly in terms of the maximum, this being obtained at the epicentre, and the abscissas represent distances in terms of the depth to the centre of the sphere. In the same figure are also shown the surface anomaly profiles across a very long, horizontal cylindrical mass, at various depths, perpendicular to the plane of the figure.

Fig.95, after Lindblad and Malmqvist (1938) shows calculated gravity profiles across a number of sheet-like, vertical ores of width 20 m, all sheets having their lower surface 200 m below the ground and with the depth to the top varying from 0 to 100 m. The density of the ore is assumed to be 1.0 g/cm^3 higher than that of the surrounding rock.

Fig.96 shows the ideal shapes of a class of geological structures often met with in practice. These are: (A) a vertical step in the bedrock or, to put it differently, a sudden increase of the overburden thickness, (B) a vertical step as in (A) but the overburden having a constant thickness, (C) a sudden increase of overburden thickness accompanied by a corresponding decrease in the thickness of the rock lying immediately underneath and (D) an outcropping vertical fault.

The structures in Fig.96A–D differ in geological detail but from the point of view of gravity anomalies they all reduce to the single structure shown in Fig.96E, which is termed as a "semi-infinite" slab. This is easily seen as follows.

For example, in (A), the slab between the surface and the plane a–a has the same gravity effect everywhere. Similarly the effect of the rock below the plane b–b is everywhere the same. Hence, the gravity variation on the surface will be due to two slabs of differing density, one extending towards the left, the other towards the right. For mathematical purposes this system in turn may be replaced by a single slab as in Fig.96E, having a density equal to the difference of densities between the two slabs.

Similar considerations apply to the structures in Fig.96B and C.

The fault structure in Fig.96D, however, is equivalent to several slab-pairs and not just one pair. The gravity effect of the fault will be the sum of the effects of the various pairs, each pair being replaced by a single slab like that in (E) at the appropriate depth.

Fig.96F shows the calculated gravity profiles due to semi-infinite

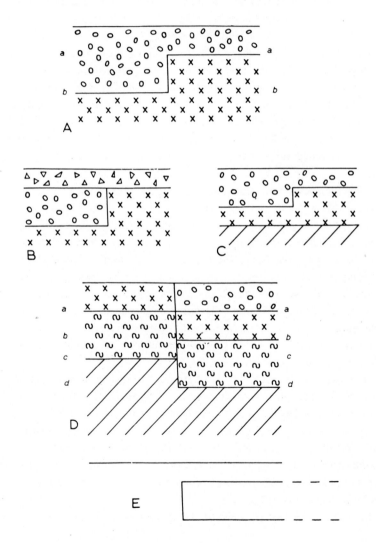

slabs having one vertical face and differing in density by 1.0 g/cm³ from the surrounding rock. Gravity profiles across the structures in Fig.96A–D will resemble these curves.

If ρ is the density contrast of a slab and h its thickness (in m) the total change of gravity anomaly across it is 0.4191 ρh g.u. irrespective of the depth at which the slab is situated (0.1277 ρh if h is in ft.).

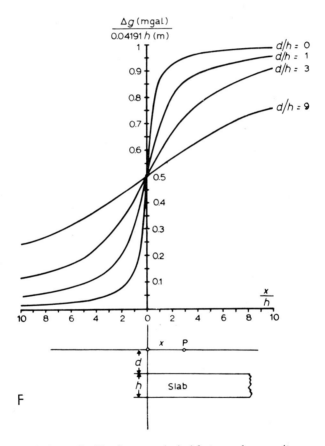

Fig.96. Ideal shapes (A–D) of some geological features whose gravity anomalies are calculable from the anomaly of a semi-infinite slab (E). Gravity profiles across a semi-infinite slab of thickness h and depth d for various values of the ratio d/h (F). The ordinates also represent values of Δg(g.u.)/0.4191h(m)

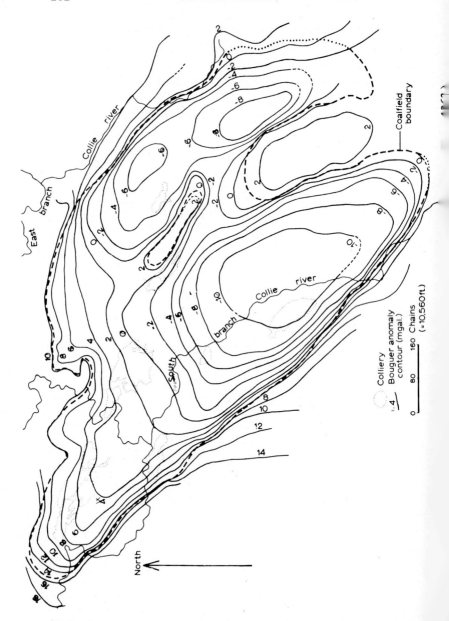

The change is also independent of the slope of the lateral face of the slab. Hence the density X thickness product of a slab can be directly estimated from its gravity anomaly.

The horizontal gradient of the anomaly due to a semi-infinite slab is steepest vertically above its lateral face and it is steeper the shallower the slab. The position of the maximum gravity gradient has been used, for example, for delineating the boundaries of coal basins and other structures with gentle dips. Fig.97 is an example of a coal-basin survey in Australia and it will be noticed that the edge of the basin is marked by the high gradients in the Bouguer anomaly.

Fig.98 shows a case where the measured gravity profile has a simple shape but the structure giving rise to it consists of a complicated system of faults and slabs.

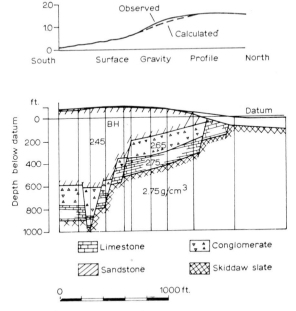

Fig.98. Gravity profile across a complicated fault system in Cumberland (1 mgal = 10 g.u.). (After Domzalski, 1955a.)

REGIONAL AND LOCAL GRAVITY ANOMALIES

The gravity anomalies of orebodies are almost always found to be superimposed on those due to structures like faults, contacts, anticlines etc. (cf. Fig.100). These latter effects are perceptible over large distances, owing to the relatively large dimensions of the structures concerned, and are therefore called regional anomalies in contrast to

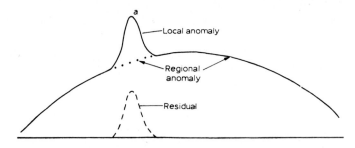

Fig.99. Superimposition of regional and local gravity anomalies.

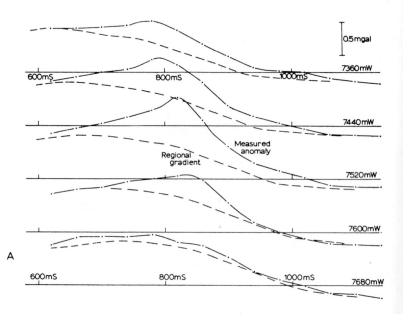

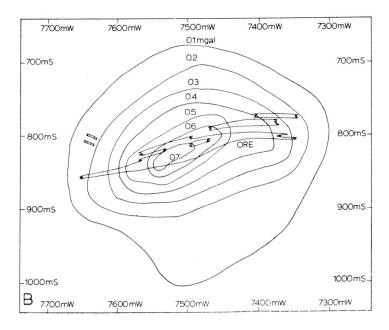

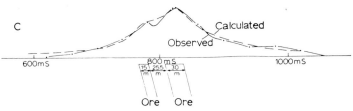

Fig.100.A. Gravity profiles across the Udden sulphide orebody, northern Sweden. (Courtesy of BGAB.) B. Residual gravity map of the Udden sulphide body. Contours in mgal(1 mgal = 10 g.u.). C. Observed and calculated gravity anomalies along one profile crossing the Udden sulphide body in part B. Density contrast 0.68 g/cm³. (Courtesy of BGAB.)

the anomalies of small-scale structures like orebodies, which are termed local.

To bring out the local anomalies in relief, the regional effects are often removed by graphical smoothing as illustrated in Fig.99. Here a local anomaly *a* is supposed to be superimposed on a broad regional anomaly, such as may be due to, say, an anticline. The regional effect has been sketched by freehand (dotted curve) and on subtracting it from the observed curve we get the local anomaly. The procedure is, of course, subjective but in a clear-cut instance, such as the hypothetical one in this figure, there is little room for significantly different alternatives for smoothing the regional.

Mathematical methods for separating regional and local anomalies have also been proposed. These are based on suitably averaging the gravity anomalies around each observation point out to some distance and subtracting the average from the field at the point itself. The difference thus obtained is called the residual anomaly. Mathematical methods have the advantage that a particular method leads to the same numerical result irrespective of the interpreter. On the other hand, almost any number of analytical methods can be devised leading to more or less different separations. Analytical methods involve a great deal of computational work but this can be programmed on electronic computers. This subject has been discussed in a number of articles (Nettleton, 1954; Grant 1954).

GRAVITY MEASUREMENTS ON THE UDDEN SULPHIDE BODY
(SWEDEN)

An example of the superposition of local and regional anomalies is afforded by the gravity measurements on a sulphide body in the Skellefteå ore district of northern Sweden. Fig.100A shows a set of gravity profiles (Bouguer anomalies) across this approximately 340 m long body.

All the profiles suggest a regional trend, with high values in the north and low ones in the south. The trend is most clearly seen along the profiles 7360W and 7680W, as well as on a number of profiles further towards the east and the west.

Along the profiles 7200W and 7800W (not shown), the influence of the ore is apparently negligible. The anomalies along these profiles were, therefore, ascribed entirely to a regional trend. On each of the intermediate profiles a regional trend was then sketched in such a way that its shape changed gradually from the shape along profile 7200W to that along 7800W. Note, for example, that the inflexion point is moved successively southwards.

The regional anomaly was subtracted from the observed (Bouguer) anomaly at each station and the gravity map shown in Fig.100B was prepared from these residuals. The residual anomaly contours conform well to the shape of the orebody. Fig.100C shows the residual anomalies along profile 7520W and, in dashed line, the calculated gravity anomalies of two parallel, dipping ore sheets, each 200 m long having a density 3.38 and embedded in a rock (tuffs, amphibolite-skarn and quartz porphyries) of density 2.70 g/cm^3. The agreement between the two is striking but it should be mentioned that quite a wide choice of densities and sheet dimensions give equally good fits.

EFFECT OF OVERBURDEN ON GRAVITY ANOMALIES

The cause of the regional gradient in the above example is not known but at least two explanations can be suggested. According to one, the gradient is due to a near-vertical contact of two rock formations differing in density from each other. The gravity change corresponding to the assumed regional trend from the north to the south is 8 g.u. If this be due to a contact of two slabs of thickness h and a density difference ρ, we put:

$$0.4191\ \rho h = 0.8\ \text{g.u}$$

from which it follows that:

$$\rho h = 19.2\ \text{m}$$

If the density difference between the rocks on the hanging-wall and the footwall side of the ore is 0.1 g/cm^3 — which appears to be about the maximum permissible — the slab thickness should be of the order of 200 m.

The alternative explanation rests on the fact that the Bouguer corrections in the measurements have been made assuming a constant overburden thickness. If there is a systematic increase in overburden thickness towards the south, it will produce the observed decrease of anomalies in that direction, because the overburden material (moraine) is lighter than the bedrock.

This brings us to an important problem in ore prospecting, namely the estimate of the extent to which observed gravity variations may be due to variations in the overburden.

The simplest case we may have to cope with is that of a light overburden resting on a denser bedrock. Ideally, if the overburden thickness were known at all points, one could calculate the necessary corrections much in the same fashion as terrain corrections and sub-tract them from the observed anomalies. However, this ideal is usually both uneconomical and impractical. We must therefore proceed in a different way and be content as a rule with estimating certain limiting values for the possible overburden variations.

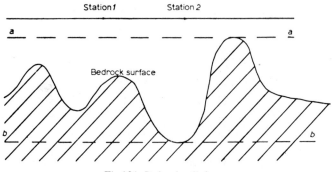

Fig.101. Bedrock relief.

Suppose we have an irregular bedrock surface as in Fig.101. Let g_1, g_2 be the observed gravity values (Bouguer anomalies, which we have elsewhere denoted by Δg) at two stations, and suppose for the sake of concreteness that $g_1 > g_2$. If now the gravity variations on the surface are due entirely to the changes in overburden thickness, the difference $\Delta g = g_1 - g_2$ must simply be due to the unequal attractions exerted at stations *1* and *2* by the infinite, inhomogeneous slab lying between the horizontal planes a and b, through the uppermost and lowermost points of the bedrock surface. Thus:

$$\text{(Effect of slab } a-b \text{ at station } 1\text{)}$$
$$-\text{(Effect of slab } a-b \text{ at station } 2\text{)} = \Delta g \qquad (8.10)$$

Suppose that we replace the inhomogeneous slab $a-b$, whose thickness h is evidently the maximum relief of the bedrock surface, by a homogeneous slab composed entirely of the lighter overburden of density ρ_1. The gravity effect of this slab at all points on the surface and therefore also at station 2, will be $0.4191\,\rho_1 h$ (cf. p.242), which is certainly less than the effect of the actual slab. Therefore:

$$\text{Effect of slab } a-b \text{ at station } 1 - 0.4191\,\rho_1 h > \Delta g \text{ g.u.} \qquad (8.11)$$

Suppose now that the slab $a-b$ is replaced by one composed wholly of the bedrock (density ρ_2). The attraction of this slab, namely $0.4191\,\rho_2 h$, at station 1, is certainly *greater* than that of the actual slab which, in parts, contains the lighter overburden material. Therefore, if we replace the first term on the left-hand side in (8.11) by $0.4191\,\rho_2 h$ the inequality will still be true, so that:

$$0.4191\,\rho_2 h - 0.4191\,\rho_1 h > \Delta g$$

that is:

$$0.4191\,\rho h > \Delta g$$

or:

$$\rho h > 2.39\Delta g \qquad (8.12)$$

where $\rho = \rho_2 - \rho_1$ is the density difference between overburden and bedrock. This formula yields an estimate of the *minimum* value of the *maximum variation* in overburden thickness, needed to explain the observed difference of anomalies at two stations.

If this estimate of the bedrock relief turns out to be implausible in view of other evidence, the difference of gravity must be attributed to causes other than overburden variations.

The inequality (8.12) can be improved, in the sense that a still higher "minimax" estimate than that provided by it can be obtained. Towards this purpose we replace Δg by $\Delta g_{max.}$, the *maximum* observed gravity difference between two points in the area, and ρ by $\rho_{min.}$, the *minimum* plausible density difference between overburden and bedrock. Then:

$$h > 2.39 \, \frac{\Delta g_{max.}}{\rho_{min.}} \qquad (8.13)$$

In the example discussed in the last section, the total regional gravity anomaly was 8 g.u. The density of the bedrock in the area cannot be lower than 2.65 g/cm^3 while the density of the overburden (moraine) is probably not higher than 2.15 g/cm^3. Hence the minimum plausible density difference appears to be 0.50 g/cm^3. Therefore:

$$h > 2.39 \, \frac{8}{0.50} = 38.3 \quad m$$

Thus, if the regional gradient in that example be due to overburden variations, a possibility which has been mentioned above, the relief of the bedrock in the area must be at least 38 m.

In respect of the argument used in deriving it the inequality (8.12) is typical of the inequalities met with in the theory of gravity interpretation. Some of these were already mentioned (without proof) in the section *Key variables of gravity interpretation* (p.255).

MASS ESTIMATES

Although a given set of gravity data can be explained by a variety of mass distributions, it can be proved that the total anomalous mass in every such distribution is always the same and, what is more, the mass can be determined from observed gravity data alone. This theorem is of great importance in ore prospecting.

Firstly, the theorem enables us to estimate ore reserves without the necessity of making any assumptions concerning the geometry and depth of an orebody. Secondly, it provides a check on the estimates of reserves based on drilling, trenching and other mining work. Thirdly, if the shape of the orebody is complicated even extensive drilling may fail to give an adequate idea of the reserves involved, in which case gravity measurements are sometimes found to yield more reliable estimates.

For the proof of the theorem the reader may be referred to Hammer (1945). Here we shall only indicate the practical procedure in the application of it.

Let Δg be the mean anomaly (g.u.) within a small element ΔS (m^2) of the area of measurement; form the product $\Delta g \times \Delta S$. Then, the total anomalous mass is given by:

$$M = 2.39 \ \Sigma(\Delta g \times \Delta S) \quad \text{metric tons} \tag{8.14}$$

where Σ denotes that the products $\Delta g \times \Delta S$ are summed up over the whole area.

If the areal element ΔS is in square feet and the mass in long tons:

$$M = 0.218 \ \Sigma(\Delta g \times \Delta S) \quad \text{long tons} \tag{8.15}$$

By the anomalous mass we mean the difference $V\rho_2 - V\rho_1 = V(\rho_2 - \rho_1)$, between the actual mass $(V\rho_2)$ of an orebody of volume V and density ρ_2, and the mass $(V\rho_1)$ of the host rock of density ρ_1 occupying an identically shaped volume. However, the actual mass of the body is given by:

$$2.39 \ \frac{\rho_2}{\rho_2 - \rho_1} \ \Sigma(\Delta g \times \Delta S) \quad \text{metric tons} \tag{8.16}$$

and cannot be estimated without making some plausible assumption concerning the densities ρ_2 and ρ_1. It should be noted that if Δg is expressed in mgal the factor 2.39 in the formulae (8.12)–(8.16) has to be replaced by 23.9 and the factor 0.218 in (8.15) by 2.18.

It should be noted that eq. (8.14) yields an estimate of the *net* mass excess. Thus, if two masses, one lighter and the other heavier than the host rock occur beside each other the formula yields the difference of the two mass-excesses and this will be quite different from the anomalous mass corresponding to either of them.

Similarly, if regional gradients due to contacts, deep-seated masses or the like exist, the estimate will automatically contain the anomalous mass corresponding to such structures. Consequently, if we wish to obtain the mass of an orebody in such a case, the regional effects must be removed first and a map of residual anomalies prepared, before applying eq. (8.14).

Gravity estimates of the anomalous mass are particularly easy if the map shows a fairly simple and regular pattern. For Fig.100B, for example, where the regional gradient has been removed, an estimate can be arrived at as follows.

The mean gravity anomaly within the area between the contours for 0.2 and 0.3 mgal is considered to be 0.25 mgal, that between the contours for 0.3 and 0.4 mgal to be 0.35 mgal and so on. Then the areas between successive contours are determined by drawing the map on a ruled graph paper (or by accurate weighing of the pieces cut from the map). In the case at hand the anomalies outside the 0.1 mgal contour were assumed to be zero, so that the contribution of the effectively infinite area outside it to the sum $\Sigma \Delta g \Delta S$ was zero. The remaining contributions gave the sum:

$$(0.15 \times 102 + 0.25 \times 44 + 0.35 \times 26 + 0.45 \times 23.5 + 0.55 \times 12.5$$
$$+ 0.65 \times 7 + 0.7 \times 3)400 = 59.50 \times 400 \quad (\text{mgal m}^2)$$

Hence, the anomalous mass represented by the orebody in Fig.100B is approximately:

$$23.9 \times 59.50 \times 400 = 568,820 \quad \text{metric tons}$$

Assuming densities 3.38 and 2.70 g/cm^3 for the ore and the host rock, the actual mass of the ore is estimated to be 2.83 million tons, which is not far from the drillhole estimate.

A more accurate estimate can be obtained by repeating the procedure after drawing intermediate isoanomaly contours as well as the contours outside the 0.1 mgal contour.

As the anomalies of shallow masses fall rapidly below the accuracy of measurement as we go outwards from the anomaly centre, while those of deep masses persist to great distances, the neglect of anomalies at large distances from the centre, as in the above example, is equivalent to neglecting the effect of the deep-lying parts of a mass. But at large distances from an anomaly centre the stray geological anomalies tend to mask the ore anomalies so that the latter cannot be separated out. Hence, estimates according to eq. (8.14) usually do not yield much information about the mass contained in the deeper parts of an orebody. In one sense, therefore, the mass estimate yielded by eq. (8.14) is a minimum.

A FURTHER EXAMPLE OF A GRAVITY SURVEY

This example, from the Svappavaara iron ore field in northern Sweden, is due to Werner (1961). It is chiefly of interest from the point of view of the extra information that a gravity survey can provide, in addition to that provided by a magnetic survey. The Svappavaara iron ores contain magnetite as well as haematite but the latter, being practically non-magnetic, cannot be detected by means of a magnetometer.

Fig.102 shows the gravity and magnetic maps of the Svappavaara iron orefield. There are two orebodies, the Gruvberget body in the left portion of the map and the Leveäniemi in the right one. To start with we notice that the gravity picture is much more regular than the magnetic one, especially for the Gruvberget body. This suggests that while the magnetite in the bodies is irregularly distributed, each ore mass as a whole is fairly regular in shape.

The strong magnetic anomalies ($> 64,000\gamma$) on the northern part of the Gruvberget body indicate the sub-outcrop of the magnetite ore in it. Along its continuation to the south there is a gravity top of 5 mgal (near the cross) but significant magnetic anomalies are absent here. This gravity top is now known to be associated with rich haematite ore.

In the case of the Leveäniemi body there is an area of strong magnetic anomalies between 32,000 and 64,000γ to the south of the cross but the gravity anomalies show no corresponding top and are considerably weaker than one would expect. Similarly the band of

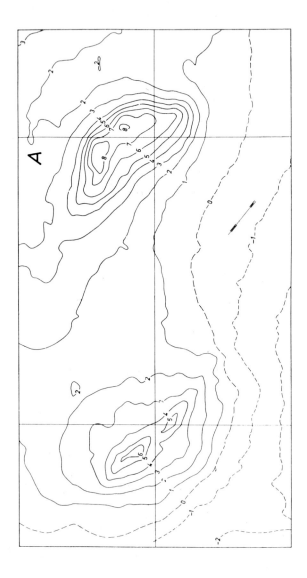

strong magnetic anomalies on the west does not appear on the gravity map. On the other hand the magnetic values are weak in the centre of the Leveäniemi area, but the gravity ones reach their maximum here (owing to massive haematite). A comparison of the gravity and

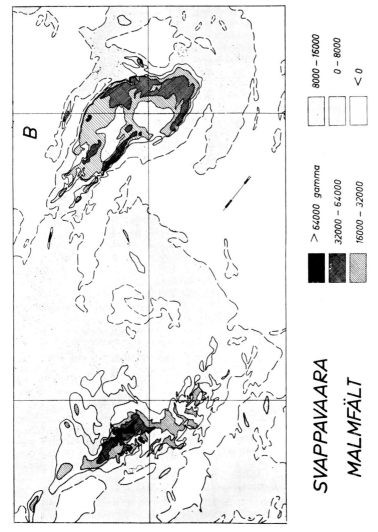

Fig.102. Gravity (A) and magnetic (B) maps of the Svappavaara iron-ore field. Distance between the two vertical lines in the centre is 4,000 m (1 mgal = 10 g.u.) (Courtesy of S. Werner, Stockholm.)

magnetic maps suggests that the Leveäniemi orebody has a core of massive haematite and the magnetite is distributed peripherically around it in relatively thin bands.

Werner (1961) states that the development work has shown that the gravity map in the Svappavaara field gives a more realistic picture of the distribution of the ore than the magnetic map.

It should be observed that the information above has been obtained by simple qualitative considerations. The Svappavaara anomalies allow, however, reliable quantitative calculations to be made on account of their relatively regular patterns. These have been made and Werner informs that the gravity mass estimates, in particular, have been strikingly confirmed by recent work in the area.

Magnetic calculations can also be used to obtain estimates of the size of an orebody. However, such estimates are not reliable unless the remanence of an orebody is well known (cf. section *Interpretation of magnetic anomalies*, p.46). This uncertainty does not arise in gravity measurements. There seems little doubt that gravity methods will be used much more extensively in future, even on highly magnetic ores, with the specific intention of obtaining reliable estimates of the ore reserves.

UNDERGROUND AND SHAFT MEASUREMENTS OF GRAVITY

Very few underground gravity measurements have been reported but the advantage of such measurements in ore prospecting seems well established. It is not possible to discuss underground measurements here in detail and the interested reader is referred to a series of papers by Domzalski (1953, 1954, 1955a, 1955b) who has given some of the most extensive accounts of such work. Consult also a paper by Algermissen (1961).

As with surface gravity measurements, underground measurements must also be corrected for latitude and elevation differences of the stations from the base, and for the attraction of the slab of rock material between the base level and the station level. The first two corrections are given by eq. (8.3) and (8.4) but the last one, the

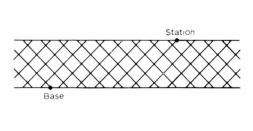

Fig.103. Underground Bouguer correction.

Bouguer correction in underground measurements, is not 0.4191 ρ g.u./m but 0.8382 ρ g.u./m, that is, exactly twice. The reason will be clear by reference to Fig.103. The slab between the station and the base exerts a downward attraction equal to 0.4191 ρh g.u. on the field station but an *upward* attraction of the same strength on the base station. The total gravity difference between the station and the base, due to the slab, is therefore 2 $\times$ 0.4191 ρh. This amount must be subtracted from the measured gravity at a station if the station is above the level of the base and added if it is below.

Underground measurements may require "terrain corrections" for shafts, mine galleries, cross-cuts, mined-out ore and other excavations.

SECOND VERTICAL DERIVATIVES OF GRAVITY ANOMALIES

A problem that often arises in gravity and magnetic interpretation involves the separation of the effects of shallow structures from slowly-varying effects, such as those due to contacts and deep-lying masses. The residual method of separation was touched upon in section *Regional and local gravity anomalies* (p.264). It was pointed out there that the residual anomaly cannot be determined uniquely, whether by smoothing or analytically, the reason being simply "the axiomatic fact that a whole cannot be divided into two (or more) unique parts without the imposition of restricting condition(s)".

The basic indeterminacy of residuals has led to the suggestion that the effects of shallow and deep masses can be separated by what are known as second vertical derivatives. The argument is as follows.

Suppose we have a point mass at a depth z. Its maximum gravity anomaly occurs vertically above it and is given by:

$$g = \frac{C}{z^2} \qquad (8.17)$$

where C is a constant (Newtonian gravitational constant times the mass).

The gravity anomalies of two equal point masses, one at a depth of 1 unit and the other at a depth, say, of 5 units will be in the proportion 25 : 1.

Now, differentiating eq. (8.17) twice with respect to z, we get the second vertical derivative:

$$g'' = \frac{6C}{z^4} \qquad (8.18)$$

We see that the second derivative of the anomaly of the shallower mass will be greater than that of the anomaly of the deeper mass in the proportion $5^4 : 1^4 = 625 : 1$. Thus the second derivative has accentuated the effect of the shallow mass, and it would seem at a first glance that the measurement of second derivatives would provide us with a method of separating shallow and deep structures with some measure of certainty.

However, it can be shown that a knowledge of second derivatives of gravity is inherent in the knowledge of the gravity anomalies themselves so that the second derivatives do not provide any information not already present in the gravity data. If the gravity anomalies are known sufficiently accurately and at sufficiently closely spaced points, the second derivatives can be calculated from them (Parasnis, 1972, p.58). Further, any combination of masses that explains a set of second derivative values must also explain the corresponding values of gravity and vice versa. Hence the inherent ambiguity in gravity (and magnetic) interpretation is in no way reduced by a knowledge of second derivatives, in whatever manner they are obtained. The ambiguity can only be reduced by geological knowledge.

The particular advantage that second derivatives may possess in some practical instances lies in a different direction and arises entirely because they create an "optical" illusion which makes it easier to spot local anomalies in analysing gravity (and magnetic) maps. In that connection it is well to remember that, paradoxically enough, the higher the accuracy and denseness of gravity observations, the less is the advantage of calculating second derivatives, even if they are then calculable to a higher degree of precision.

Many schemes of second derivative calculations have been proposed. All of them demand a close and regular network of observation points. One of the simplest (due to Nettleton 1954) is as follows.

Let g_0 be the anomaly at an observation point P of a square grid (Fig.104) and g_1, g_2, g_3, g_4 be the anomalies at the stations which are the nearest neighbours of P. Then the second vertical derivative at P is given by:

$$g_0'' = \frac{4}{S^2}(g_0 - \bar{g}) \quad \text{g.u./m}^2 \tag{8.19}$$

where $\bar{g}$ is the mean of g_1, g_2, g_3, g_4 and S is the grid spacing.

Some serious shortcomings of second vertical derivatives should be borne in mind.

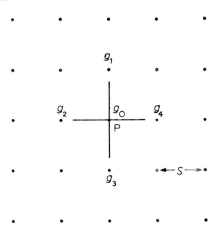

Fig.104. Square grid of gravity or magnetic observations.

Fig.105. A. Bouguer anomaly map of the J-jaure titaniferous iron-ore area, Sweden. Contours in mgal (10 g.u.). (Courtesy of BGAB.) B. Second derivative of the gravity map in part A. Contours: 0 (dashed), ± 0.1, ± 0.2, ± 0.4 in units of 0.0025 mgal/m².

Second derivatives are much more sensitive to terrain irregularities than gravity anomalies themselves. Further, the derivatives of a gravity field (of whatever order) possess more maxima, minima and zeroes than the field itself. These, it should be noted, are not independently connected to mass excesses or deficiencies as the maxima and minima in the gravity field but are the result of straightforward algebraic properties. Consequently, a second derivative map presents a "patchy" picture and is often so cluttered with "spurious" positive and negative anomaly centres as to be misleading.

Fig.105A shows the Bouguer anomaly map of an area in northern Sweden, containing fairly compact lenses of titaniferous iron ore in gabbro. The two principal lenses are immediately evident from the maxima in the anomalies. The general trend of the contours suggests a southward as well as westward regional gradient. Considering the geology, there is hardly any doubt that this gradient is due to a contact of gabbro and granite bending somewhat like the contours.

Fig.105B shows the second derivative map of the area. The lenses are clearly evident on this map also and the slowly-varying effect of the regional gradient has practically disappeared. However, a number of small maxima and minima of no structural interest appear on the map. To decide whether some of these are significant or not, one is forced to revert to the original gravity map and, of course, to geological observations.

CHAPTER 9

Seismic Methods

INTRODUCTION

The seismic methods of prospecting exploit the fact that the velocity of elastic waves is different in different rocks. When elastic waves generated, for example, by a dynamite shot propagate through the ground, they suffer reflections and refractions at the interfaces between rocks in which their velocities are different. Strictly speaking it is necessary for reflections to occur that the acoustic impedances of adjoining media be different, the acoustic impedance being the product of the elastic velocity and the density of a medium.

From a study of the arrival times of seismic waves at a number of selected points it is possible then to infer the positions of the various interfaces at which the waves are reflected and refracted.

TYPES OF ELASTIC WAVES

A solid body is capable of transmitting two principal kinds of elastic waves within itself. These are known respectively as the longitudinal and transverse waves. Both are "body waves", being transmitted through the interior of the body.

When longitudinal waves travel through a body, its particles vibrate to and fro in the direction of the wave propagation, and the body is compressed in some parts but dilated in others at any instant. Longitudinal seismic waves are akin to ordinary sound waves.

During the propagation of transverse waves the particles of a body vibrate in a direction perpendicular to the direction of wave propagation. As a consequence, small deformations arise in the body, roughly in the manner that a square element of it is transformed constantly into a rhombus and back again into a square and so on. The waves on a violin string are transverse waves (but they give rise to longitudinal waves in the air).

The frequency of longitudinal and transverse seismic waves ranges between about 15 c/sec and 100 c/sec.

Longitudinal waves are also called compressional or primary waves and generally denoted by the symbol P. Transverse waves are alternatively known as shear or secondary waves and commonly denoted by the symbol S.

Besides the longitudinal and compressional waves other types of elastic waves can also exist in a heterogeneous body, notably the Love and Rayleigh waves. However, these are not body waves but are confined to the interfaces between media of different acoustic impedances. We shall not enter into a discussion of these.

Both P and S waves are generated in the ground when a seismic shot is exploded or a sharp blow is imparted to the ground by means of a hammer, and are propagated simultaneously. On reflection or refraction, a wave can change its character. Thus, a P wave may be reflected as a P or an S wave. Such waves and their subsequent transformations are denoted by appropriate combinations of the symbols P and S, e.g., PP, PS, SP, PPS etc.

In contrast to the properties, such as the magnetic susceptibility or the electric resistivity, the elastic (i.e., seismic) velocities in specific rocks vary within relatively narrow limits. In fact, in a given area they often remain constant to such an extent that geological strata can be identified on the basis of the observed seismic velocities. Table VI gives a list of longitudinal and transverse elastic velocities in some rocks, ores and common substances. It will be seen that the longitudinal waves travel faster than the transverse ones. Fluids, e.g., water or air, do not possess any shear strength, which means that the geometrical shape of a fluid element can be deformed by an infinitesimally small force, and hence fluids cannot transmit transverse waves.

TABLE VI

VELOCITIES OF LONGITUDINAL SEISMIC WAVES

Material	Velocity[1] (m/sec)	Source
Water	1,450	standard value
Soil layer	100–500	⎫
Sand, loose moraine	200–800	⎪
Clay, silt, gravel	500–1,500	routine refraction work
Compact moraine	1,500–2,700	carried out in Scandinavia
Weathered fissured bedrock	1,900–4,000	and Canada
Granite and greenstone	4,000–5,500	⎪
Gabbro	5,500–6,800	⎭
Limestone		
Cretaceous	2,200	Maurin and Eblé (Heiland, 1946)
Carboniferous	3,000–3,600	Barsch and Reich (Heiland, 1946)
Ordovician	4,090 (⊥ bedding) 5,320 (∥ bedding)	Weatherby, Born and Harding (Heiland, 1946)
Quartz porphyry	4,870–5,330	
Sulphide ore with pyrite, zinc blende	3,950–6,550	Baule and Arensmeyer (1954)
Black shales with pyrrhotite	3,890–5,500	

[1] Small seismic velocity differences between two rock formations do not exclude the possibility of reflections at their interface because the reflection coefficient is determined by the difference in acoustic impedance (product of seismic velocity and density).

SCOPE OF SEISMIC MEASUREMENTS IN ORE PROSPECTING

The suggested applications of seismic prospecting methods in the search for ores are twofold, firstly, a direct search for ores by delineating contacts of ores and host rocks, and secondly the determination of overburden thicknesses and the thicknesses of sedimentary strata.

The method that has been tried in a direct seismic search for ore horizons has been, for the most part, the reflection method described in the next section. It has been used overground as well as underground. It is evident from Table VI that the elastic velocity contrasts between ores and host rocks (particularly if the latter are crystalline) will, in general, be very small and since orebodies constitute relatively thin sections of the ground their influence on the propagation of elastic waves through the ground may be expected to be small. This is the principal reason why seismic methods have met with a very limited success in the direct search for ores.

As for the other aspect of seismic methods in ore prospecting, the need to know overburden thicknesses arises in the detailed interpretations of gravity anomalies (cf. section *Effect of overburden on gravity anomalies*, p.267), while a knowledge of the thicknesses of sedimentary strata is of great importance in prospecting for coal, gypsum, sulphur beds etc. Both the reflection and refraction methods have been employed in, for example, coal basin surveys (Thyer, 1963). The determination of overburden thicknesses for possible gravimeter corrections is of considerable interest in areas where the crystalline basement rocks are overlain by glacial moraine or soil cover having a relatively high density contrast with the bedrock.

Although depth-to-bedrock determinations are very commonly undertaken nowadays for engineering purposes they are not very widespread as aids in gravity interpretation, one restricting factor being the cost of seismic surveys. Now that relatively cheap and easily operated seismic outfits like the hammer seismograph models (Stam, 1962; Johansson, 1965) are commercially available, the use of seismic data as an aid in gravity interpretation is likely to grow.

GENERATION, DETECTION AND REGISTRATION OF SEISMIC WAVES

By far the most common method of generating seismic waves is to explode dynamite charges. The method has the advantage that the required energy can always be obtained by the use of a sufficient amount of explosive. Moreover, provided proper precautions are taken, explosives are convenient to handle. The main drawback of explosives is that there is always an inherent danger of injury to personnel and damage to property so that very rigorous safety precautions must be taken.

Other ways of producing seismic waves have been tried, e.g.

hammer blows or powerful electric sparks, but the energies obtained by them are not always sufficient for deep investigations. For shallow investigations, the hammer seismograph outfits, in particular, seem to be well suited.

Seismic waves are detected by geophones of which the most common types are the electromagnetic ones. A coil attached to a frame is placed between the poles of a magnet which, in turn, is suspended by leaf springs. The frame is in firm contact with a closed tight housing provided with a spike or blade for driving the geophone in the ground. The coil moves with the ground while the magnet remains virtually stationary on account of its large inertia and the relative movement of the two produces an electrical oscillating voltage.

The voltage from the geophone is amplified, filtered suitably depending upon the frequencies in the ground motion to be registered, and fed into the recorder where it sets a tiny galvanometer into oscillations. A mirror carried by the galvanometer reflects a light beam on to a moving recording film where the seismic waves are thus ultimately recorded.

Modern reflection seismic outfits also record the waves magnetically on magnetic discs, tapes or drums. The hammer seismographs record seismic impulses as small marks made on a paper.

Geophones are small light-weight assemblies and the output of several of them (for example, 12 or 24) is normally recorded simultaneously on as many channels.

A photographic seismic record also has time lines superimposed on it so that events such as the arrival of waves can be determined accurately (within a millisecond). A typical reflection seismic record is shown in Fig.106. Fig.107A is a block diagram of a seismic equipment and Fig.107B is a photograph of the ABEM Trio refraction unit.

THE REFLECTION METHOD

The principle of the seismic reflection method is shown in Fig.108 where the simple case of a single reflecting horizon is envisaged. A ray

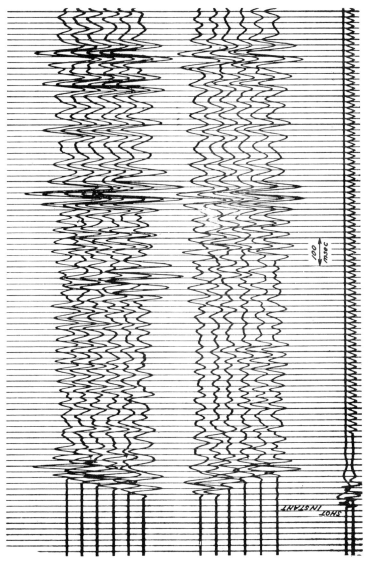

Fig. 106. Typical seismic record. (Courtesy of British Petroleum Co. Ltd., London.)

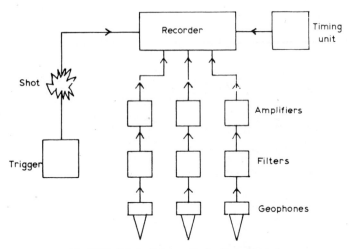

Fig.107A. Block diagram of seismic equipment.

Fig.107B. Refraction seismic equipment Trio. The middle unit is the recorder. On the right is the amplifier box as seen from the front side, on the left the same box seen from its rear. In the foreground, one geophone with spike. The complete geophone cable, the shot cables and the shot box are not shown. (Courtesy ABEM Company, Stockholm.)

starting from a shot S is reflected at a point R of the interface between two horizontal layers and arrives at the detector G. If h is the thickness of the upper stratum and the ray arrives at G, t sec after the shot:

$$t = \frac{2h}{V_1} \qquad (9.1)$$

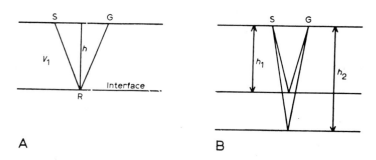

Fig.108. Principle of the seismic reflection method. A. Single interface. B. Two interfaces.

where V_1 is the velocity of the seismic wave in the upper stratum — the shot–detector distance is small compared with the depth of the reflecting horizon so that it is permissible to replace the actual path length 2SR by $2h$ in writing eq. (9.1).

In practice, an array of geophones is placed at a relatively short distance from the shot, usually in a straight line.

The disturbance arriving at a geophone is partly signal and partly noise due to surface waves created by wind, traffic, etc., and by the shot itself. If only one geophone were to be used to record the waves, there will be no way of telling whether a particular wiggle on the record is due to noise or to signal. However, noise disturbances would not be expected to be exactly in phase at all the geophones. On the other hand a reflection signal from a subsurface velocity interface arrives at all the geophones almost simultaneously on account of the very short mutual distance between the geophones and produces a characteristic "lining-up" pattern on the seismogram (see Fig.106). To each such pattern corresponds one reflection (single or multiple).

For two interfaces as shown in Fig.108B, the reflection from the first interface arrives at a time:

$$t_1 = \frac{2h_1}{V_1} \qquad\qquad (9.2)$$

while the reflection from the second interface arrives at a time:

$$t_2 = \frac{2h_1}{V_1} + \frac{2(h_2 - h_1)}{V_2} \tag{9.3}$$

If the velocities V_1 and V_2 are known the thickness h_1 is calculated first from eq. (9.2) and then substituting in eq. (9.3) we get also the thickness h_2. The times t_1 and t_2 are read from the seismogram record. These equations can be generalized in an obvious manner for any number of interfaces, but it is clear that the velocities of the seismic waves must be determined by separate experiments. Such experiments are usually made with the refraction method.

THE REFRACTION METHOD

When seismic waves pass from one medium to another in which they have a different velocity they are refracted. The law of refraction is simple. If the ray incident on the interface between two media makes an angle i_1 with the normal to the interface, the refracted ray in the adjoining medium makes an angle i_2 with the normal (Fig.109) and:

$$\frac{\sin i_2}{\sin i_1} = \frac{V_2}{V_1} \tag{9.4}$$

where V_1 and V_2 are the seismic velocities in the two media.

If V_2 is greater than V_1 we have $\sin i_2 > \sin i_1$ and therefore $i_2 > i_1$. Thus the refracted ray makes a larger angle with the normal, i.e., a smaller angle with the interface than the incident ray.

If the incident ray makes a particular angle i_c such that:

$$\sin i_c = \frac{V_1}{V_2} \tag{9.5}$$

$\sin i_2 = 1$ so that $i_2 = 90°$. In this case the refracted ray travels along the interface and the angle of incidence is called the critical angle.

Now consider an overburden of thickness h resting on a substratum having a greater seismic velocity (Fig.109B). A critically incident ray SA will be refracted so that it travels along the line $AB_1 B_2$ ... along

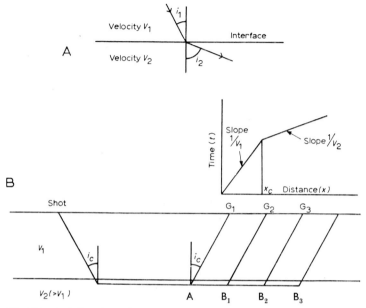

Fig.109. A. Refraction of seismic waves. B. Refraction of seismic waves at critical angle.

the interface, but at various points such as B_1, B_2 etc., its energy reemerges in the upper medium, along rays making angles i_c with the normals at these points. These rays reach the surface of the ground at points G_1, G_2 ... etc.

If we place a number of geophones along a straight line from the shot, the first ray to arrive at the nearer geophones will be the direct ray travelling along the surface, e.g., SG_1. However, at the more distant geophones the first ray to arrive will be the refracted ray because it travels part of the path with the higher velocity V_2 and overtakes the direct ray. Therefore if we plot the first-arrival times against the distance from the shot, the first few arrival times will fall on one straight line and the rest on another straight line, the slopes of the lines depending upon the velocities V_1, V_2. In fact the reciprocals of the slopes are equal to the respective velocities as indicated in Fig.109B.

Having determined the velocities in this manner from the time–distance graph, we get the thickness of the upper layer from the "break-point" at which the two lines intersect. If x_c is the distance of the break point from the shot it can be shown that the thickness is given by:

$$h = \frac{x_c}{2} \sqrt{\frac{V_2 - V_1}{V_2 + V_1}}$$

Simple nomograms exist from which the depth h can be read off without calculations once the velocities and the break-point are determined from the graph (Meidav, 1960).

Another method of determining h is as follows. The second segment (slope $1/V_2$), if produced, will intersect the time-axis at a point corresponding to a definite time t_1. This is the so-called intercept-time. Then it can be shown that:

$$h = \frac{V_1 t_1}{2 \cos i_c} \tag{9.6a}$$

$$= \frac{t_1}{2} \frac{V_1 V_2}{\sqrt{V_2^2 - V_1^2}}$$

$$= \frac{t_1}{2} \frac{\eta}{\sqrt{1 - \eta^2}} \quad \text{where } \eta = V_1/V_2 \tag{9.6b}$$

If the interface between the upper layer and the substratum is not parallel to the ground surface but makes an angle θ with it, the slope $1/V_2$ of the second segment will not be the same when the shot is placed on the up-dip side and the geophone set-up on the down-dip side, as in the reverse case. Therefore, two apparent velocities V_d and V_u, in shooting down-dip and up-dip respectively will be obtained. The slope of the first segment ($1/V_1$) giving the upper-layer velocity is the same for both shootings. The angle of dip can be determined from the relation:

$$\theta = \frac{1}{2} \left\{ \sin^{-1} (V_1/V_d) - \sin^{-1} (V_1/V_u) \right\} \tag{9.7a}$$

where $\sin^{-1}x$ denotes the angle whose sine is x. The velocity V_d is less than the velocity V_u.

The critical angle i_c is given by:

$$i_c = \tfrac{1}{2} \left\{ \sin^{-1}(V_1/V_d) + \sin^{-1}(V_1/V_u) \right\} \qquad (9.7b)$$

and the velocity in the second layer by $V_2 = V_1/\sin i_c$.

If h is the vertical depth of the interface below a shot-point and t is the intercept-time obtained when shooting from the shot-point in question, then h is again given by the formula (9.6a).

Fig.110A shows a refraction seismic record with the shot-instant (on trace 0) and the "kicks" due to the first arrivals at 12 geophones planted in a straight line.

Fig.110B is an example of the time–distance curves obtained with one and the same geophone set-up but with shots in opposite directions. Either curve consists of two main segments. We shall neglect the weathered layer in which the shots show delays of 2.5 msec and 4.4 msec. The case is then reduced to a two-layer problem and the velocity in the upper layer is found to be 1,100 m/sec. This is characteristic of the moraine in the area. The apparent velocities given by the second segment are not equal. Shooting from the left we get a velocity of 3,100 m/sec and from the right 8,500 m/sec. From eq. (9.7a) we have:

$$\theta = \tfrac{1}{2} \left\{ \sin^{-1}\frac{1,100}{3,100} - \sin^{-1}\frac{1,100}{8,500} \right\} = 6.7°$$

and:

$$i_c = \tfrac{1}{2} \left\{ \sin^{-1}\frac{1,100}{3,100} + \sin^{-1}\frac{1,100}{8,500} \right\} = 14.1°$$

Further, eq. (9.5) gives:

$$V_2 = 1,100/\sin(14.1°) = 4,512 \text{ m/sec}$$

and from eq. (9.7a) we get, for the vertical depth below the left shot:

$$h = \frac{1,100 \cdot 14.5 \cdot 10^{-3}}{2\cos(14.1°)} = \frac{15.95}{1.940} = 8.3 \text{ m}$$

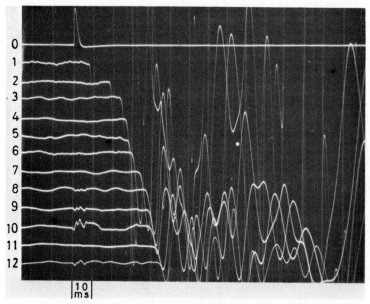

Fig.110A. A refraction seismic record showing shot instant (break in trace 0) and kicks due to first arrivals at 12 geophones (traces 1–12).

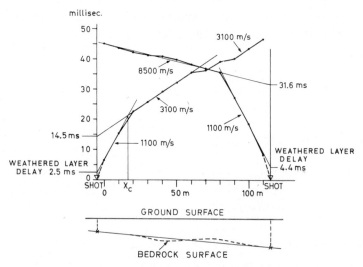

Fig.110B. Time–distance curves shooting up-dip and down-dip. Area: Flarken, northern Sweden. (Courtesy BGAB.)

Similarly, for the right-hand shot, $h = 18.0$ m.

The irregularities in the time-distance curves can be explained by a slight undulation of the bedrock surface as shown. If the weathered layer is taken into account somewhat more complicated formulas are needed but in the present instance the layer is rather thin (0.5–0.8 m) and the above estimates of the bedrock depth may be found adequate for many purposes.

ILLUSTRATIONS OF SEISMIC MEASUREMENTS IN ORE PROSPECTING

Siderite district of the Siegerland (Germany)

This example is due to Schmidt (1959). The Siegerland iron-ore district lies some 55 km east of Bonn. The ore is siderite (iron carbonate, $FeCO_3$) with an average of 30–32% Fe and 6-7% Mn and belongs to the lowest part of the Lower Devonian. The lodes of commercial value occur in a relatively small area and quite irregularly distributed as fillings of fissures and cracks, 1–2 m in thickness and at the most 200–300 m in length. They dip mainly vertically.

The seismic measurements were undertaken as the ore in the district was being exhausted and no other geophysical methods were judged to be useful for prospecting for more ore of this type.

The measurements were carried out underground in the Neue Haardt mine with geophone set-ups firmly attached to the walls of an adit. As the shot points were also in hard rock, the frequencies of the recorded seismic waves were considerably higher (200–600 c/sec) than in ground surveys. As the wavelengths were then shorter than usual, there was the advantage that small thicknesses interbedded in the host rock stood a good chance of being detected.

However, the reflection times were generally very short because of the high velocities (5,000 m/sec) and the limited distances available for the measurements. Consequently, the reflection events on the record tended to be masked by the initial general unrest after the shot, making it necessary to use suitable electric filters in recording the waves.

Fig.111 shows the plan of the 925-m level. With the geophones

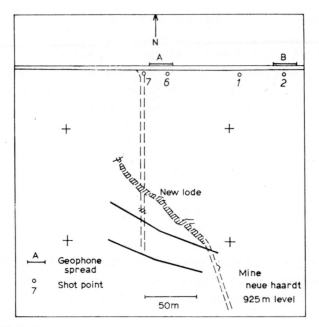

Fig.111. Reflection horizons in the Neue Haardt mine, Siegerland, Germany.
(After Schmidt, 1959).

along the stretch A in the gallery, shots were exploded at points *1* and
2 and with the geophones along the stretch B at *6* and *7*. The heavy
lines show the two parallel reflecting horizons indicated by the results
and interpreted as representing the interfaces of siderite veins and the
host rock. The occurrence of a new lode of commercial value just in
this part of the field was considered improbable on geological grounds
but an adit (the dotted line) hit a previously unknown ore vein.

The vein was 3—4 m thick, about 100 m long on this level and lay
somewhat to the north of the seismic horizons.

Sulphur limestone in Sicily (Italy)

An application of the seismic reflection method in the search for
sulphur limestone has been reported by Cassinis (1958).

The sulphur layers or "series" in Sicily occur sandwiched between
Pliocene clays on the top and a very thick series of Miocene clays at

the bottom. The sulphur series itself usually comprises, from top to bottom, white marls ("Trubi"), gypsum, limestone, the foraminiferous marls of the "Tripoli" and, in some cases, salt lenses. The thickness of the "series" varies from about 10 to about 100 m and the problem is to locate the gypsum and limestone horizons in which the sulphur occurs.

Electrical methods were previously used as they seemed promising on account of the great contrast of resistivities between the Pliocene clays (2–3 Ωm) and limestone (20–40 Ωm). But the results were often unsatisfactory due to dipping layers, shallow inhomogeneities, faults etc. Moreover, the resistivities of the "Trubi" and the lower sections of the sulphur series are sometimes very similar. Hence the seismic method was attempted, although it also encountered difficulties of its own on account of the very rough topography.

The reflecting horizons indicated a regular syncline and were considered, on the basis of geology and auxiliary refraction measurements, to arise from the lower part of the sulphur series. A test well encountered a thin section of gypsum, 315 m below the surface, underlain by honeycombed limestone.

In regard to this survey Cassinis states further that the results showed: ". . .that the seismic method can be a useful guide to the evaluation of the lower part of the "sulphur series" . . . While the velocity of the overburden is quite constant, about 2.2 km/sec, the velocity of the sulphur layers varies from 3 to about 4 km/sec. The highest values were found to correspond to solid gypsum or limestone and the smallest to honeycombed layers, i.e., to more favourable conditions for mineralization."

The application of seismic methods to ore prospecting is still mainly in the trial stage and, for the present at any rate, seismic methods play a very subordinate role in the search for ores. Therefore we shall not enter further into them here. The interested reader will find more details about seismic methods in general in Menzel (1958) and Dobrin (1952).

CHAPTER 10

Radioactive Methods

INTRODUCTION

The nuclei of certain elements disintegrate spontaneously emitting energetic corpuscular and electromagnetic radiations, and in doing so are transformed into nuclei of other elements. The daughter elements may also be radioactive in their turn. The corpuscular radiations emitted are the alpha (α) and beta (β) particles, which are helium nuclei and electrons respectively. The α particles carry a positive electric charge, the β particles a negative one, except that some artificial radioactive nuclei emit positrons which are positively charged particles. The electromagnetic radiation consists of gamma (γ) rays which are X-rays but of very short wavelength and therefore possessing a high energy.

There are over 50 naturally occurring radioactive nuclei and over 800 artificially produced ones. Natural radioactivity is confined principally to the disintegration products of three elements: neptunium, uranium and thorium. Besides these, several other naturally occurring radioactive isotopes of other elements are known, chief among which are the isotopes of potassium and rubidium. Two other examples are the rare-earth elements samarium and lutecium.

The three radiations emitted by radioactive nuclei lose part of their energy on encountering matter, but to different degrees. The α particles are stopped completely by very small thicknesses of matter (e.g., a few microns of aluminium) but the range of β particles is much greater, say about 50 μ in aluminium. The intensity of γ rays decreases continuously as they pass through matter so that they have no definite range and could theoretically be detected across any thickness of matter. However, a practical limit to their detection exists since the intensity gradually falls below the sensitivity and noise of the detecting instruments. For practical purposes γ rays may be assumed to be completely stopped by about 30–50 cm of hard rock, or by a somewhat greater thickness if the overburden is loose debris.

All the three radiations are capable of ionizing the air or gas through which they pass and, in doing so, they render the air or gas electrically conducting. The γ rays are moreover capable of producing small flashes of light (scintillations) when they impinge on certain crystals, e.g., zinc sulphide, scheelite, anthracene etc. These are the two effects by which radioactive radiations are detected.

SCOPE OF THE METHOD

Radioactivity is a property of the nucleus and is therefore not affected by the chemical form in which a radioactive element occurs. Consequently, it can reveal the presence of the element irrespective of the complexity of the particular chemical compound. It is clear from the ranges of the α, β and γ rays that only the γ rays can be used in the search for radioactive elements in the earth's crust, since the α and β particles will be completely stopped by the slightest overburden like soil, humus, clay etc.

The geophysical search after radioactive elements in the earth's crust is primarily a search after places with abnormal γ radiation. However, not all radioactive elements emit γ rays and their deposits cannot then be located unless a daughter element present in the deposit emits these rays. Thus, uranium is located indirectly by the γ radiation given off by one or more of its products, notably radium.

The location of radioactive elements is not the only use to which radioactive methods can be put. Since all rocks, igneous as well as sedimentary, contain traces of radioactive elements, the methods can also be used for geological mapping provided different rocks, strata and facies have significantly different radioactivity. Impressive work of this sort in Washington County, Md., U.S.A., has been reported by Moxham (1963). Again, Giret has reported the use of radioactive methods for determining granite boundaries (Giret, 1961).

RADIOACTIVE DECAY AND RADIOACTIVE EQUILIBRIUM

The rate of radioactive disintegration is always the same for nuclei of a particular species and unaffected by conditions like pressure, temperature and chemical composition, but it varies enormously from one radioactive nucleus to the other.

Radioactive decay of a substance takes place at a rate such that the number of radioactive atoms which will disintegrate within 1 sec is proportional to the total number of the radioactive atoms present. It can be shown that if N_0 is the number of atoms at any particular instant, the number remaining after t seconds is:

$$N = N_0 e^{-\lambda t} \qquad (10.1)$$

where λ is known as the decay constant. The equation can also be written as:

$$-\lambda t = \ln \frac{N}{N_0} = 2.303 \times \log_{10} \frac{N}{N_0} \qquad (10.2)$$

Suppose that after a time $t_{1/2}$, only one half the atoms are remaining so that $N/N_0 = 1/2$. Then:

$$-\lambda t_{1/2} = 2.303 \times \log 0.5 = -0.693$$

or:

$$t_{1/2} = \frac{0.693}{\lambda} \qquad (10.3)$$

The time $t_{1/2}$ after which only half as many atoms remain as at the start is called the half-life of the radioactive nucleus. The half-lives of radioactive nuclei vary from a fraction of 10^{-6} sec to $> 10^{11}$ years. The half-life of ^{238}U is about 4,560 million years.

Radioactivity is measured in röntgens (r) per hour. One röntgen is the amount of radiation that will produce 2.083×10^9 pairs of ions per cm^3 of air at standard temperature and pressure. In geophysical work a smaller unit, the microröntgen per hour (1 $\mu r = 10^{-6} r$) is generally employed.

Radioactive decay produces a new element which may itself be radioactive like its parent and disintegrate into another element and so on. If the parent element is left to itself it will, after a certain time, come into equilibrium with its products so that as many atoms of a member in the series are being formed per second as are disintegrating. The quantities N_1, N_2, N_3 etc., of a number of radioactive elements in equilibrium with each other and their half-lives t_1, t_2, t_3 etc., are related as:

$$\frac{N_1}{t_1} = \frac{N_2}{t_2} = \frac{N_3}{t_3} = \ldots \ldots \tag{10.4}$$

Hence if all the half-lives in the series are known, the assay of any one element will provide a knowledge of the quantities of the other elements in radioactive equilibrium with it.

Quantitative estimates of the content of uranium or thorium from radioactive intensities measured in the field are often attempted. If a single element, say uranium, were present, a comparison of the observed intensity with that produced by a standard source containing a known weight of uranium could give an estimate of the uranium content of a deposit. However, products of the decay of uranium will usually be present in the deposit. They will affect the observed radioactive intensity and an estimate of the uranium content cannot be reliably made unless the degree of radioactive equilibrium in the deposit can be ascertained.

RADIOACTIVITY OF ROCKS

The radioactivity of rocks is naturally dependent upon the amounts of uranium and thorium and of their daughter products like radium, polonium, radon etc. Uranium occurs in pegmatites and granites in the form of a very complex mineral known as uraninite. Certain metalliferous veins containing tin, copper, or lead and silver also carry uranium, sometimes in appreciable quantities. The uranium of some deposits occurs in metamorphosed lavas and in sediments.

Thorium occurs in placer deposits like monazite sands but also as primary mineral in granites and gneisses.

Rocks like pegmatite, granites and gneisses are therefore disposed to show high radioactivity. However, the radioactivity of rocks is a much more common phenomenon since an isotope of potassium ^{40}K is also found to be radioactive. Although this isotope forms only about 0.012% of the potassium in the earth's crust, it contributes very significantly to the radioactivity of rocks on account of the very widespread occurrence of potassium itself, in acid igneous rocks as orthoclase and microcline feldspars as well as muscovite, and in their alteration product as alunite. Besides, saline sedimentary deposits, especially shales, contain much potassium in the form of sylvite and carnallite.

Table VII, after Moxham (1963) shows the average uranium, thorium and potassium content of common rock types together with their equivalent uranium (eU). Equivalent uranium is the amount of U necessary to impart to the rock a radioactivity equal to its observed activity. It is seen that granites and shales show the largest radio-activity, while the activity of limestone, sandstone and basalt is about that produced by a distribution of approximately 2–3 p.p.m. U.

The immediate consequence of the radioactivity of common rocks is that radioactivity detectors show a high background effect in granitic and sedimentary areas which may mask the radioactive uranium and thorium deposits.

TABLE VII

AVERAGE RADIOACTIVE CONTENTS OF ROCKS
(After Moxham, 1963)

Rock type	Chemical composition			γ-ray equivalents[1]		
	U (p.p.m.)	Th (p.p.m.)	K (p.p.m.)	eU_{Th} (p.p.m.)	eU_K (p.p.m.)	Total eU (p.p.m.)
Granite	5	18	$3.8 \cdot 10^4$	8	9.5	22.5
Shale	3.7	12	$1.7 \cdot 10^4$	5	4.2	12.9
Limestone	1.3	1.1	$0.27 \cdot 10^4$	0.5	0.7	2.5
Sandstone	0.45	1.7	$0.64 \cdot 10^4$	0.8	1.6	2.8
Basalt	0.5	2	$0.5 \cdot 10^4$	0.9	1.2	2.6

[1] $eU_{Th} = 0.45$ chemically determined Th, $eU_K = 2.5 \cdot 10^{-4}$ chemically determined K.

INSTRUMENTS AND FIELD PROCEDURE

Two types of prospecting instruments are available for radioactive surveys. These are the Geiger counter and the scintillation counter, both of which are constructed to detect γ radiation.

A radioactive deposit emits a spectrum of γ-rays, that is, γ-rays of a number of more or less well-separated, discrete frequencies. The higher the frequency of a γ-ray, the higher is its energy. It is customary to describe the spectrum in terms of energy levels, instead of frequencies or wavelengths as for the spectrum or ordinary light, and the energy is in turn expressed in million electron volt (MeV). One MeV is one million times the energy acquired by an electron in falling through a potential difference of one volt.

Either counter can be constructed in two principal modes. The *differential* spectrometer records only radiation falling within predetermined upper and lower energy limits. If the energies are very close to each other the detector is said to respond to a channel or line, and if they are wide apart it is said to respond to a window. The *integral* spectrometer is set to exclude radiation below a predetermined energy level, the threshold, and records all the radiation having energies greater than this level.

The choice of the detector will largely depend upon the purpose and the requirements of a survey. Channel spectrometers can identify individual radioactive nuclides while integral spectrometers will be found to be more useful for a reconnaissance survey.

The Geiger counter employs a sealed tube which has a thin central wire anode (positive electrode) surrounded by a cylindrical cathode (negative electrode). The tube is filled with some gas (usually a mixture of argon and alcohol or amyl acetate) and a high voltage is applied across the electrodes. Normally the gas is electrically nonconducting and no current passes through the tube but when γ radiation falls on the tube, the gas is ionized and the ions and electrons produced rush to the electrodes. This causes an electrical current pulse to pass through the tube. The pulse can be made audible in a headphone by means of suitable electronic circuits.

The scale of the Geiger counter reads the pulse rate in counts/min.

The scintillation counter, which has replaced the Geiger counter in much modern work, employs the fact that certain crystals emit a flash of light (scintillate) when they absorb γ rays. The scintillations can be detected by special devices, known as photomultiplier tubes, amplified and read on a meter.

While practically every γ ray entering the scintillation counter produces a tiny flash in the crystal, only about one in a hundred γ rays brings about ionization of the Geiger tube gas. Hence, the sensitivity of the scintillation counter to γ radiation is much higher than that of the Geiger counter. Scintillation counters have been constructed which differentiate the counts due to radiations of different energy and this, for example, enables one to distinguish between uranium and thorium deposits.

Ground radioactivity surveys are not difficult to carry out provided certain normal precautions are observed. In reconnaissance surveys, the observer walks slowly along the lines of measurement, stopping occasionally to take accurate readings. If there is evidence of radioactive occurrrence in the area, detailed measurements are made in a grid pattern at close intervals, say 5—10 m. The instrument is then placed on the ground or slightly above it and the count is read.

Owing to the γ rays in cosmic radiation and the atmosphere and owing to the general radioactivity of rocks, there is always a background count which must be determined in every area and subtracted from the readings. A count is not usually considered to be significant unless it is 2—3 times the background.

In the interpretation of radioactivity surveys it is common practice to plot the counts on a map and draw curves of equal radioactivity. The centres of high radioactivity can be immediately recognized if present, but their interpretation in terms of radioactive deposits must be made with due consideration to the local geology and topography. For example, small but almost outcropping pegmatite veins will often give a higher count than uranium or thorium occurrences lying at a greater depth. Purely geometrical effects must also be watched for. Thus, a valuable deposit may be shielded by rubble or by topographic irregularities and therefore fail to register a significant count.

A radioactivity map prepared from data cited by Eve and Keys

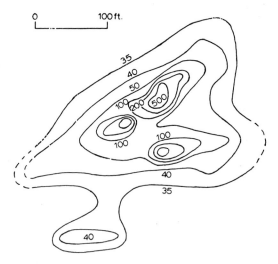

Fig.112. Radioactivity map of a claim in the Goldfields area, Canada; scintillo-meter count. (Source of data: Eve and Keys, 1956, p.317.)

(1956) is shown in Fig.112. Other examples of radioactive prospecting will be found in Brownell(1950) and Ridland (1945).

AIRBORNE RADIOACTIVE PROSPECTING

The scintillation counter has been adapted to the measurement of surface radioactivity from the air. A number of large thallium-activated sodium iodide crystals coupled in parallel are employed in such counters and the count is recorded automatically on a strip of moving paper. The crystals are shielded from cosmic radiation by lead screens, except for the faces pointing downward.

Aerial radioactivity surveys are often carried out in conjunction with airborne magnetic and electromagnetic surveys. As with ground surveys they provide information about the radioactivity of the ground within the uppermost 0.5–1 m only.

Considerable progress has been made in the quantitative estimates of the surface radioactivity and of the uranium content of the ground

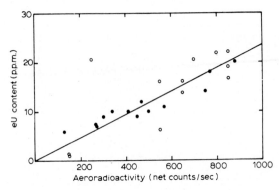

Fig.113. Equivalent uranium content of soil samples in Washington County and Texas Coastal Plain area as a function of aeroradioactivity. ○ = Washington County samples (eU content calculated). ● = Texas Coastal Plain samples (eU content by radiometric analysis). (After Moxham, 1963.)

from airborne measurements. The uranium content is expressed in these estimates as the equivalent uranium (eU) in parts per million. This includes, besides the uranium itself, the quantities of thorium and potassium converted into the quantity of uranium needed to produce the same γ-ray emission.

Fig.113, after Moxham(1963), shows the eU content of soil samples in Washington County and Texas Coastal Plain area against the aeroradioactivity (counts/sec) observed in these areas (apparently at a height of 2,500 ft.). The relation suggested is:

$$eU(p.p.m.) = 0.023 \times \text{aerial activity} \quad (counts/sec)$$

Moxham has further shown that the surface radioactivity in Washington County is linearly related to the aeroradioactivity and can also be estimated from it.

It should be noted that the above relation is only true for extended sources of radiation and that the estimated eU content of the ground is not to be considered reliable unless the sources are in radioactive equilibrium (see the section *Radioactive decay and radioactive equilibrium*, p.300). For example, Moxham believes that the scatter in the diagram of Fig.113 "...probably results mainly from radioactive disequilibrium through loss of the radon daughters." Furthermore, in all quantitative interpretation of radioactive anomalies aiming to calculate the size of the source or the grade x area product, the phenomenon of mechanical and chemical dispersion in the immediate vicinity of the orebody must be given consideration. The interested reader will find a very good account of the subject in Moxham (1964).

CHAPTER 11

Airborne Magnetic and Electromagnetic Methods

INTRODUCTION

It was mentioned in Chapter 10 that radioactive measurements can be carried out from the air. The same is true of magnetic and electro-magnetic measurements. The physical principles behind airborne work are, of course, the same as those behind ground work. The difference between the two types of work arises in the details of instrumentation and operation which, for airborne work, are much more complicated.

From the point of view of prospecting the principal and immediate aim of airborne measurements, as well as of ground ones, is the separation of areas which appear to be barren from those which appear to hold promise of ore. However, a great deal of regional structural information can also be obtained, particularly from airborne measurements. In this respect, airborne work has the advantage that it permits a rapid accumulation of data over very large areas. Consequently, the costs of an airborne survey per square kilometre or per line-kilometre are many times smaller than the costs of a corresponding ground survey, provided the area is sufficiently large. For small areas, fixed costs usually rule out the application of airborne methods. Moreover, aerial work can be carried out over terrain like jungles, swamps, mountains, glaciers etc., to which access may be difficult for ground survey-ing parties.

One, two or all the three types of airborne measurements can be made simultaneously at little extra cost and registered alongside each other, together with the flight data.

The costs of an airborne survey depend on a number of factors, such as the type of aircraft used (fixed-wing or helicopter), distance of survey area from the base, size of the area, line-spacing, navigation systems employed and so on.

Fixed-wing surveys generally cost less than helicopter surveys but there are conditions (mountainous areas) in which fixed-wing aircraft is useless for low flying and only a helicopter can serve the purpose.

Line-spacing is an important factor in the planning of an airborne survey. It must strike a proper balance between costs on the one hand and the anomaly detail desired on the other. It depends also on the survey height. For fairly great flight heights, say 1,000 ft., which are often employed in magnetic and radiometric surveys, the spacing is usually between 1/4 and 1 mile or 500 m and 2 km. Electromagnetic surveys must be carried out at rather low heights, say 30–150 m or 100–500 ft., and the spacing is then usually 125–250 m or 400–1,000 ft.

Navigation in airborne surveys can be carried out in different ways. If good aerial photographs are available and there is sufficient topo-

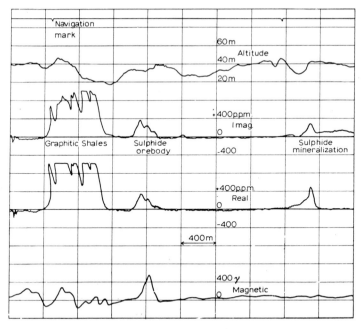

Fig.114. Record of an airborne survey. Profile approximately in the centre of the area in Fig.122. (Courtesy of BGAB.)

graphic detail (lakes, rivers, streams, land forms, roads etc.), it is quite convenient to check the course against topography, simultaneously making marks at suitable intervals in the aerial photograph, as well as on the data recording film, when the aircraft passes over a recognizable feature.

If aerial photographs are not available, a camera can be installed which takes an instantaneous photograph of a piece of the ground beneath the aircraft. If the exposures are synchronized appropriately with the data recording film, the flight path can be reconstructed from the mosaic of photos. However, even with a camera installation there may be the difficulty that the terrain has no or very few recognizable features. Navigation must then be based on electronic systems like Shoran, Lorac, Decca, Doppler, etc. Electronic navigation adds considerably to the survey costs.

Lastly, the height of the aircraft must be suitably determined continuously during flight and recorded alongside the geophysical data (Fig.114).

LIMITATIONS OF AIRBORNE SURVEYS

The primary limitation of airborne surveys is that, even with excellent navigational facilities, there is often considerable uncertainty in the position of geophysical indications obtained from the air. Further, airborne measurements necessarily imply a decrease in resolution which means that two neighbouring indications may tend to merge into one another giving the impression of only one indication, although this disadvantage is offset to some extent by the fact that the readings are continuous rather than discrete as in ground surveys; but, on the whole, there is a loss of anomaly detail in airborne work. It is, therefore, not generally advisable to undertake operations like exploratory drilling, trenching, shaft-sinking etc., on aerial indications without some sort of confirmatory work on the ground.

Finally, it must be realized that the depth penetration of airborne methods (below ground surface) is considerably less than that of the ground methods. The magnetic method is not at such a serious disadvantage in this respect but the electromagnetic methods (with one exception) are hardly capable of indicating orebodies below a maximum depth of, say, 50 m (150 ft.). One should realize that airborne methods "skim off the cream" as it were, while the really deep-lying ores or structures require ground methods for their detection.

MAGNETIC AIRBORNE WORK

Magnetometers for ground surveys, with the exception of the proton magnetometer, are designed for use on a stable platform and cannot therefore be employed in an aeroplane without cumbersome modifications. The instruments used in aerial work are actually modifications of the fluxgate or the proton type. The principle of the proton magnetometer is briefly described in Parasnis (1972, p.13); that of the fluxgate type is described below.

The intensity of magnetization in a magnetizable material such as iron increases with the magnetizing field, until a state of saturation is reached after which further increase of the field produces no increase in the magnetization. If the material is subjected to a sinusoidally alternating magnetic field of moderate strength, its magnetization will also be sinusoidal. The action of the fluxgate depends on the fact that in certain high permeability materials like permalloy, fields as weak as the earth's normal field (about 0.5 G) produce a state of near-saturation. If a small sinusoidal magnetizing field is then impressed, the magnetization of the permalloy does not follow a pure sine wave form but a distorted one with truncated tops. The amount of distortion can be exhibited by means of suitable electronic circuits, as the deflection of a meter or a pen, proportional to the ambient field.

Airborne magnetometers employ three mutually perpendicular fluxgate elements (small strips of permalloy) mounted in a gimbal system. Two of them serve as positioning elements automatically taking up orientations in which the magnetic field acting on them is zero. The third element is then necessarily in the direction of the maximum field strength, that is along the direction of the earth's total intensity vector. In this version, the fluxgate airborne instruments measure the anomalies (ΔT) in the magnitude of the total field. No information is obtained about the direction of the field.

Theoretically, vertical intensity measurements provide more information about the earth's magnetic field than total field ones (Parasnis 1972, pp.56–59), and airborne magnetometers for vertical field measurements should prove to be of very great advantage. Unfortunately, the accuracy at present attainable in such airborne measurements (about 50 γ) is much inferior to the accuracy of total field measurements (about 1–2 γ).

Airborne magnetic measurements must be corrected for the drift of the magnetometer and for diurnal variation. The latter correction is, however, needed in case of exceptionally accurate surveys, but a check on the state of the geomagnetic field must always be kept and measurements discontinued in case of severe magnetic storms.

When all the flight lines have been measured the values of the magnetic field are read off (nowadays mostly by means of automatic data processing machines) at suitable points on each recorded profile. The values are plotted on a map and isoanomaly lines are then drawn in the usual manner.

The aeromagnetic maps obtained with fluxgate instruments show contours of *anomalies* above an arbitrary zero, the earth's (normal) total field being compensated during measurement. The maps with proton magnetometers show lines along which the magnitude of the *total field* has definite values. Such lines are often called isodynamic lines. Anomaly maps in this case will have to be obtained by subtracting the normal field, as a separate operation.

EXAMPLES

The applications of airborne measurements of the magnetic field are very diverse and are best illustrated by examples.

Fig.115 shows a case, after Lang (1960), where aeromagnetic measurements succeed in distinguishing a weakly magnetic granodiorite intrusive massive from highly magnetic lavas. The boundary between

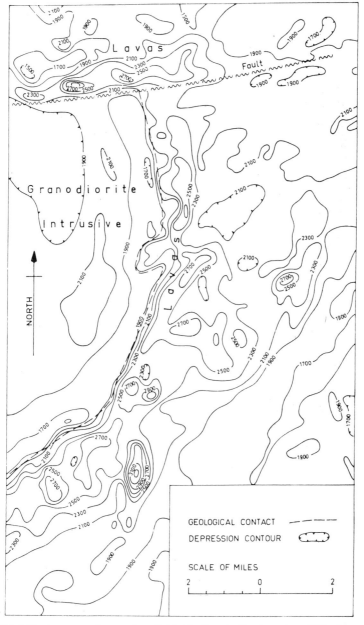

Fig.115. Aeromagnetic map in a district in Canada. Contours in γ. (After Lang, 1960.)

the two formations is recognized on the map from the crowding of magnetic contours along it or, in other words, from a sharp gradient in the field intensity (cf. Chapter 3, section *Magnetic effects of broad zones*, p.59). Within the lava formation there are many tops or magnetic "highs" which indicate local and variable concentrations of magnetic material and/or variations in the magnetization intensity.

An almost east—west running feature in the north part of the map is indicative of a fault which occurs there.

It should be noted that the pattern of magnetic anomalies over the lavas is very irregular suggesting that the formation is not uniform. Large areas of supposedly uniform rocks, igneous as well as sedimentary, are often found in this way to be magnetically inhomogeneous, although surface geological observations may reveal no obvious petrographic differences.

Igneous dikes may show up on an aeromagnetic map. Fig.116, due to H.F. Scott, shows the effect of olivine and quartz diabase dikes in sedimentary strata. The north—east trending olivine diabase is associated with relatively high magnetic anomalies while the north—south running quartz diabase dikes are indicated, but barely, by the bulging of the isoanomaly lines in this direction. Had the sedimentary host rocks been slightly more magnetic, however, the effect of the quartz diabase would probably not be recognized.

Many other geological situations exist in which aeromagnetic maps provide information about regional trends, dips, fold axes etc. Examples of aeromagnetic anomalies on orebodies occur in sections *Example of an airborne survey* (p.333) and *Examples of the combination of geophysical methods* (Chapter 12, p.342).

INTERPRETATION OF AEROMAGNETIC MAPS

The basic ideas in the interpretation of aeromagnetic maps are not very different from those in the interpretation of ground maps. Thus, the main feature on which attention should be focussed to start with is the "texture" of the anomaly field, that is the trends, sizes, configurations etc, of the various anomaly centres, the occurrence of

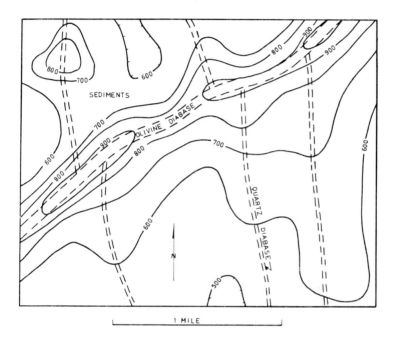

Fig.116. Mapping of igneous dikes from aeromagnetic data. Contours in γ.
(After Scott, 1955.)

sharp gradients etc. These features should be correlated as far as possible with known geological observations.

Indications of dip and plunge can also be obtained from aeromagnetic anomalies but particular attention must be paid to the effect of transverse magnetization of the causative bodies in the earth's field. Also, the possible effect of the remanent magnetization of rocks and ores, which can completely upset inferences, if neglected, should be constantly borne in mind (Balsley and Buddington, 1958; Green, 1960; Bath, 1962; Hood, 1963; Jahren, 1963; Carmichael, 1964). In magnetic latitudes which are not too low, many of the qualitative considerations in Chapter 3, concerning vertical field anomalies, may be applied without serious error to total field anomalies.

Aeromagnetic anomalies can be subjected to quantitative interpretations, just as ground anomalies can, for estimating the depth, length, size, dip etc., of the features causing them but this requires recourse to special diagrams and charts, since the present-day airborne magnetometers measure only the total intensity of the earth's field so that the formulas in Chapter 3 are not directly applicable.

It will be beyond the scope of this book to include an exhaustive catalogue of total-field master curves meeting a variety of situations. Such curves have been published by Zietz and Henderson (1956), Henderson and Zietz (1957), Gay (1963), Henderson and Wilson (1964), Vacquier et al. (1951) and others.

Two sets of curves, which will be found to be useful in a large

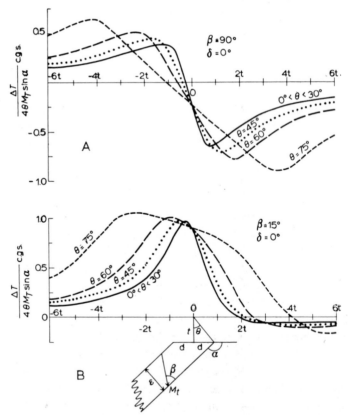

Fig.117. Master curves for calculating total-field magnetic anomalies above sheet-like bodies. See Appendix 9 for explanation. (After Bath, 1962.)

number of cases arising in practice, are, however, given in Fig.117. The figure is drawn after Bath (1962) and can be used to calculate total-field anomalies along profiles crossing sheet-like magnetic formations of very great strike-length and depth extent. The manner of its employment is indicated in Appendix 9.

Fig.118 shows a comparison of calculated and observed total-intensity curves across three profiles crossing the Biwabik Iron Formation (Ridge area) in Minnesota, U.S.A. The anomalies directly above the outcrop are negative because the component of total magnetization parallel to the formation is directed "upwards". As the earth's field in the area is directed almost at right angles to the ore sheet, the induced magnetization parallel to the ore is weak, of the order of 15 A/m, and the total magnetization (average 110 A/m) is almost entirely due to strong remanence, whose component parallel to the sheet is directed "upwards".

AIRBORNE ELECTROMAGNETIC METHODS

Airborne electromagnetic methods may be primarily classified into *active* and *passive* systems. In active systems the transmitter as well as the receiver is airborne; in passive systems only the receiver is airborne and the primary field source is either stationary on the ground or consists of natural or artificial fields (e.g., afmag, VLF) due to distant sources, over which the designer has essentially no control. The classification is applicable to ground systems also. We shall first treat the active systems and deal with the passive systems later (p.327).

In principle, the active airborne e.m. systems are nothing but moving source–receiver ground systems lifted up into the air. However, the technical problems associated with this project are intricate and the following brief comments do far from justice to the ingenuity with which they have been solved by different workers.

Firstly, measurements at discrete points are not possible in airborne systems so that continuously recording instruments must be employed which respond instantaneously to the input signal.

Secondly, it is necessary to realize the following. The primary field

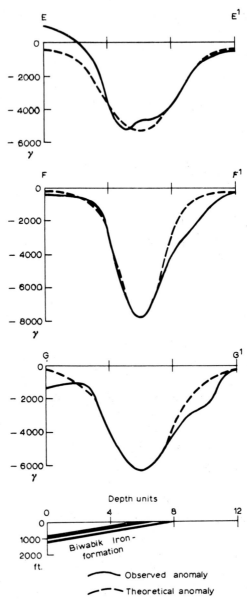

Fig.118. Calculated and observed aeromagnetic anomalies along three profiles across the Biwabik Iron Formation, U.S.A. (After Bath, 1962.)

of a transmitting coil falls off inversely as the cube of the distance from the coil. The secondary field of the currents induced in a sub-surface conductor is proportional to the primary field at it and suffers a further decrease in returning to the receiving coil, at a rate somwhere between the inverse first and third powers of the distance depending upon the geometry of the conductor. Therefore the signal will vary at a rate between that represented by the inverse third and the sixth powers of the height of an airborne system above a conductor or, more properly, by an inverse power of the "height—coil separation" ratio[1]. Consequently, relatively small increases in the flying height, such as might be necessitated by terrain conditions, are likely to con-siderably reduce the signals to be recorded. Hence, the sensitivity of the recording instruments must be high.

Finally, the relative movement of the coils of a moving source—receiver system produces a variation in the primary field at the receiver, which may be misinterpreted as an anomaly. To illustrate the problems that have to be overcome in airborne e.m. systems using fixed coil distance we may note the following.

The sensitivity aimed at in the determination of the secondary field at the receiver coil in many systems is 10 p.p.m. of the primary field. If the coils are separated by 10 m, a change of only one third of a *millimetre* in the separation alters the field at the receiver by 10 p.p.m. Complicated compensation techniques must, therefore, be devised to correct for such minute changes which easily arise due to the flexing of the mountings or wings, vibrations of the aircraft, temperature changes etc.

CLASSIFICATION OF ACTIVE AIRBORNE E.M. SYSTEMS

A rather great variety of active airborne electromagnetic systems have been proposed differing in the aircraft employed, the normal flight height, frequencies, coil separations etc. The systems are often known by the name of the contracting company or the organization which

---

[1] The variation is according to the inverse first to third power for ratios less than about 0.7.

developed them. This is unfortunate because it tends to obscure the fact that many of these systems are identical to each other, except for relatively minor details like the choice of frequency. However, there is a rational scheme of classification and this is shown in Fig.119A.

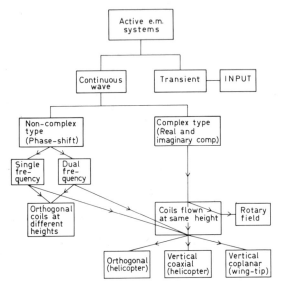

Fig.119A. Classification of active airborne electromagnetic systems.

Fig.119B. Vertical coplanar coils, with axes in the flight direction, mounted on the wing tips of a small aircraft. (Courtesy of BGAB.)

It will be seen that the various systems fall broadly into only two classes.

In the class of systems in which the transmitter and the receiver are flown at the same height, being mounted on the wingtips, on a beam under a helicopter, or in two different planes flying in tandem, the positions of the coils with respect to each other are truly fixed, except for possible small changes in the two-plane operation. These systems may, therefore, also be referred to as fixed-separation systems.

In the systems in which the transmitter and the receiver are flown at different heights, the receiver trails behind the plane at the end of a cable, usually about 500 ft. long. The orientations of the coils with respect to each other are only nominally fixed in these systems because turbulence in the air often causes the receiver at the end of the cable to dive and plunge. For a reason which will appear later these systems may be referred to as phase-measuring or quadrature systems.

FIXED-SEPARATION SYSTEMS

The coil distance in the fixed-separation systems depends very much upon the type of aircraft used. The Canadian Aero Otter system uses a spacing of 62 ft. (19 m) between two vertical coplanar coils mounted on the wing-tips, while the same configuration is employed by the Boliden Mining Company of Sweden with a spacing of 13 m (43 ft.). The latter is illustrated in Fig.119B. The Canadian Aero Sikorsky system employs vertical, coaxial coils separated by 60 ft., while exactly the same configuration is mounted by the American Metals Company below a Bell helicopter with a spacing of 20 ft. between the coils.

The choice of fixed-wing or helicopter aircraft for carrying an e.m. system is an economic and practical question that has little to do with the scientific principles behind airborne electromagnetic prospecting. For example, the vertical, coaxial configuration just referred to has also been used with the coils mounted on a fixed-wing aircraft.

A note must be added here concerning the so-called rotary field method because this differs radically from other fixed-separation systems. The transmitter of the rotary field method consists of two mutually orthogonal coils. The fields transmitted by the two coils are of the same frequency but $90°$ out of phase with each other, that is, the one attains its maxima and minima a quarter period earlier than the other. The receiver, mounted in another plane, likewise consists of two orthogonal coils and what is measured is the difference of amplitudes and phases of the fields picked up by the two receiver coils separately. The sensitivity of the system is about 0.3–0.5% (3,000–5,000 p.p.m.) of the primary field strength at the receiver. It can be shown that reasonably small changes in the distance between the .planes (150–300 m) do not affect the field components at the receiver. More details of the system may be found elsewhere (Törnquist, 1958; Hedström and Parasnis, 1958, 1959).

The frequencies currently used in the various fixed-separation e.m. outfits apparently range from 320 to 4,000 c/sec but higher or lower frequencies could also be used. From the geophysical point of view, it is desirable that fixed-separation airborne systems be constructed in which the choice of frequency is flexible, to suit the overburden conditions in an area, but such a development is not at present within sight.

The fixed-separation systems measure the real as well as the imaginary components of the field. As we saw in section *Real and imaginary components* (p.110), where the significance of these components was explained, the ratio Re/Im for the secondary field provides an approximate measure of the quality of a subsurface conductor, or rather a measure of the product "electric conductivity x size". This information, although subject to some uncertainty, is valuable for the planning for further geophysical work on an indication.

PHASE-MEASURING OR QUADRATURE SYSTEMS

In the systems in which the transmitter is mounted in an aeroplane and the receiver towed at the end of a long cable, a registration of the real or in-phase component is out of the question. The reason is that the real component constitutes a measure of the strength of the electromagnetic field picked up by the receiver and the strength varies violently when the transmitter—receiver orientation alters on account of the movements of the receiver due to air turbulence.

On the other hand, the *phase* of the field picked up by the receiver, with respect to the phase of the primary field, represents merely a difference between the times at which the alternating transmitting and receiving fields attain their respective maxima or minima, and is therefore essentially independent of the variations in the coil-orientation. Hence, in the systems of the second class it is found practicable to record only the phase shift of the field acting on the receiver (cf. section *The phase angle and the vector diagram*, p.108).

Of course, a variety of transmitter—receiver orientations can be conceived for phase-measuring systems but only two of them seem to have been utilized in practice.

In the Aerophysics Anson system (fixed-wing), both coils are in a vertical plane, parallel to the flight direction, but at different heights and the phase-shift is measured at a single frequency (140 c/sec). Measurements of phase-shift at a single frequency cannot tell whether a conductor detected is good or poor because, as will be clear from Fig.120 showing the variation of phase-shift with conductivity, a given

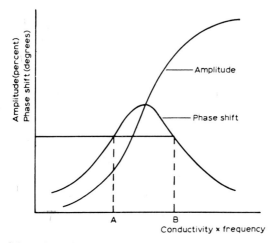

Fig.120. Schematic variation of the amplitude and phase of the secondary electromagnetic field with the electric conductivity.

phase-shift may be caused by either of two types of conductors, a good one (*b*) and a poor one (*a*).

To overcome the lack of information in the single frequency system, a dual frequency method has been tried. This employs, however, a horizontal transmitter coil and a vertical receiver coil trailing at the end of a 500 ft. long cable. The phase-shift responses are measured at 400 and 2,300 c/sec and the ratio "low-frequency response/high-frequency response" provides a measure of the conductivity, the ratio being greater than 1.0 for good conductors and less than 1.0 for poor ones. The sensitivity of the system is about 0.05—0.10 degree, or about 0.1—0.2% (1,000—2,000 p.p.m.), a phase-shift of 1° being the equivalent of 1.75% of the primary field.

A limitation of purely phase-measuring systems is that very good conductors (for example, massive sulphide bodies with considerable pyrrhotite, e.g., that in Fig.50B) *embedded in non-conducting host rock* produce extremely small, almost zero, phase shifts. Such ores will therefore not be detected by phase measurements alone. However, this limitation is often off-set in practice if the host rock (or the overburden) has an appreciable conductivity because, in this case, phase-displaced secondary currents are induced in the host rock (or the overburden) also. These are collected by the ore conductor which then produces a phase anomaly manifesting its presence despite its high electric conductivity and small intrinsic phase shift.

Fig.121A shows typical responses of different systems to a vertical sheet-like conductor.

INPUT

If instead of a continuous, sinusoidal electromagnetic field, a transient field is generated by a sudden pulse of electric current in a transmitting coil, it induces transient currents in a conductor in its path. When the transient primary field disappears, the currents continuously decay on account of the resistance of the conductor and finally vanish altogether. Their secondary electromagnetic field is naturally also transient and induces a continuously decaying voltage in a receiving coil. The greater the resistance of the conductor, the faster the decay, while in a good conductor the currents can keep on circulating for a longer time and the decay of the receiver voltage is also slower.

The above idea has been used by Barringer Research Corporation of Canada in devising their INPUT (*In*duced *Pu*lse *T*ransient) method of electromagnetic prospecting.

A large wire-loop is strung from the aircraft nose, around each wing tip and beneath the tail. Pulses of the order of two kilowatt are sent through this horizontal transmitter several hundred times a second. A receiver coil trailing on a cable, up to 150 m long, picks up the decaying signal from the ground conductors, during the period between two consecutive pulses. The receiver voltage is sampled at a series of different preselected times (channels) from about 200 μsec after the cessation of a pulse to about 2,000 μsec, and the signals on the different channels are registered alongside each other (Fig.121B).

The system thus effectively registers the decay curve of the secondary field. A low late-channel signal, relative to the first channel, indicates a rapid decay and a poor conductor. It is essential throughout to refer channel strengths to one single channel (usually number 1), in assessing the rate of decay, because the absolute value of the signal depends on the primary field actually acting on the conductor, for the inevitable variations in which no correction is possible.

The record in the left-hand part of Fig.121B was obtained across the Aitik pyrite and chalcopyrite deposit, the resistivity survey on which is illustrated by Fig.70A. The rate of decay indicates a medium conductor. On the right-hand side is the record across another deposit in the area and the slow rate of decay here indicates a low resistivity. It is also of interest to note that a buried bare cable gives a distinct INPUT indication. However, the fast rate of decay in this case is not indicative of the resistivity of the cable material itself (copper), but the resistivity of the overburden, the transient currents in which are "sucked up" by the cable.

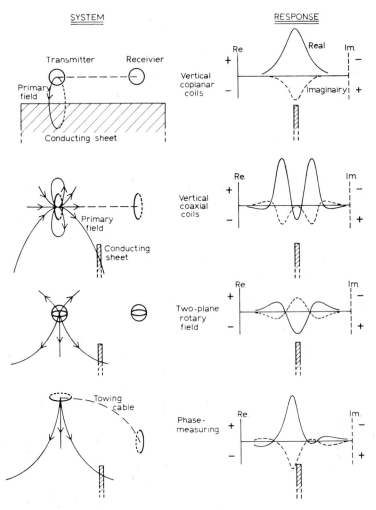

Fig.121A. Typical responses of different airborne e.m. systems to a vertical sheet-like conductor.

PASSIVE AIRBORNE E.M. SYSTEMS

As mentioned previously the afmag and VLF methods (p.317) fall into this class. Both these systems have been adapted to airborne

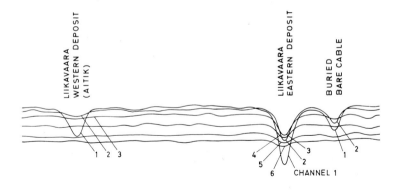

Fig.121B. Airborne INPUT profile in northern Sweden. (Courtesy BGAB.)

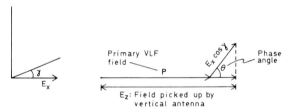

Fig.121C. Radiophase method, electric vectors.

work. The principles involved are as in ground work and need no repetition here. The technique of measurement differs, however, because of operational difficulties. In the airborne version of the Afmag method the natural audio-frequency field is picked up by two mutually orthogonal coils. The axis of each makes nominally an angle of 45° with the horizontal. The axes lie in the same vertical plane. If A is the amplitude of the magnetic field vector and θ its tilt from the horizontal, the voltage in one coil is proportional to $A\cos(45-\theta)$ and that in the other coil to $A\cos(45+\theta)$. The ratio f of these two voltages is $\cos(45-\theta)/\cos(45+\theta)$ and after expanding the cosines, it follows that:

$$\tan\theta = \frac{f-1}{f+1}$$

which gives the tilt.

In the airborne radiophase method which utilizes VLF fields, not only the magnetic vector but also the electric vector associated with the VLF electromagnetic wave is sensed.

If we consider Fig.53B we shall see that the electric vector at any point is normally vertical and thus perpendicular to the magnetic vector, which is horizontal, and both the vectors are perpendicular to the direction of propagation of the VLF wave which is radially outward from the transmitting antenna. In the vicinity of a conductor there also appears a small horizontal electric field due to the secondary wave emitted by the conductor. Ideally this field could be measured by simply connecting a receiver antenna, a horizontal wire of suitable length, to a voltage detector. However, the primary vertical field is 100–200 times larger than the secondary horizontal electric field and even very small departures of the receiving antenna from the horizontal will cause a "spurious" signal in it, essentially the component of the vertical field along the antenna. As such departures are inevitable during flight, a measurement of simply the electric field in the receiving antenna is meaningless.

The radiophase method obtains a measure of the horizontal electric field by using one vertical and one (nominally) horizontal antenna as follows.

Suppose that the receiving antenna makes an angle γ with the horizontal (Fig.121C). Then the component of a horizontal field E_x is $E_x \cos\gamma$ along the antenna. This field is not, in general, in phase with the field E_z picked up by the vertical antenna (called a whip-antenna). If θ is the phase difference between the primary VLF field P and $E_x\cos\gamma$ then we see from Fig.121C that the amplitude of the component of $E_x\cos\gamma$, $90°$ (one quarter period) out-of-phase with E_z is $E_x\cos\gamma \sin\theta$ (see pp.108–109).

The radiophase method measures this component as a fraction of the voltage E_z in the (strictly vertical) whip-antenna, that is, the quantity $E_x \cos\gamma \sin\theta/E_z$. This is treated as a measure of the secondary field E_x. It should be noted further that $E_z = P + E_x\cos\gamma \cos\theta \approx P$, since E_x is much smaller than P, and may be treated as being constant.

A similar approach is employed in measuring the *magnetic* field.

DEPTH-PENETRATION AND EFFICIENCY OF AIRBORNE E.M. SYSTEMS

There has been a great deal of discussion concerning the depth-penetration of airborne electromagnetic systems and the question is still not satisfactorily settled. The question is too complicated to be exhaustively treated here but a few remarks will help the reader to understand its nature. Reference should also be made to section *Depth-penetration of electromagnetic methods* (p.150) in reading the following.

The principal factors governing the depth down to which an e.m. system can "see" are: (*1*) recording sensitivity, (*2*) coil separation, (*3*) flight height, (*4*) frequency, (*5*) near-surface effects, and (*6*) conductor geometry and conductivity.

The depth-penetration is greater the higher the recording sensitivity but it is also greater, the larger the coil-separation. Further, other factors being the same, a system that can be flown nearer to the ground has an inherent advantage over one that must be flown at great heights. This puts the cable-towed-receiver systems at a great disadvantage because they are normally flown at heights of 500–600 ft. (150–180 m), or more, in order that the receiver at the end of the 500 ft. long cable may not hit the ground in case of turbulence. The fixed-separation systems can be flown as low as 30–50 m (single plane) or 60–100 m (two-plane) under most conditions.

The effect of superficial conductors is greater the higher the frequency. Hence low frequency systems have a better depth penetration than high frequency ones. However, it is probably safe to say that the depth-penetration is not too critically dependent upon the choice of frequency, within the range, say, 300–900 c/sec.

The depth-penetration, taking into account only the four purely instrumental factors (sensitivity, spread; flight height and frequency), can be estimated from laboratory experiments on metal models. We shall call this the ideal depth-penetration. Its magnitude for various systems is shown in Table VIII, assuming that the conductor to be detected is a vertical sheet of great length and medium resistivity embedded in a non-conducting host rock.

However, the effective depth-penetration of a system depends on

TABLE VIII

DEPTH-PENETRATION OF VARIOUS AIRBORNE E.M. SYSTEMS

System	Flight height	Sensitivity	Ideal depth-penetration for vertical sheet[1]	Approx. figure for geological noise	Effective depth-penetration for vertical sheet[2]
Fixed separation					
20 m (60 ft.) (single plane)	30–50 m	10–50 p.p.m.	80–120 m	50–100 p.p.m.	60–80 m
250 m (800 ft.) (two plane)	70–100 m	0.3–0.5%	200 m	1–2%	100–140 m
Phase-measuring[3] dual frequency (150 m)	150 m (500 ft.)	0.05°–0.1° (0.1–0.2%)	50–80 m	0.5–0.7%	20–30 m
	100 m (300 ft.)		100–150 m		50–60 m

[1] Identical with effective depths in may areas (e.g., polar regions).
[2] These figures and their proportions depend essentially on the geologic noise in the area and the position of the conductor.
[3] Receiver on towed cable.

yet another factor, namely the more or less random electromagnetic variations (geologic noise) caused by local changes in the conductivity and dimensions of the near-surface layers (soils, moraine, watertable, clays etc.). To be recognized as such, indications of ore must stand significantly above the geologic noise which depends, apart from the properties of the ground, on the transmitter–receiver separation and the flight height. The smaller the separation the better does the system pick up stray, local variations; the greater the flight height the smaller the anomalies from deep conductors in relation to those of near-surface layers.

The geologic-noise levels of various systems and their estimated effective depth-penetrations are also given in Table VIII. The conclusions in this table are based upon model experiments made at the ABEM Company of Stockholm, the Boliden Mining Co., Boliden (Sweden) and on data concerning the dual frequency system published by Paterson (1961).

It is interesting to note that, although the ideal depth-penetration of the towed-receiver dual frequency system is about the same as that of a 20 m-fixed-separation system, its actual or effective depth-penetration may be considerably less. This is due partly to the great height at which the towed-receiver system must, of necessity, be flown.

In a review article on airborne electromagnetic systems, Pemberton (1962) quotes the depth-penetration of practically all airborne systems as 200–275 ft. (60–85 m) below ground surface but he gives no hint of how the estimate was arrived at. Perhaps, the estimate refers to the ideal depth-penetration, that is, Pemberton does not seem to have given adequate consideration to the geologic noise. Even then it is difficult to reconcile Pemberton's depth-penetration estimates with the results of model experiments on which Table VIII is based.

Finally, the geometry of a conductor also affects the maximum depth at which the conductor may lie and yet respond sufficiently well to an airborne system. Clearly, the bigger the conductor the greater the depth at which it may lie and yet be detected by an electromagnetic system. However, it seems very difficult to formulate general rules in this respect since orebodies occur in all shapes and sizes, and it does not seem profitable to pursue this aspect further here.

The depth-penetration is not the only criterion of the electro-magnetic efficiency of an airborne system. Another important criterion is the minimum size that a conducting orebody must have, to be detected by the system which is used. Here, the advantage rests with systems using small coil-separations.

If the coil-separation is small an orebody need not have a very large size before it gives a relatively strong indication. If the separation is large, the dimensions of the conductor must also be large. As a rough rule, we may say that for a vertical sheet-conductor to be detected, its length must be at least $1/4-1/2$ the transmitter—receiver distance. It follows also that systems using very small coil-separations can map more detail than those using relatively large separations but, again, the spacing of flight lines will also determine the amount of detail that can be mapped.

INTERPRETATION OF AIRBORNE ELECTROMAGNETIC ANOMALIES

As with magnetic measurements the interpretation of airborne electro-magnetic results can hardly be said to differ from that of ground ones and any difference there may be arises principally because of the large scale of the airborne survey.

Information concerning the length and strike of a conductor can be derived more or less directly from a perusal of a map of airborne anomalies. For the determination of the dip and plunge of a conductor it is more profitable to study the recorded profiles of anomalies rather than the plan-map. Generally, these parameters are estimated from the distortion in the shape of a profile which would have a known shape if the dip were vertical. For example, a symmetrical profile may be distorted into an asymmetric one. However, such determinations require a good knowledge of the response of the system in question to conductors of different geometry and attitude. Laboratory model curves are of great assistance in this respect. Unfortunately no adequate collections of such curves have so far been published except, to some extent, for the dual frequency system (Paterson, 1961).

Estimates of conductor depths in electromagnetic work cannot be based on half-widths of anomaly curves, as they can be in magnetic measurements. The principle of e.m. depth determination, where such a determination can be validly made, is rather different. It can be shown that two electromagnetic observational quantities, for example, real-component and imaginary-component anomalies or low-frequency and high-frequency response, suffice in certain simple cases of conductor geometry to determine the depth as well as the conductivity x size product. However, such an interpretation needs suitable model experiment curves (e.g., Fig.48B).

In following an electromagnetic anomaly from one profile to the adjacent, particular attention must be paid to the altimeter record to ensure that variations in the anomaly magnitude or eventually a disappearance of the anomaly is not due to altitude variations. This caution applies to the interpretation of magnetic and radioactive surveys also.

It should be borne in mind while interpreting the data of electromagnetic methods, whether airborne or ground, that quite worthless but fairly good conductors like lakes, marshes, rivers, clay pockets, thin ore veins, fractures and fissures in the bedrocks etc., also tend to give rise to strong indications. These can be eliminated sometimes by a study of the terrain map and by combining the electromagnetic results with aeromagnetic ones, although the elimination may not always be possible beyond doubt.

These few comments should make it clear that the interpretation of airborne electromagnetic anomalies is a matter of experience as well as collation with data other than the purely electromagnetic ones.

EXAMPLE OF AN AIRBORNE SURVEY

Fig.122A is a map of the real-component anomalies measured over a small part of the Skellefteå ore district of Sweden. It was obtained with a fixed-separation system consisting of vertical, coplanar coils mounted on the wing tips of a small aircraft, with axes perpendicular to the flight direction, the separation being 13 m. The system was

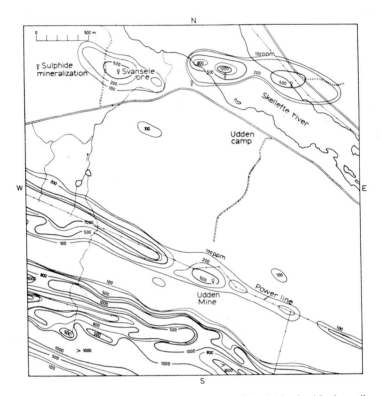

Fig.122A. Map of airborne real-component anomalies obtained with the coil system in Fig.119B. Contours in p.p.m. Frequency 3,500 c/sec. Flight direction perpendicular to strike. Mean ground clearance 30 m. Area: part of the Skellefteå orefield, northern Sweden.

flown in the north—south direction, i.e., approximately at right angles to the geological strike at a ground clearance of 30 m.

The contours represent anomalies in parts per million of the primary field at the receiver. Contours below 100 p.p.m. are not drawn as they are judged to represent the total noise, instrumental plus geological.

Perhaps the most striking feature of the map is the pair of anomaly belts in the south within which the anomalies reach values of more than 1,000 p.p.m. Both these belts correspond to graphitic shales. These shales often serve as guiding horizons in the Skellefteå ore field.

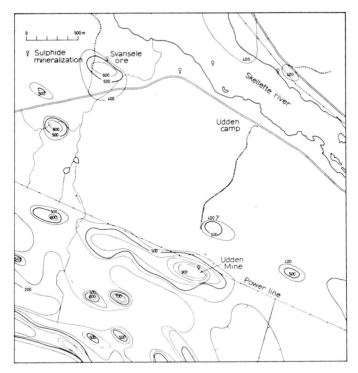

Fig.122B. Total-intensity aeromagnetic anomaly map of the area in part A. Contours in γ. (Courtesy of BGAB.)

The southernmost one continues, with approximately the same trend and undiminished maximum anomaly, for several tens of kilometers to the east as well as the west.

The adjoining, more northern belt, is not as continuous although it can be traced to the east and the west. The anomalies within it are sometimes due to sulphide ores, one of which is marked on the map. The gravity anomaly on this ore was, incidentally, discussed in section *Gravity measurements on the Udden sulphide body (Sweden)*, p.266. A power line happens to run almost parallel to this belt within the area of the map and is the cause of the weak anomalies (100–200 p.p.m.) in the eastern part of the belt. The strong anomalies in the west, however, owe their origin to graphitic shales, one piece of evidence being that the anomalies and the power line diverge completely from each other immediately west of the western boundary of the figure. Another piece of evidence is that the strong electromagnetic anomalies are associated with magnetic ones but the weak eastern ones are not.

In the north there are three distinct anomaly centres, all of which correspond to strong sulphide mineralization, one in fact to the Svansele orebody discussed on p.145.

Fig.122B is a map of airborne magnetic anomalies over the same area. It is evident that the graphitic shales are associated with magnetic disturbances, caused no doubt by pyrrhotite impregnation. The pattern of magnetic anomalies shows, however, that the pyrrhotite distribution is highly irregular.

Of the three electromagnetic indications in the north, one (that over the Svansele ore) is associated with magnetic anomalies, which checks well with the fact that the Svansele orebody is known to contain considerable pyrrhotite. The southerly dip of the ore shows up clearly in the aeromagnetic indication (cf. Fig.51).

Several instances will be recognized of magnetic indications without corresponding electromagnetic ones. These probably represent poor disseminations of pyrrhotite and magnetite.

CHAPTER 12

Combination of Geophysical Methods

INTRODUCTION

Every geophysical method has its own limitations in the type of information it provides concerning the hidden masses below the ground. A combination of two or more geophysical methods generally yields further information and may thereby help to reduce the ambiguity inherent in the interpretation of geophysical data. In fact, the less is known about the geology of an area the greater the need for obtaining extra geophysical information.

It is not possible to formulate guiding rules about the number or type of different geophysical methods that should be used in a particular prospecting problem. The decision will depend very much upon local topographical, geological and mineralogical conditions and, not least, upon economic considerations. Experience and judgment are probably far better guides in this respect than any number of pre-set rules, but a few remarks of a general character should indicate the nature of the extra information sought by combining geophysical methods and comparing their results.

For example, magnetic anomalies prove the existence of magnetic masses but cannot tell whether the masses are magnetite or pyrrhotite-bearing bodies. If an additional self-potential survey shows a strong anomaly, the presence of pyrrhotite may reasonably be suspected.

However, an absence of a self-potential anomaly will not necessarily indicate magnetite in the above hypothetical case, because the existence of SP effects requires rather special conditions even if sulphides be present. In particular, the mineralization must lie at a very shallow depth. If it lies at a considerable depth SP surveys will not reveal it so that the ambiguity between magnetite and pyrrhotite will persist. If an electromagnetic survey is then made and shows an anomaly, a conductor like a pyrrhotite–pyrite mass may be suspected (although magnetic masses also show electromagnetic anomalies but mostly of a special character).

However, an electromagnetic survey often does not reveal all the conductors if they happen to lie very close to each other which, on the other hand, a resistivity survey will generally do.

In electrical mapping there is sometimes a doubt as to whether certain strong indications are caused by conductors like zones of crushed rock or by sulphide impregnation. If a magnetic anomaly is obtained at the same place the latter alternative becomes more plausible since many sulphide bodies contain pyrrhotite (and even magnetite) as an accessory mineral.

Again, a strong electromagnetic anomaly can be caused by thin sulphide conductors as well as thick ones, and a gravimeter survey may be able to distinghuish between the two possibilities.

Similarly a magnetic survey may be decisive if electrical mapping has indicated a structure with high resistivity and the question arises whether it is a dike of diabase or gabbro or some other rock, because the former are often strongly magnetic.

Zones of serpentinite can be located magnetically but the pyrrhotite-bearing sulphide impregnations, which are often found on their margins, will not be distinguishable magnetically from the serpentinite. An electromagnetic survey may be of help in locating the sulphides if they are present.

Obviously, instances of the above type can be multiplied.

THE LOCATION OF GEOPHYSICAL INDICATIONS

Having made surveys with several methods, we should naturally want to know how their results are to be compared with each other. More specifically we want to compare the "indication" obtained with the different methods.

Clearly, it is meaningless to compare, for example, a magnetic anomaly (γ) at a point with the electric self-potential (mV) at it because the two are quite different physical quantities. What we can, and do, compare is the *pattern* of geophysical anomalies obtained by one method with that obtained by another. It is the pattern that tells us where a subsurface mass is likely to lie, how deep it is buried and so on.

One way to compare the patterns is to draw an isoanomaly map on a transparent paper and place it on a corresponding map obtained with another method. Another way is to draw profiles in the two methods, one below the other, or in different colours. If the anomaly patterns are very similar to each other it would be plausible to assume that the causative body or set of bodies is the same in either case. Otherwise, the masses responsible for the two kinds of anomalies must be more or less distinct. For instance, if the magnetic maximum on a profile does not coincide with the electromagnetic indication this may be because the orebody has more or less well separated pyrrhotite and pyrite zones, the former giving the magnetic, the latter the electromagnetic indication.

At this stage we are led to the following question: what features on an anomaly map or profile obtained with a particular method correspond to those obtained with another method?

Because the shapes of anomalies obtained with different methods are not exactly alike, and it is desirable to have some short-cut to the comparison. In some methods we have minima over the ore masses, in others we get maxima, still others show inflexion points and so on.

Fortunately, the question can be answered in a rather simple manner, despite the diversity of the methods and procedures employed in geophysical work. In the following we shall confine attention to profiles rather than to isoanomaly maps but the reasoning can be extended to cover the latter case.

All geophysical anomalies can be broadly divided into two classes: the symmetric and the antisymmetric. Their characteristics are as follows.

An (ideal) symmetric anomaly has two identically shaped halves, any of which can be brought into coincidence with the other by means of a single reflection (in the axis of symmetry). The anomaly profiles on the left-hand side in Fig.123 are all symmetric ones, the dotted line being the axis of symmetry.

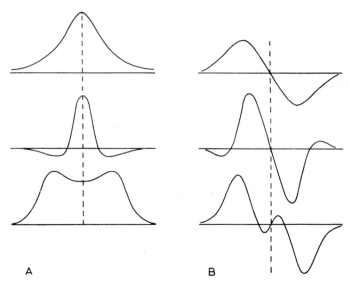

Fig.123. A. Symmetric anomaly profiles. B. Antisymmetric anomaly profiles.

An (ideal) antisymmetric anomaly also has two identically shaped halves, but to bring any one of them into coincidence with the other, *two* reflections are needed, one in the *x*-axis and the other in the *y*-axis. The anomaly profiles on the right-hand side in Fig.123 are antisymmetric. A good practical example of the somewhat complicated shape of the bottom curve will be found in Parasnis (1972, p.37).

Of course, these ideal shapes are not met with in practice, although it is surprising how often excellent approximations to them *are* observed. Anyway, an actual anomaly profile can generally be referred unambiguously to one of the two classes, disregarding the obvious impossibility in case it is highly disturbed by "noise". This is true, even if the profile departs considerably from the ideal shape, because what determines the symmetry class is not the exact shape of the profile as such but the number of extreme points (maxima and minima) on it.[1]

The symmetric class has an odd number of extreme points, the antisymmetric class has an even number of them. On this criterion the

[1] Ambiguity in classification is usually due to the practical impossibility of exactly ascertaining the flanks of a profile. Gentle dips may also lead to an ambiguity.

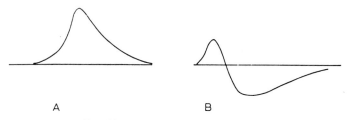

Fig.124. Asymmetric anomaly profiles.

profiles in Fig.124A and 124B can be classified as symmetric and antisymmetric respectively, although their actual shapes are far from the respective ideal ones.

The practical bearing of the above classification is in the location of the indication point on a profile.

The centre of a causative body lies below the central maximum (or minimum) if the profile is symmetric, and below a point midway between the two innermost extrema (which of course, have opposite signs) if the profile is antisymmetric. These are the points which may be called the "indications" in the respective cases and followed up from profile to profile in preliminary interpretation. A detailed interpretation will entail a closer inspection of the shapes of the profiles.

It is more correct to say that what is located in this simple manner is the centre of the causative system and this may not actually lie within any anomalous mass. For example, the bottom curve (say the vertical magnetic anomaly) in Fig.123A may correspond to a single broad zone of magnetic material, in which case the centre of the zone will be located below the central minimum, or to two *separate* ore sheets, one below each maximum in which case the point below the centre of the profile will correspond to a barren region.

Similarly, the departure of an anomaly profile from the ideal shape will also necessitate appropriate modifications in the above rule. This should be particularly borne in mind when the geological dips in an area are known to be gentle. But it is clear that we now have some sort of standard procedure for defining where the indication on a profile lies and to what point on a profile of another shape it corresponds. Nevertheless, real skill in comparing and interpreting geophysical maps can only be acquired with considerable practice.

TABLE IX

CLASSIFICATION OF INDICATIONS YIELDED BY DIFFERENT METHODS
IN MINING GEOPHYSICS

Symmetric	Example	Antisymmetric	Example
ΔZ for net vertical magnetization	Fig.7,8, 10B,13	ΔH for net vertical magnetization	Fig.8
ΔH for net horizontal magnetization	Fig.15	ΔZ for net horizontal magnetization	Fig.15
SP	Fig.26	SP gradient	Fig.26
Two-frame e.m.	Fig.40	Tilt-angle with vertical loop as primary source	Fig.33
Compensator(horizontal component)	Fig.125	Compensator (vertical component)	Fig.42,43
Turam ratio and phase difference	Fig.44		
Moving source–receiver	Fig.49		
Gravity ("closed surfaces")	Fig.95, 100C	Gravity (faults, slabs)	Fig.98

We can now systematize the profile shapes obtained with the
various geophysical methods as is done in Table IX.

EXAMPLES OF THE COMBINATION OF GEOPHYSICAL METHODS

The reader will probably have noticed that examples of the combination of geophysical methods are scattered throughout this book so
that a special section on this topic may appear to some as superfluous.
However, we shall consider two further instances below.

The Västra Maurliden discovery (*Skellefte ore field, Sweden*)
This example is due to Werner (1961). The prospecting campaign
in the area started with the moving source–receiver (slingram) method
using horizontal coils. The Västra Maurliden indication did not show
up as anything spectacular, being like a large number of other indications obtained in the area. However, when the indications were
subsequently screened by gravimeter measurements, the Västra
Maurliden slingram indication showed a distinct gravimeter anomaly

having a regular shape (Fig.125). Magnetic, electromagnetic compensator and electric mise-à-la-masse (see p.195) measurements then followed. No significant magnetic anomalies were found. The results of the other two measurements are shown in Fig.125.

The electromagnetic anomaly shows a centre with negative field values which gradually fade away into weak positive anomalies. The picture indicates a steeply dipping orebody with an upper surface whose contour coincides approximately with the −5% anomaly contour.

The maximum gravity anomaly is about 2.3 mgal and occurs at almost the same place as the electromagnetic centre. The outer gravity contours show, however, that the real centre of the strong gravity anomaly lies some distance towards the northwest.

Drillings established the existence of the Västra Maurliden ore.

The mise-à-la-masse electric potential map in Fig.125 covers a larger area and is therefore displayed on a smaller scale. This survey was carried out after the drillings. The part of the map that corresponds to the other two maps in Fig.125 is shown by a dotted line. Again, the indication is strong. Moreover, of all the geophysical indications, this one gives the clearest evidence of the northwest—southeast strike of the orebody.

The electromagnetic, gravimeter and mise-à-la-masse anomalies along the line A−A are also shown in Fig.125, together with a section of the ore. (The electrode in the ore was negative.)

The ore is almost vertical, about 50 m thick, and consists of compact pyrite. Its southwestern contact with the bedrock is sharp but on the northeastern side there is a 20 m broad pyrite-impregnation zone. The depth to the top of the ore is about 15 m but decreases towards the northeast.

The profile shows that the electromagnetic anomaly delineates only the compact ore. The gravity anomaly, on the other hand, is evidently also influenced by the impregnation zone, and the electric measurements indicate the entire sulphide occurrence. However, no distinction between the compact ore and the impregnation is possible on the basis of the electric anomalies because the values are almost constant (and very low) over the sulphide zone.

Electromagnetic anomaly *(% normal field)*

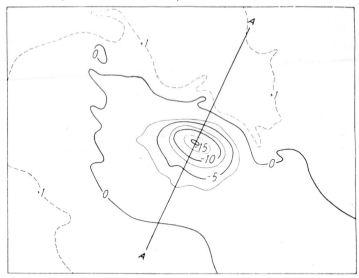

Bouguer anomaly *(mgal)*

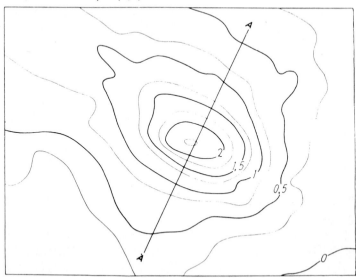

Potential (mV)

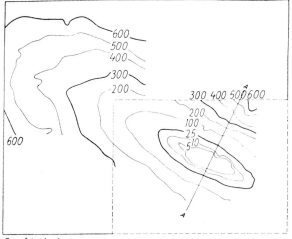

Profil A-A

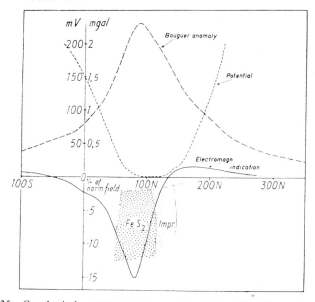

Fig.125. Geophysical measurements on the Västra Maurliden discovery, northern Sweden. The e.m. anomalies are in the horizontal component and obtained with a long earthed cable as primary source. Electric potential anomalies are mise-à-la-masse measurements. (After Werner, 1961; courtesy of S. Werner, Stockholm.)

Estimates of mass based on the gravimeter map lead to a total anomalous mass of 2 million metric tons which includes the compact ore as well as the impregnation zone but not the mass corresponding to the anomaly zone to the northwest.

The very clear continuation of the electric anomalies along the strike to a considerable distance towards the northwest and the less distinct one of the gravity anomalies indicate that the mineralization continues in this direction. That it cannot be rich is shown by the absence of electromagnetic anomalies in this part. An alternative explanation is that the orebody plunges towards the northwest.

The Tervaskoski orebody (Norrbotten county, Sweden)

This example is from the records of the Boliden Mining Co., Sweden. The initial discovery of the Tervaskoski orebody is to be credited to aeromagnetic measurements, an isoanomaly chart of which is shown in Fig.126A. There is a fairly regular magnetic centre, although the contours are more tightly packed in the northeast than in the southwest where their spacing increases.

A distinct negative minimum is present on the south-eastern side of the eastern part of the anomaly.

A map of the ground measurements (Fig.126B) reproduces the main features of the aeromagnetic map but shows much more detail, this despite the low height (40 m) and the close line-interval (125 m) at which the aerial survey was carried out. Note also that the aerial and ground indications do not occur at exactly the same place.

Above all, the ground survey shows that the distribution of the magnetic material is much more irregular in the northeastern part of the mass than in the southwestern one. The boundary of the magnetic zone is indicated by the sharp gradient and may be tentatively identified with the zero-anomaly contour.

The gradient of magnetic anomaly at the edges of the mass is not as sharp in the southwest as in the northeast and, in fact, is very diffuse near the western corner of the area. Further, there are distinct negative minima of the order of $-2,000\gamma$ surrounding the northeastern part of the mass on three sides, like water surrounding a peninsula. However, no negative minima are discernible in the southwest. We shall presently see that the differences between the anomaly patterns in the northeastern and southwestern parts of the area are of great significance and can be explained in a reasonable manner.

Fig.126C is an electromagnetic ground map (moving source— receiver, horizontal coils, 60 m separation, frequency 3,600 c/sec) of the real component. Its pattern is strikingly different from that of the magnetic map.

In the first place we notice that only the northeastern part of the magnetic anomaly shows up on the electromagnetic map and that electromagnetic anomalies are practically non-existent in the south- west. In fact, the boundary between the two areas is quite sharp and coincides roughly with the dot—dash line. What does this mean? Clearly, the electric conductors in the southwestern part must be deeper than the depth-penetration of the electromagnetic system used, while those in the northeast are much shallower.

Before accepting this conclusion we must analyze an argument that there are no electric conductors in the southwestern part.

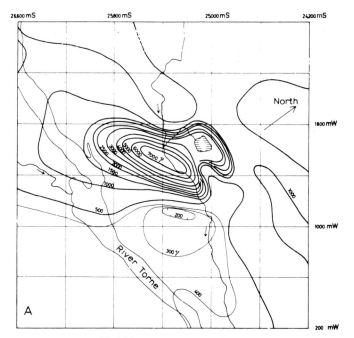

Fig.126A. (Legend see p.349).

We note that the electromagnetic anomalies in the northeastern part of the massif are positive. Actually the anomalies with the horizontal moving source—receiver system on such extensive electric conductors at shallow depth should be negative (Parasnis, 1972, p.120). Now this is only true if the conductors are non-magnetic, which is what we have tacitly assumed, for example, in the discussions of electromagnetic anomalies in Chapter 5. However, if a conductor has a high magnetic susceptibility the field from the transmitter of the e.m. system induces a strong oscillating magnetism in the conductor in addition to electric currents. The field from this oscillating magnetism also affects the receiver and if the susceptibility is sufficiently high it outweighs the field due to the induced currents. Since this purely magnetic field is positive the observed electromagnetic anomalies will also be positive in such case. This applies to the real or in-phase

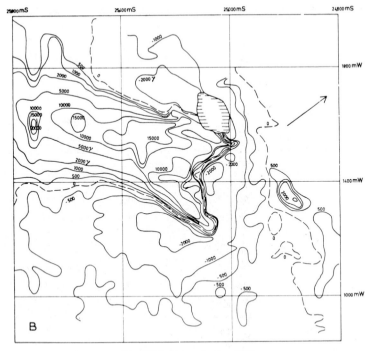

Fig.126B. (Legend see p.349).

component of the field picked up. The sign of the imaginary or out-of-phase component will not be affected.

The observed positive sign of the real component in the north-eastern part of the Tervaskoski massif leaves no doubt that it is the permeability of the magnetic zone that is responsible for the electro-magnetic anomalies. But, to all appearances, the magnetic material in the southwestern part of the massif must also have a high magnetic susceptibility, yet it fails to show up on the electromagnetic map. The explanation can only be the one cited above, that the material south-west of the dot—dash line lies deeper.

Now, it is in the area approximately southwest of the dot—dash line that the magnetic anomalies become more regular. It is here that

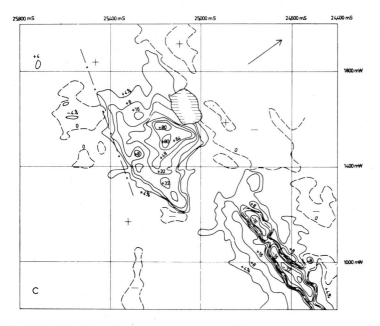

Fig.126.A. Total-intensity aeromagnetic anomaly map of the Tervaskoski iron-orebody, northern Sweden. Flight height 40 m. B. Ground magnetic map (vertical field anomalies) of the Tervaskoski iron-orebody. C. Electromagnetic (moving source—receiver) map of the Tervaskoski area. Coil-separation 60 m. Frequency 3,600 c/sec. (Courtesy of BGAB.)

the gradients marking the boundary of the magnetic zone are gentle and it is here that the magnetic negative side-minima are absent.

Piecing together all the bits of the puzzle we find the inference that the depth to the anomalous mass is greater to the southwest of the dot—dash line to be very plausible.

The fact that the maximum magnetic anomalies in both regions are approximately equal despite the probable depth-difference is understandable because the magnitude of the anomalies on broad zones is not critically dependent on the depth to the top.

Only a few drillholes have so far been placed on the magnetic massif. These have proved rich magnetite ore.

The dot—dash line probably represents a geological fault but this inference cannot be checked by any surface observations because outcrops of the bedrock in this moraine covered area are totally lacking.

The electromagnetic map (Fig.126C) shows another important feature; this is the long indication, in the lower right-hand quadrant, striking east—west. This feature continues for a considerable distance to the east outside the area shown. The anomalies here are negative (more than -32% at maximum), as we should expect them to be on non-magnetic conductors, which checks with the fact that the indication does not show up on the magnetic map. Drillholes on this indication have encountered sulphide mineralization with some copper. The dip of the mineralization is to the south, as is evident from the fact that the positive side-maxima are stronger on the southern flank ($+16\%$) than on the northern one ($+8\%$).

It is interesting to observe that the direction of the geological fault inferred above is approximately the same as that of the sulphide indication. This may be a coincidence but it does open a field for speculation and is of undoubted heuristic value.

These two, and the other examples discussed elsewhere in the book, will amply demonstrate the usefulness of combining different geophysical methods. Further examples may be found in a large number of case histories which have been published (e.g., European Association of Exploration Geophysicists, 1958; Canadian Institute of Mining and Metallurgy, 1959; Granar, 1963; Laurila, 1963; Puranen, 1963).

Simple Method of Determining the Magnetic Susceptibility and Remanence of Approximately Spherical Rock and Ore Samples

The method described below is rough but very useful for obtaining quick estimates of the susceptibility and remanence, provided the magnetic material in the sample is distributed more or less uniformly.

The magnetic anomaly of a homogeneously magnetized sphere, at a distance r (m) from its centre, along a line parallel to the magnetization (A/m) is:

$$F = (\frac{\mu_0}{4\pi}) \frac{2IV}{r^3} \, \text{Wb/m}^2 = 200 \frac{IV}{r^3} \, \text{gamma}$$

where I is the net intensity of magnetization and V the volume (m^3) of the sphere. However, $I = I_i \pm I_r$ depending upon whether the induced intensity, I_i, has the same or the opposite direction as the remanent intensity, I_r.

The vertical field anomaly of an approximately spherical rock or ore sample can be measured by reading an ordinary magnetometer before and after placing the sample below the instrument with the total magnetization vertical (and therefore pointing towards the needle). The needle of the magnetometer must be orientated east— west in order to eliminate the effect of induction due to the horizontal component of the earth's field. Suppose that, to start with, $I = I_i + I_r$ and that the anomaly is ΔZ_1. Turn the sample upside down. The direction of the induced magnetization due to the earth's vertical magnetic field will be unchanged but that of I_r will be reversed. Hence, in the second case $I = I_i - I_r$. We now have:

$$\Delta Z_1 = \frac{200(I_i + I_r)V}{r^3} \, \text{gamma}$$

$$\Delta Z_2 = \frac{200(I_i + I_r)V}{r^3} \, \text{gamma}$$

Adding the two equations:

$$\Delta Z_1 + \Delta Z_2 = \frac{400 I_i V}{r^3}$$

Subtracting:

$$\Delta Z_1 - \Delta Z_2 = \frac{400 I_r V}{r^3}$$

The first equation gives I_i and the second I_r. The volume of the sample may be measured by displacement or by weighings in air and water.

Now if Z is the vertical field (flux density, Wb/m^2) of the earth, the corresponding magnetizing force (A/m) is Z/μ_0 (p.22). Since the induced intensity of magnetization is equal to the susceptibility times the magnetizing force, we have $I_i = \kappa_i (Z/\mu_0)$, that is:

$$\kappa_i = \frac{\mu_0 I_i}{Z} \qquad (Z \text{ in Wb/m}^2)$$

$$= \frac{400 \pi I_i}{Z} \qquad (Z \text{ in gamma})$$

or by substituting for I_i from the equation above:

$$\kappa_i = 4\pi \frac{r^3}{V} \cdot \frac{\Delta Z_1 + \Delta Z_2}{4Z} \quad \text{(rationalized SI)}$$

The susceptibility in the unrationalized system is obtained by dividing κ_i given by this formula by 4π. Now κ_i is the net susceptibility of the sample and not that (κ) of the material of the sample. The latter is obtained from:

$$\kappa = \frac{\kappa_i}{1 - (\kappa_i/3)}$$

where the denominator takes account of the "demagnetization factor" owing to which the susceptibility as given by $\mu_0 I_i/Z$ is too low.

If the geological body from which the sample is taken has through-

out a composition identical with that of the sample, the net susceptibility of the body as a whole in situ is given by:

$$\kappa_e = \frac{\kappa}{1 + N\kappa}$$

where N is the demagnetization factor. It is this value which must be
used in calculating the magnetic effect of the body. N depends on the
shape of the body and can, in general, be only crudely estimated. It
also depends on the direction in which the net magnetization of the
body is postulated to be. Tables of N for prismatic bodies are given by
Sharma (1968).

The method described above presupposes an appreciable vertical
field and is unsuitable in very low magnetic latitudes. In these areas a
horizontal-field magnetometer (of the compensation type) should be
used. The instrument is oriented so that the needle is free to swing in
the vertical plane through the local magnetic meridian. If the sample is
placed below the magnetometer, then:

$$\kappa_i = 4\pi \frac{r^3}{V} \cdot \frac{\Delta H_1 + \Delta H_2}{2H}$$

where ΔH_1, ΔH_2 are the fields with the sample pointing north and
south respectively and H is the horizontal component of the earth's
field at the place.

If samples are to be reasonably small, say 10—15 cm across at the
most, the lowest susceptibility that can be determined with any
accuracy with the above crude methods is about 1—2 (rationalized SI).

In general, I_i and I_r will have different directions and as their
mutual orientation will be unknown, we look upon the value of I_r
obtained as above to be the vertical component of the remanent intensity in the particular position of the sample. To find the total
remanence, mark three mutually perpendicular axes AB, CD, EF on
the sample (by pairs of oppositely placed coloured dots for example)
and take 6 anomaly measurements in the above fashion, 2 corresponding to each axis. Then we get three values I_{i1}, I_{i2}, I_{i3} for the
induced intensity and three I_{r1}, I_{r2}, I_{r3} for the remanent intensity.
The latter may be positive or negative, the former will be positive and

equal to each other within the errors of measurement, unless the sample has strong magnetic anisotropy. For the isotropic case, the mean of I_{i1}, I_{i2}, I_{i3} is adopted for calculating κ from the equation above while the total remanent intensity is given by the vector sum $I_r = \sqrt{(I_{r1}^2 + I_{r2}^2 + I_{r3}^2)}$. The direction cosines of I_r (the cosines of the angles made by I_r with the three mutually perpendicular axes chosen) are I_{r1}/I_r etc., so that the orientation of the remanent intensity within the sample can also be determined. Fig.127 shows the eight possible directions of I_r with respect to the fixed axes chosen relatively to the sample.

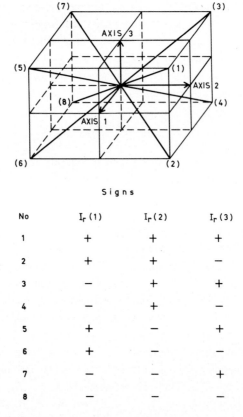

Signs

No	$I_r(1)$	$I_r(2)$	$I_r(3)$
1	+	+	+
2	+	+	−
3	−	+	+
4	−	+	−
5	+	−	+
6	+	−	−
7	−	−	+
8	−	−	−

Fig.127. Direction of the remanent magnetic vector of a sample.

Magnetic Anomaly of Pole Systems

(1) By reference to Fig.128A, which shows a point negative pole of strength m at a depth a, it will be seen that the field at P is $\Delta T = (\mu_0/4\pi)\,(m/r^2)$ Wb/m^2 (cf. p.23). The vertical and horizontal components of ΔT are:

$$\Delta Z = \Delta T \cos\theta = \frac{\mu_0 m}{4\pi r^2}\cdot\frac{a}{r} = \frac{\mu_0 m a}{4\pi (x^2 + a^2)^{3/2}}$$

$$\Delta H = \Delta T \sin\theta = \frac{\mu_0 m}{4\pi r^2}\cdot\frac{x}{r} = \frac{\mu_0 m x}{4\pi (x^2 + a^2)^{3/2}}$$

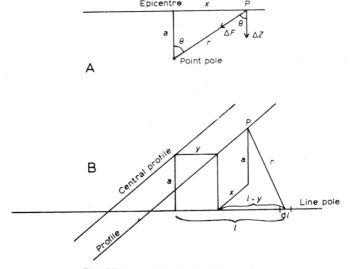

Fig.128.A. A point pole. B. A line pole.

Since $(\mu_0 m)/(4\pi a^2) = \Delta Z_{\max}$, the value of ΔZ at $x = 0$, which is also the maximum value of ΔZ, these two equations can be written as:

$$\frac{\Delta Z}{\Delta Z_{\max.}} = \frac{1}{(x_a{}^2 + 1)^{\frac{3}{2}}}$$

$$\frac{\Delta H}{\Delta Z_{\max.}} = \frac{x_a}{(x_a{}^2 + 1)^{\frac{3}{2}}}$$

where $x_a = x/a$.

Both sides are now dimensionless and the equations can be used for calculating the anomalies of a point pole at any depth, provided we understand that the distances are expressed in terms of the depth.

With an equal and opposite pole at a depth a' (representing the lower surface of a pencil-like orebody) the net vertical intensity is:

$$\Delta Z = \frac{\mu_0 ma}{4\pi(x^2 + a^2)^{\frac{3}{2}}} - \frac{\mu_0 ma'}{4\pi(x^2 + a'^2)^{\frac{3}{2}}}$$

$$= \frac{\mu_0 m}{4\pi a^2}\left\{\frac{1}{(x_a{}^2 + 1)^{\frac{3}{2}}} - \frac{1}{(x_a{}^2 + n^2)^{\frac{3}{2}}}\right\}$$

if we put $a' = na$. In this case:

$$\Delta Z_{\max.} = \frac{\mu_0 m}{4\pi a^2}\left(1 - \frac{1}{n^2}\right) = \frac{\mu_0 m(n^2 - 1)}{4\pi a^2 n^2}$$

Hence:

$$\frac{\Delta Z}{\Delta Z_{\max.}} = \frac{n^2}{n^2 - 1}\left\{\frac{1}{(x_a{}^2 + 1)^{\frac{3}{2}}} - \frac{n}{(x_a{}^2 + 1)^{\frac{3}{2}}}\right\}$$

A similar expression can be obtained for ΔH.

(2) A line pole of strength λ per unit length is shown in Fig.128B. An element of length $\mathrm{d}l$ at a distance l from the centre of the pole may be considered to be a point pole of strength $\lambda \mathrm{d}l$. By the above, its

vertical field anomaly at P on an arbitrary profile distant y from the centre is:

$$\frac{\mu_0 \lambda \mathrm{d}la}{4\pi r^3} = \frac{\mu_0 \lambda \mathrm{d}la}{4\pi \ \{x^2 + a^2 + (l - y)^2\}^{\frac{3}{2}}}$$

Integrating from $-l$ to $+l$ with respect to l, if the length of the pole is $2l$ and the centre of the pole is at $y = 0$, we get the total vertical field anomaly due to the line pole as:

$$\Delta Z = \frac{\mu_0 \lambda a}{4\pi} \cdot \frac{1}{x^2 + a^2} \left[\frac{l + y}{\{x^2 + a^2 + (l + y)^2\}^{\frac{1}{2}}} + \frac{l - y}{\{x^2 + a^2 + (l - y)^2\}^{\frac{1}{2}}} \right]$$

which can also be reduced to a dimensionless form but this may be left to the reader as an exercise.

For an infinitely long line pole the expression for the vertical field anomaly reduces to the simple one:

$$\Delta Z = \frac{\mu_0 \lambda a}{2\pi(x^2 + a^2)}$$

According to eq.3.2 (p.22) the vertical magnetization intensity $(\kappa Z/\mu_0)$ where κ is the susceptibility and Z is the vertical magnetic field, is equal to the pole strength per unit area. Hence m for a "point" pole of area A may be replaced by $A\kappa Z/\mu_0$, and the total pole strength $2l\lambda$ of a line pole by $2lb\kappa Z$, that is, λ in the equations above by $b\kappa Z/\mu_0$.

A rectangular block may be imagined to be composed of thin strips. If the upper and lower surfaces of each strip are considered as line poles of opposite sign, the anomaly of a block can be obtained by integrating the anomaly of a line pole in the appropriate manner.

The Magnetic Field of a Large Rectangular Loop Carrying an Electric Current

The simple but interesting results on p.131 — eq. (5.4) and (5.5) — do not appear to be very well known. For the reader who wishes to verify them, the following hint may be given.

By the law of Biot and Savart the magnetic field (B) of a current-carrying cable of length l at a point distant d from it on the perpendicular erected at one of its extremities is:

$$B = \frac{\mu_0 I}{4\pi d} \cdot \frac{l}{l^2 + d^2}$$

where I is the current through the cable.

Semi-absolute Calculation of the Electromagnetic Field Components from Turam Reduced Ratios and Phase Differences

We recall that the reduced ratios yield the quantities V_1/V_2, V_2/V_3 etc., and the phase differences the quantities $\alpha_2 - \alpha_1$, $\alpha_3 - \alpha_2$ ...etc. The reciprocal of the first ratio is V_2/V_1 and assuming the amplitude of the vertical field at point 1 to be arbitrarily 1.0, the reciprocal becomes V_2 and gives the amplitude at point 2. Dividing V_2 by the next ratio we get $V_2/(V_2/V_3) = V_3$ and so on. If the phase α_1 of the field at point 1 is arbitrarily assumed to be zero, successive additions of the measured phase differences give the phases α_1, α_2, α_3 ... etc., at points 1, 2, 3 ... etc.

The procedure of calculation is illustrated in Table X by reference to actual observations along the profile 720E across the Kimheden orebody (cf. Fig.44).

Columns 6 and 7 show the quantities $V\cos\alpha$ and $V\sin\alpha$ which are the in-phase and out-of-phase components of the resultant vertical field (cf. Fig.35) expressed in terms of the normal field at each point, this field being reckoned as 1.000.

The phase lag of the field for a sheet-like conductor, as the orebody in question, should be approximately constant at all points. The explanation of column 7 in this respect is as follows.

The phase shows a lag (almost constant minus values) south of the point 385N. In the neighbourhood of 385N there is a sudden reversal of phase and at points north of 385N the phase is positive. This is a geometrical effect because the vertical component of the secondary field is directed downwards on this side of the conductor but upwards on the southern side (cf. Fig.32) so that the lag appears as an apparent lead. The true phase lag of the field is half-way between the almost constant positive and negative values, i.e., about $-30°$ or one twelfth of a period. At the frequency used (350 c/sec) this means that the

TABLE X

CALCULATION OF ELECTROMAGNETIC FIELD COMPONENTS FROM TURAM RATIOS AND PHASE DIFFERENCES

Point	Reduced ratio	Phase diff.	Amplitude V	Phase α	V cos α	V sin α	Point
480N	Cable						
450N			1.000	0.00	1.000	0.000	450N
	0.975	0.50					
440N			1.026	0.50	1.026	0.0089	440N
	0.960	0.30					
430N			1.070	0.80	1.069	0.0150	430N
	0.955	0.42					
420N			1.120	1.22	1.119	0.0239	420N
	0.965	0.50					
410N			1.162	1.72	1.161	0.0341	410N
	0.960	1.30					
400N			1.210	3.02	1.209	0.0637	400N
	0.970	0.10					
395N			1.248	3.12	1.246	0.0678	395N
	1.005	− 0.50					
390N			1.241	2.62	1.240	0.0567	390N
	1.090	− 3.20					
385N			1.139	− 0.58	1.139	−0.0058	385N
	1.305	−12.3					
380N			0.872	−12.88	0.850	−0.1944	380N
	1.490	−19.0					
375N			0.585	−31.88	0.496	−0.3085	375N
	1.360	−15.8					
370N			0.431	−47.68	0.290	−0.318	370N
	1.165	− 7.30					
365N			0.370	−54.98	0.212	−0.303	365N
	1.060	− 2.0					
360N			0.349	−56.98	0.190	−0.292	360N
	1.015	− 0.20					
355N			0.340	−57.18	0.185	−0.286	355N
	1.010	+ 0.20					
350N			0.341	−56.98	0.186	−0.286	350N
	0.990	0.90					
340N			0.344	−56.08	0.192	−0.286	340N
	0.975	1.20					
330N			0.353	−54.88	0.203	−0.288	330N
	0.975	0.80					
320N			0.362	−54.08	0.212	−0.293	320N
	0.975	0.40					
310N			0.371	−53.68	0.220	−0.299	310N
	0.980	0.20					
300N			0.378	−53.48	0.225	−0.304	300N

resultant electromagnetic field attains its maxima and minima (1/12) × (1/350) = 0.24 msec *after* the primary field (cf. section *The phase angle and the vector diagram*, p.108).

Electric Potential Due to a Point and a Line Current Electrode Placed on the Surface of a Homogeneous Ground

Point electrode

Describe a hemispherical shell of radius r and thickness dr with the point electrode as the centre. The area of the shell is $2\pi r^2$. All the current (I) injected by the electrode passes across the shell and if the electric resistance of the shell is dR, then by Ohm's law, the potential difference across it is $IdR = dV$. Applying eq. (6.1), p.163, for the definition of the electric restivity of the ground we have:

$$dR = \frac{\rho\,dr}{2\pi r^2}$$

Hence:

$$dV = \frac{I\rho}{2\pi} \cdot \frac{dr}{r^2}$$

Integrating from r to ∞, the potential at a distance r is seen to be:

$$V = \frac{I\rho}{2\pi}\frac{1}{r}$$

if the potential at ∞ is assumed to be zero.

Line electrode

We consider first an infinitely long line electrode through which a current J per unit electrode length is entering the ground. Describe a semicylindrical shell of radius r and thickness dr with the electrode as the axis. Then, the resistance of a shell of unit length is:

$$dR = \rho\,\frac{dr}{\pi r}$$

and by the same reasoning as above:

$$V = C - \frac{J\rho}{\pi} \ln r$$

where C is a constant which depends on the distance at which the potential is arbitrarily assumed to be zero.

The potential of a finite line electrode can be found by a process of integration starting from the potential of a point electrode. The expression for the apparent resistivity for a line electrode layout like that shown in Fig.65 is:

$$\rho_a = \frac{\pi}{J} \cdot \frac{\Delta V}{S - T}$$

where:

$$S = \sinh^{-1}\left(\frac{b-y}{x-l}\right) + \sinh^{-1}\left(\frac{b+y}{x-l}\right) - \sinh^{-1}\left\{\frac{b+y}{2L-(x-l)}\right\}$$

$$-\sinh^{-1}\left\{\frac{b-y}{2L-(x-l)}\right\}$$

and T = same expression as S with $x - l$ replaced by $x + l$, $\sinh^{-1}x$ denotes the hyperbolic sine and may be expressed alternatively as $\ln\{x + \sqrt{(1+x^2)}\}$.

Method of Images

The electric potential due to a point electrode in certain simple types of resistivity distributions, of which Fig.61 is an example, can be calculated by a method based on optical analogy and known as the method of electrical images. It may be illustrated by application to this figure.

Consider a single point current-electrode on the surface of the ground but in medium *1*. Let us think of it as a source of light. An observer in medium *1* sees the direct light from the source and the light reflected at the plane of partition between media *1* and *2*, but the latter light will be dimmed owing to reflection. According to the result in the last appendix, the electric potential of the actual source ("the intensity of the light" as seen by the observer) is $(I\rho_1/2\pi)\cdot(1/r)$ where r is the distance of the observer from the source. The potential of the image source may be written as:

$$k\,\frac{I\rho_1}{2\pi}\,\frac{1}{r_1}$$

where r_1 is the distance of the mirror image of the source in the partition and k is a sort of "reflection coefficient". The total potential in the first medium is therefore:

$$V_1 = \frac{I\rho_1}{2\pi}\left(\frac{1}{r}+\frac{k}{r_1}\right)$$

An observer in medium *2* sees only the light of the actual source but only the fraction $(1 - k)$ is transmitted through the boundary since the fraction k is reflected at it. The potential in medium *2* can therefore be written as:

$$V_2 = (1 - k) \frac{I \rho_2}{2\pi} \frac{1}{r_2}$$

where r_2 is the distance of the observer in medium 2 from the source.

On the boundary (where at all points $r = r_1 = r_2$) the potential must be the same whether it is calculated from the one expression or the other. It follows that:

$$\rho_2(1 - k) = \rho_1(1 + k)$$

or, solving for k, we get:

$$k = \frac{\rho_2 - \rho_1}{\rho_2 + \rho_1}$$

As k is known the potentials are now completely determined. If a second (negative) electrode is placed on the surface of the ground its potentials may be calculated in a similar manner and the total potentials in each medium determined by superposition.

APPENDIX 7

Gravity Anomalies

The basis for calculating gravity anomalies is Newton's law of gravitation which states that the attraction exerted by a *point* mass M on a unit point mass at a distance r from it is $F = GM/r^2$ where G is the universal gravitational constant[1]. Considering the point mass M as a point volume ΔV of density ρ we can write:

$$F = \frac{G\rho\Delta V}{r^2}$$

If F is expressed in g.u., the volume ΔV in m^3 and ρ in g/cm^3 and r in m it is found *experimentally* that

$$G\rho = \frac{20}{3} \times 10^{-2} \, \rho \, \text{g.u./m}$$

The attraction F is along the line joining the two masses and its vertical component is, by definition, the gravity anomaly if the unit mass is on the earth's surface.

Any mass, whether of uniform or non-uniform density, can be divided into very small elements ΔV within each of which the density can be considered to be constant and equal to the local value ρ. The unit mass (the point of observation) will be at different distances from each of the volume elements but their attractions at it can be separately calculated from the formula above and, on adding the vertical components of these attractions, we get the gravity effect of the entire mass.

(*1*) Sphere and cylinder. It can be shown that a sphere attracts an

---

[1] Rather, this is a deduction from Newton's law which is more general in its statement.

external mass as if the entire mass of the sphere were concentrated as a point mass at its centre. The gravity anomaly of a buried sphere on the ground surface can be calculated formally in exactly the same fashion as the vertical magnetic field of a point pole (Appendix 1). We have:

$$\Delta g = \frac{GMa}{(x^2 + a^2)^{\frac{3}{2}}}$$

where a is the depth and x the horizontal distance from the epicentre on the surface.

An infinitely long cylinder attracts an external mass as if the mass of the cylinder were concentrated along its axis as a line mass. The gravity anomaly of a buried horizontal cylinder can be calculated in exactly the same manner as the magnetic vertical field anomaly of an infinitely long horizontal line pole. We have:

$$\Delta g = \frac{2G\mu a}{x^2 + a^2}$$

where μ is the mass of the cylinder per unit length and a is the depth to the axis.

(2) A prism of infinite length along the strike (Fig.129). Let the x

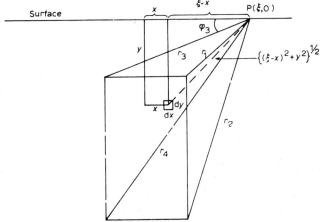

Fig.129. A long prism striking perpendicular to the plane of the figure.

and y coordinate axes be parallel to the sides of the prism, the x-axis being horizontal and the y-axis vertical. Let the origin be at a point on the surface vertically above the centre of the prism.

Let a small square element of the prism have a side dx parallel to the x-axis and a side dy parallel to the y-axis and be situated with its centre at the point (x,y). The volume of the element per unit length (along the strike) is $dxdy$ and the mass per unit length of this elemental prism is $\rho dxdy$. Such a small element may be considered to be a line mass and its gravity anomaly at a surface point P (coordinate $\xi,0$) is given by the formula above, namely:

$$\frac{2G\rho y\,dxdy}{(\xi - x)^2 + y^2}$$

since y is the depth of the element. Integrating this expression from $x = -\frac{b}{2}$ to $+\frac{b}{2}$ and $y = y_1$ to $y = y_2$ where $\frac{b}{2}$ is half the width of the prism and $(y_2 - y_1)$ is its thickness we get:

$$\Delta g = \int_{y_1}^{y_2} \int_{-\frac{b}{2}}^{\frac{b}{2}} \frac{2G\rho y\,dxdy}{(\xi - x)^2 + y^2}$$

$$= 2G\rho \int_{-\frac{b}{2}}^{\frac{b}{2}} \ln \left\{ \frac{(\xi - x)^2 + y_2^2}{(\xi - x)^2 + y_1^2} \right\}^{\frac{1}{2}} dx$$

The last integral can be evaluated by parts but we shall not carry out the integration in detail. On introducing the lengths and angles shown in the figure, the result of the integration can be expressed in the form:

$$\Delta g = 2G\rho \left\{ x \ln \frac{r_1 r_4}{r_2 r_3} + b \ln \frac{r_2}{r_1} + y_2(\Phi_2 - \Phi_4) - y_1(\Phi_1 - \Phi_3) \right\}$$

A different derivation of this formula and special cases of it leading to the anomalies of geological faults, infinite slabs etc., are treated in Parasnis (1972).

APPENDIX 8

Depth Estimates of Some Simple Mass Shapes

TABLE XI

TABLE XI

DEPTH ESTIMATES OF SOME SIMPLE MASS SHAPES FROM THE MAXI-
MUM GRAVITY ANOMALY ($\Delta g_{max.}$) AND THE MAXIMUM HORIZONTAL
GRADIENT ($\Delta g'_{max.}$)

Concentrated mass (point mass)	Very long mass (line mass)	Geological fault (sharp flexure)
$0.86 \dfrac{\Delta g_{max.}}{\Delta g'_{max.}}$	$0.65 \dfrac{\Delta g_{max.}}{\Delta g'_{max.}}$	$\dfrac{1}{\pi} \dfrac{\Delta g_{max.}}{\Delta g'_{max.}}$

The throw of a fault can be estimated as explained in section *Gravity profiles across simple structures*, p.261.

Notes on the Master Curves in Fig.117 for Total Field Magnetic Anomalies

The curves are calculated for a sheet striking in the east—west direction ($\delta = 0°$), and for two magnetization directions ($\beta = 15°$ and $\beta = 90°$).

Assume a depth t to the top of the sheet in some plausible way. Read off the values of $\Delta T/4\theta M_T \sin \alpha$ at the various x-coordinates. The values are fractions between 0 and 1.0. Multiply each value by a suitable constant (like 5,000, for example) to obtain the correct order of magnitude of the anomalies in γ. Plot the scaled-off anomalies on the measured profile. The constant that yields the best fit with the observed curves we shall call c. Then:

$$4\theta M_T \sin \alpha = c$$

In this expression θ is the angle shown in Fig.117 and is expressed in radians ($1° = 0.0175$ radian). M_T is the total magnetization. The tangent of the angle θ is the ratio d/t.

If two of the three quantities θ, M_T and α (the dip) are known the third is easily determined from this equation. In practice, θ and α can in general be estimated from an inspection of the aeromagnetic map and geological data respectively and the equation then suffices to yield the total magnetization M_T.[1]

---

[1] These curves yield the magnetization in electromagnetic c.g.s. units.

Elliptic Polarization of the Electromagnetic Field

The general theory of elliptic polarization, although it involves no further basic concepts than in the analysis below, is algebraically cumbersome. We shall therefore consider here only the two most important practical cases, namely, when the primary field is horizontal and when it is vertical. In Fig. 130 $P\cos\omega t$ represents the horizontal primary field and $S\cos(\omega t-\epsilon)$ the secondary field making an angle γ with the horizontal. The latter lags behind the primary field by the angle ϵ.

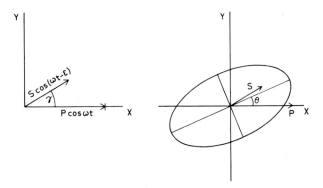

Fig. 130 Elliptic polarization.

Let X, Y be the total fields in the horizontal and the vertical directions. Then, as is easy to see:

$$X = P\cos\omega t + S\cos\gamma\cos(\omega t - \epsilon)$$
$$Y = S\sin\gamma\cos(\omega t - \epsilon)$$

Now, $\cos\omega t = \cos(\omega t-\epsilon+\epsilon) = \cos(\omega t-\epsilon)\cos\epsilon - \sin(\omega t - \epsilon)\sin\epsilon.$

From the equation for Y we have $\cos(\omega t - \epsilon) = Y/S\sin\gamma$. Hence:

$$\sin(\omega t - \epsilon) = \frac{(S^2\sin^2\gamma - Y^2)^{\frac{1}{2}}}{S\sin\gamma}$$

Therefore $\cos\omega t$ can be calculated. Inserting the values of $\cos\omega t$ and $\cos(\omega t - \epsilon)$ in the equation for X we get:

$$XS\sin\gamma - Y(S\cos\gamma + P\cos\epsilon) = -P\sin\epsilon(S^2\sin^2\gamma - Y^2)^{\frac{1}{2}}$$

Squaring both sides and rearranging the terms we obtain:

$$(S^2\sin^2\gamma)X^2 - 2S\sin\gamma(S\cos\gamma + P\cos\epsilon)XY + \{(S\cos\gamma + P\cos\epsilon)^2 + P^2\sin^2\epsilon\}\,Y^2 = P^2 S^2\sin^2\gamma\sin^2\epsilon$$

This is the equation of an arbitrarily oriented ellipse in the X-Y plane.

The resultant of $P\cos\omega t$ and $S\cos(\omega t - \epsilon)$ describes therefore an ellipse in this plane, the plane contained by the primary and secondary field vectors at a point. This plane is called the plane of polarization. It can be shown that the resultant is identical with that of two fields, one along the major axis of the ellipse and one along the minor axis but 90° out of phase with each other.

The angle made by the plane of polarization with the horizontal, that is, *the dip* (p.102) is, in the present case, 90°. The angle θ made by the major axis of the ellipse with the horizontal, *the tilt*, is obtained from a formula in coordinate geometry according to which $\tan 2\theta = 2h/(a-b)$ where $2h$ is the coefficient of the XY term and a, b are the coefficients of the terms in X^2 and Y^2 respectively. It follows that:

$$\tan 2\theta = -\frac{2S\sin\gamma(S\cos\gamma + P\cos\epsilon)}{S^2\sin^2\gamma - (S^2\cos^2\gamma + 2PS\cos\gamma\cos\epsilon + P^2)}$$

In the tilt-angle methods the angle θ is determined by tilting a search coil, held with its plane perpendicular to the plane of polarization, until the signal is minimum. In this position, only the field represented by the minor axis is cutting the coil. The above equation is not needed for determining θ.

The construction in Fig.32A is strictly valid only if S is $180°$ behind P in phase. A similar construction is also possible if the phase difference is $0°$. However, it is not possible to give a strictly valid *simple* construction for any other difference in phase, although qualitatively the tilt-angles behave as shown in Fig.32A for all phase differences.

If the primary field is vertical (Fig.32B) the dip of the plane of polarization is again $90°$ but the tilt is given by:

$$\tan 2\theta = -\frac{2S\cos\gamma(S\sin\gamma + P\cos\epsilon)}{(S^2\sin^2\gamma + 2PS\sin\gamma\cos\epsilon + P^2) - S^2\cos^2\gamma}$$

The derivation of this equation may be left to the reader as an exercise.

FORTRAN Source-programs for Calculating the Vertical Field Magnetic Anomaly due to an Inclined Prism and the Gravity Anomaly of a Two-dimensional Feature of Arbitrary, Uniform Cross-Section

Program ZPRISM for the vertical field anomaly of a long prism

The program calculates the bracketed expression in eq.(3.9a) at specified intervals between two given points along the ground-profile at right angles to the strike. Any number K of models, each represented by the following parameter set can be handled: width (B), dip (V), depth extent (E), transverse magnetization (T, denoted by k in eq.3.9a), x-coordinates (XMIN, XMAX) between which the calculations are to be made and interval (INT) at which the calculations are required between XMIN and XMAX.

All lengths are expressed in units of the upper-face depth. The origin of coordinates is above the midpoint of the upper face and x is positive in the direction from which the dip V (0 < V < 180) is measured. For dips within about 25° from the horizontal, the geometry in Fig.17A becomes unreasonable and eq.(3.9) is not recommended for such cases.

E is expressed as the ratio lower-face depth/upper-face depth.

Output comprises coordinate of calculation point and ΔZ in arbitrary units. ΔZ may be converted to gamma by multiplying with a suitable "amplitude factor" (=$200I_z$).

Input consists of the following card deck (apart from system cards):

Card 1: K, number of models to be handled
Card 2: B, V, E, T
Card 3: XMIN, INT, XMAX
Card pairs corresponding to card 2 and card 3 for subsequent models,
if any.

K is punched in the format I3 (Statement 2).
B is given with three decimals, format F8.3 (Statement 5).
V is given with one decimal, format F5.1 (Statement 5).
E is given with two decimals, format F7.2 (Statement 5).
T is given with four decimals, format F8.4 (Statement 5).
XMIN, XMAX, INT are integers, all in format I5 (Statement 10).

Example
K = 2
Model 1:
B = 16.000, V = 45.0, E = 10.00, T = 0.5770
XMIN = −15, INT = 5, XMAX = 15
Model 2:
B = 31.700, V = 122.0, E = 6.20, T = −0.7310
XMIN = −60, INT = 40, XMAX = 100

Output
B= 16.000 V= 45.0 E= 10.00 T= .5770

POINT	DELTAZ(ARB.UNITS)
−15	.6757
−10	1.3322
−5	2.7836
0	1.3062
5	.0406
10	−2.5930
15	−2.0449

B= 31.700 V=122.0 E= 6.20 T= −.7310
POINT   DELTAZ(ARB.UNITS)
−60   −.2380
−20   −2.8911
 20   1.3564
 60   .6067
100   .6242

The program ZPRISM is listed below. The input−output units are numbered as follows: 1 = card reader; 2 = line printer

```
C   ZPRISM
  2 FØRMAT(I3)
  5 FØRMAT(F8.3,F5.1,F7.2,F8.4)
 10 FØRMAT(3I5)
 15 FØRMAT(/2X,2HB=,F8.3,3X,2HV=,F5.1,3X,2HE=,F7.2,3X,2HT=,F8.4
 20 FØRMAT(2X,26HPOINT   DELTAZ(ARB.UNITS))
 25 FØRMAT(2X,I5,4X,F8.4)
    INTEGER XMIN,XMAX,X
    REAL L,M
    READ(1,2) K
    DØ 50 I=1,K
    READ(1,5) B,V,E,T
    S=V
    READ(1,10) XMIN,INT,XMAX
    V=V*3.1415927/180
    WRITE(2,15) B,S,E,T
    WRITE(2,20)
    DØ 45 X= XMIN,XMAX,INT
    L = X + B/2
    M = X − B/2
    IF (ABS(CØS(V) − 10E−8))   36,36,30
 30 TAN = SIN(V)/CØS(V)
    P = (L − (E −L)/TAN)/E
    Q = (M − (E −1)/TAN)/E
```

```
35 R1 = 1 + L*L
   R2 = 1 + M*M
   R3 = P*P + E*E
   R4 = Q*Q + E*E
   GØ TØ 40
36 P = L/E
   Q = M/E
40 W = ATAN(L) - ATAN(M) - ATAN(P) + ATAN(Q)
   Y = (T/2)*ALØG((R1*R4)/R2*R3))
   Z = W - Y
45 WRITE(2,25) X,Z
50 CØNTINUE
   END
```

Program D2GF for the gravity anomaly of a two-dimensional feature of arbitrary, uniform cross-section

This program is based on a generalization (see, for example, Vargova and Kolbenheyer, 1968) of the equation for Δg derived in Appendix 7. It calculates the gravity anomaly along a ground profile at right angles to the strike of the feature.

The contour of the assumed cross-section of the long feature is approximated by an n-sided polygon with sides parallel to the x and z axes (Fig.131A). The z-axis is positive downwards. The origin may be anywhere on the profile. All coordinates are absolute and in metres. Model may also be outcropping ($z = 0$ along one or more sides of the polygon).

Any number of models can be handled by the program. Starting from the uppermost and the "most positive" corner of the polygon, all the corners of a model are numbered 1, 2, ... n in the anticlockwise direction. The number n is necessarily even.

Output of the program comprises coordinate of calculation point and Δg in gravity units (g.u.) for a density contrast 1.000 g/cm^3.

Input consists of the following card deck (apart from system cards):

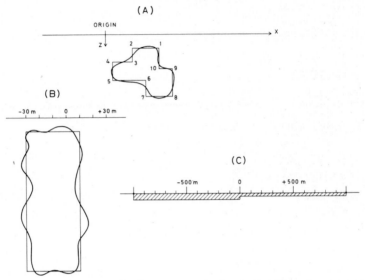

Fig.131. Approximating a cross-section by a rectangular polygon.

Card 1: K, number of models to be handled.

Card 2: N, P, D, Q for model 1 where N is the number of polygon corners, P, Q (P < Q) are the coordinates of the points between which the calculations are to be made, D is the interval at which calculations are required.

Card 3: X(1), Z(1) $x-z$ coordinates of corner 1 of model 1

Card 4: X(2), Z(2) $x-z$ coordinates of corner 2 of model 1

. . . .

Card N+2: X(N), Z(N) $x-z$ coordinates of corner N of model 1

Cards corresponding to 2,3, . . . (N+2) for subsequent models, if any.

K is punched in format I3 (Statement 2)

N is punched in format I3 (Statement 5)

P, D, Q are integers (nearest metre) in format I5 (Statement 5)

X(I), Z(I) are integers (nearest metre) in format I5 (Statement 10).

Example

K = 2
Model 1 (Fig.131B):
N = 4, P = −220, D = 80, Q = 100
X(I),Z(I) =   10, 10
           −30, 10
           −30,110
           10,110
Model 2 (Fig.131C)(Hatched structure):
N = 6, P = −160, D = 40, Q = 160
X(I),Z(I) =   1000, 0
          −1000, 0
          −1000, 40
             0, 40
             0, 20
         1000, 20

Output

POINT	ANOMALY(G.U.),DENSITY=1
−220	0.65
−140	1.44
−60	4.75
20	7.16
100	1.86

POINT	ANOMALY(G.U.),DENSITY=1
−160	16.12
−120	15.97
−80	15.67
−40	14.93
0	12.44
40	9.95
80	9.21
120	8.91
160	8.75

The program D2GF is listed below. The input–output units are numbered as follows: 1 = card reader; 2 = line printer

```
C    D2GF
  2 FØRMAT(I3)
  5 FØRMAT(I3,3I5)
 10 FØRMAT(2I5)
 20 FØRMAT(/2X,32HPOINT  ANOMALY(G.U.),DENSITY=1)
 25 FØRMAT(2X,I5,4X,F6.2)
    INTEGER P,D,Q,X,Z
    DIMENSION A(100),B(100),X(100),Z(100)
    READ(1,2) K
    DØ 50 M=1,K
    READ(1,5) N,P,D,Q
    READ(1,10) (X(I),Z(I),I=1,N)
    WRITE(2,20)
    F=−1
    E=1
 30 C=0
    IF (P−Q) 35,35,50
 35 DØ 40 I=1,N
    A(I)=X(I)−P
    IF (Z(I)) 37,36,37
 37 B(I)=(A(I)/2)*ALØG(Z(I)*Z(I)+A(I)*A(I))+
   F Z(I)*ATAN(A(I)/Z(I))
    GØ TØ 38
 36 B(I)=(A(I)/2)*ALØG(A(I)*A(I))
 38 E=F*E
 40 C=C+E*B(I)
    G=2*6.67*C/100
    ABSG=ABS(G)
    WRITE(2,25) P,ABSG
    P=P+D
    GØ TØ 30
 50 CØNTINUE
    END
```

References

Algermissen, S.T., 1961. Underground and surface gravity survey, Leadwood, Missouri. *Geophysics*, 26(2):158–168.

Anderson, L.A. and Keller, G.V., 1964. A study in induced polarization. *Geophysics*, 29(5):848–864.

Bahnemann, F., 1951. Magnetic measurements in the area of the emery deposits on the Island of Naxos. *Rept. Subs. Res. Dept., Athens*, 94 pp.

Balsley, J.R. and Buddington, A.F., 1958. Iron–titanium oxide minerals, rocks, and aeromagnetic anomalies of the Adirondack area, New York. *Econ. Geol.*, 53:777–805.

Bath, G.D., 1962. Magnetic anomalies and magnetizations of the Biwabik iron formation, Mesabi area, Minnesota. *Geophysics*, 27(5):627–650.

Baule, H. and Arensmeyer, I., 1954. *Report on Commissioned Laboratory Measurements*. Archives of the Boliden Mining Company, 3 pp.

Bhattacharyya, B.K. and Morrison, H.F., 1963. Some theoretical aspects of electrode polarization in rocks. *Geophys. Prospecting*, 11(2):176–196.

Bhimasankaram, V.L.S. and Rao, B.S.R., 1958. Manganese ore of southern India and its magnetic properties. *Geophys. Prospecting*, 6(1):11–24.

Bloh, I.M., 1962. *The Method of Electrical Mapping*. Gosgeotehizdat, Moscow, 240 pp. (in Russian).

Bosschart, R.A., 1964. *Analytic Interpretation of Fixed-Source Electromagnetic Prospecting Data*. Thesis, Univ. of Delft, 102 pp.

Browne, B.C., 1959. The earth's gravitational field. *Proc. Roy. Inst. Gt. Brit.*, 37(169):489–499.

Brownell, G.M., 1950. Radiation surveys with a scintillation counter. *Econ. Geol.*, 45(2):167–174.

Canadian Institute of Mining and Metallurgy, 1959. *Methods and Case Histories in Mining Geophysics*. Montreal, 359 pp.

Carlsborg, H., 1963. Om gruvkompasser, malmletning och kompassgångare. *Med Hammare och Fackla (Stockholm)*, 1963(23):9–108.

Carmichael, C.M., 1964. The magnetization of a rock containing magnetite and hemoilmenite. *Geophysics*, 29(1):87–92.

Cassinis, R., 1958. Geophysical exploration of sulphur limestone in Sicily (Italy). In: *Geophysical Surveys in Mining, Hydrological and Engineering Projects*. European Assoc. Exploration Geophysicists, The Hague, pp.157–169.

Collett, L.S., 1959. In: J.R. Wait (Editor), *Overvoltage Research and Geophysical Applications*. Pergamon, London, pp.50—70.

Collin, C.R., Sanselme, H. and Huot, G., 1958. An example of the use of geoexploration methods in metalliferous mining. In: *Geophysical Surveys in Mining, Hydrological and Engineering Projects*. European Assoc. Exploration Geophysicists, The Hague, pp.127—137.

Compagnie Générale de Géophysique, 1955. Abaques de sondage électrique. *Geophys. Prospecting*, 3(Suppl.3): 50 pp. (7 pp. text, 43 pp. master curves).

Cook, A.H. and Thirlaway, H.I.S., 1952. A gravimeter survey in the Bristol and Somerset coalfields. *Quart. J. Geol. Soc. London*, 107:255—286.

Davis, W.E., Jackson, W.H. and Richter, D.H., 1957. Gravity prospecting for chromite deposits in Camaguey province, Cuba. *Geophysics*, 22(4):848—869.

Dobrin, M., 1952. *Introduction to Geophysical Prospecting*. McGraw-Hill, New York, 435 pp.

Domzalski, W., 1953. Gravity measurements in a vertical shaft. *Trans. Inst. Mining Met.*, 63:429—445.

Domzalski, W., 1954. Gravity profile over the Hogs Back fault. *Mining Mag. (London)*, 71(2):73—82.

Domzalski, W., 1955a. Three-dimensional gravity survey. *Geophys. Prospecting*, 3(1):16—55.

Domzalski, W., 1955b. Relative determination of the density of surface rocks and the mean density of the earth from vertical gravity measurements. *Geophys. Prospecting*, 3(3):213—227.

Edge, A.B. Broughton and Laby, T.H., 1931. *Geophysical Prospecting*. Cambridge Univ. Press, London, 372 pp.

European Assoc. Exploration Geophysicists, 1958. *Geophysical Surveys in Mining, Hydrological and Engineering Projects*. The Hague, 270 pp.

Eve, A.S. and Keys, D.A., 1956. *Applied Geophysics in the Search for Minerals*. Cambridge Univ. Press, London, 382 pp.

Flathe, H., 1955a. Possibilities and limitations in applying geoelectrical methods to hydrological problems in the coastal areas of northwestern Germany. *Geophys. Prospecting*, 3(1):95—110.

Flathe, H., 1955b. A practical method of calculating geoelectrical model graphs for horizontally stratified media. *Geophys. Prospecting*, 3(3):268—294.

Fraser, D.C., Keevil Jr., N.B. and Ward, S.H., 1964. Conductivity spectra of rocks from the Craigmont ore environment. *Geophysics*, 29(5):832—847.

Gay, S.P., 1963. Standard curves for interpretation of magnetic anomalies over long tabular bodies. *Geophysics*, 28(2):161—200.

Gerryts, E., 1970. Diamond prospecting by geophysical methods — a review of current practice. In: L.W. Morley (Editor), *Mining and Groundwater Geophysics*. Geological Survey of Canada (Rept.26), Ottawa, 439—446.

Giret, R., 1961. La radiométrie aéroportée, outil d'exploration géologique structurale. *Geophys. Prospecting*, 9(4):582–590.

Goodell, R.R. and Fay, C.H., 1964. Borehole gravity meter and its application. *Geophysics*, 29(5):774–782.

Granar, L., 1963. Apparatus for electric potential investigations. *Geoexploration*, 1(2):22–39.

Grant, F.S., 1954. A theory for the regional correction of potential field data. *Geophysics*, 19(1):23–45.

Grant, F.S. and Elsaharty, A.F., 1962. Bouguer corrections using a variable density. *Geophysics*, 27(5):616–626.

Green, R., 1960. Remanent magnetization and the interpretation of magnetic anomalies. *Geophys. Prospecting*, 8(1):98–110.

Haalck, H., 1953. Die gravimetrischen Methoden. In: H. Haalck (Editor), *Lehrbuch der Angewandten Geophysik*. Bornträger, Berlin, pp.27–155.

Hall, D.H., 1959. Direction of polarization determined from magnetic anomalies, *J. Geophys. Res.*, 64(11):1945–1958.

Hallof, P.J., 1963. *IP case 7*. Advertisement brochure. McPhar Geophysics Ltd., Canada.

Hallof, P.J., 1964. A comparison of the various parameters employed in the variable-frequency induced-polarization method. *Geophysics*, 29(3):425–433.

Hammer, S., 1939. Terrain corrections for gravimeter stations. *Geophysics*, 4(3):184–209.

Hammer, S., 1945. Estimating ore masses in gravity prospecting. *Geophysics*, 10(1):50–62.

Hammer, S., 1950. Density determinations by underground gravity measurements. *Geophysics*, 15:637–652.

Hammer, S., Nettleton, L.L. and Hastings, W.K., 1945. Gravimeter prospecting for chromite in Cuba. *Geophysics*, 10(1):34–49.

Hawkes, H.E., 1951. A summary of the problem of magnetic exploration for chromite. *Geol. Surv. Bull., Washington*, 973-A, 20 pp.

Hedström, H., 1937. Phase measurements in electrical prospecting. *Am. Inst. Mining, Met. Engrs., Tech. Publ.*, 827, 19 pp.

Hedström, H., 1957. In defence of mining geophysics. *Geophys. Prospecting*, 5(3):231–238.

Hedström, H. and Parasnis, D.S., 1958. Some model experiments relating to electromagnetic prospecting with special reference to airborne work. *Geophys. Prospecting*, 6(4):322–341.

Hedström, H. and Parasnis, D.S., 1959. Reply to comments by N.R. Paterson. *Geophys. Prospecting*, 7(4):448–470.

Heiland, C.A., 1946. *Geophysical Exploration*. Prentice Hall, New York, N.Y., 1013 pp.

Heiskanen, W.A. and Vening Meinesz, F.A., 1958. *The Earth and its Gravity Field*. McGraw-Hill, New York, 470 pp.

Henderson, R.G. and Wilson, A., 1964. Polar charts for calculating aeromagnetic anomalies of three-dimensional bodies. *U.S. Geol. Surv. Rept., Open-File, Ser.*, 701, 13 pp.

Henderson, R.G. and Zietz, I., 1957. Graphical calculation of total-intensity anomalies of three-dimensional bodies. *Geophysics*, 22(4):887–904.

Henkel, J.H. and Van Nostrand, R.G., 1957. Experiments in induced polarization. *Mining Engr.*, 9(3):355–359.

Holm, A., 1964. An instrument for the determination of drill-hole geometry. *Geoexploration*, 2(1):20–27.

Hood, P., 1963. Remanent magnetism – a neglected factor in aeromagnetic interpretation. *Can. Mining J.*, 84(4):76.

Hutchinson, R.D., 1958. Magnetic analysis by logarithmic curves. *Geophysics*, 23(4):749–769.

Jahren, C.E., 1963. Magnetic susceptibility of bedded iron-formation. *Geophysics*, 28(5):756–766.

Jewell, T.R. and Ward, S.H., 1963. The influence of conductivity inhomogeneities upon audio-frequency magnetic fields. *Geophysics*, 28(2):201–221.

Jung, K., 1959. Zur gravimetrischen Bestimmung der Bodendichte. *Gerlands Beitr. Geophys.*, 68(5):268–279.

Jung, K., 1961. *Schwerkraftverfahren in der Angewandten Geophysik.* Geest und Portig, Leipzig, 348 pp.

Kaye, G.W.C. and Laby, T.H., 1959. *Physical and Chemical Constants.* Longmans, London, 147 pp.

Keevil, N.B. and Ward, S.H., 1962. Electrolyte activity. Its effect on induced polarization. *Geophysics*, 27 (fig.1).

Keller, G.V., 1959. Analysis of some electrical transient measurements on igneous, sedimentary and metamorphic rocks. In: J.R. Wait (Editor), *Overvoltage Research and Geophysical Applications.* Pergamon, London, pp.92–111.

Ketola, M., 1972. Some points of view concerning mise-à-la-masse measurements. *Geoexploration*, 10(1):1–21.

Kohlrausch, F., 1947. *Praktische Physik.* 1 ed., Teubner, Leipzig, 1943. Republished by Rosenberg, New York, 2:578 pp.

Lang, A.H., 1960. Prospecting in Canada. *Geol. Surv. Can. Econ. Geol. Ser.*, 7:190.

Laurila, M., 1963. The geophysical "case history" of the Kalliokylä sulfide deposit. *Geoexploration*, 1(1):16–24.

Lauterbach, R., 1956. Geophysikalische Prospektionsverfahren zur Aufsuchung und Erschliessung von Nickellagerstätten. *Z. Angew. Geol.*, 2(8/9):382–395.

Lee, E., 1963. *Magnetism.* Penguin, London, 286 pp.

Levanto, A., 1959. A three-component magnetometer for small drill-holes and its use in ore prospecting. *Geophys. Prospecting*, 7(2):183–195.

Lindblad, A. and Malmqvist, D., 1938. A new static gravity meter and its use for ore prospecting. *Ingeniörs Vetenskaps Akademien, Stockholm, Handlingar*, 146:52 pp.

Logn, O., 1964. Exploration for deep magnetite ore. *Geoexploration*, 2(2):74–106.

Lundberg, H., 1922. Practical experience in electrical prospecting. *Sveriges Geol. Undersökn., Årsbok*, 16(9):1–37.

Malmqvist, D., 1958. The geophysical case history of the Kankberg ore deposit in the Skellefte district, northern Sweden. In: *Geophysical Surveys in Mining, Hydrological and Engineering Projects*. European Assoc. Exploration Geophysicists, The Hague, pp.32–54.

Malmqvist, D., 1960. Eine Analyse des zeitlichen Verlaufes von Polarisations-indikationen nach einer Gleichstromsmethode. *Freiberger Forschungsh.*, C-81:122–136.

Marshall, D.J. and Madden, T.R., 1959. Induced polarization, a study of its causes. *Geophysics*, 24(4):790–816.

Meidav, T., 1960. Nomograms to speed up seismic refraction computations. *Geophysics*, 25(5):1035–1053.

Menzel, H., 1958. Die seismische Aufschlussmethoden. In: H.Haalck (Editor), *Lehrbuch der Angewandten Geophysik*. Bornträger, Berlin, 2:83–195.

Mooney, H.M., 1952. Magnetic susceptibility measurements in Minnesota. 1. Technique of measurements. *Geophysics*, 17(3):531–543.

Mooney, H.M. and Bleifuss, R., 1953. Magnetic susceptibility measurements in Minnesota. 2. Analysis of field results. *Geophysics*, 18(2):383–393.

Moxham, R.M., 1963. Natural radioactivity in Washington County, Maryland. *Geophysics*, 28(2):262–272.

Moxham, R.M., 1964. Radioelement dispersion in a sedimentary environment and its effect on uranium exploration. *Econ. Geol.*, 59(2):309–321.

Müller, M., 1940. Ergebnisse geoelektrischer Polarisationsmessungen. *Z. Geophys.*, 16:274–284.

Nair, M.R., Biswas, S.K. and Mazumdar, K., 1968. Experimental studies on the electromagnetic response of tilted conducting half-planes to a horizontal-loop prospecting system. *Geoexploration*, 6(4):207–244.

Néel, L., 1955. Some theoretical aspects of rock magnetism. *Advan. Phys.*, 4(14):191–243.

Nettleton, L.L., 1939. Determination of density for reduction of gravimeter observations. *Geophysics*, 4:176–183.

Nettleton, L.L., 1954. Regionals, residuals and structures. *Geophysics*, 19(1):1–22.

Nettleton, L.L., LaCoste, L. and Harrison, J.C., 1960. Tests of an airborne gravity meter. *Geophysics*, 25(1):181–202.

Neumann, G., 1932. Magnetische Untersuchungen bei Berggiesshübel in Sachsen. *Gerlands Beitr. Angew. Geophys.*, 2(1):22–68.

Nicholls, G.D., 1955. The mineralogy of rock magnetism. *Advan. Phys.*, 4(14):113–190.

Öhrn, B., 1934. Diagrams. Archives of the Boliden Mining Company.

Orellana, E., and Mooney, H.M., 1966. *Tables and Master Curves for vertical electrical sounding*. Interciencia, Madrid, 160 pp.

Parasnis, D.S., 1952. A study of rock densities in the English Midlands. *Monthly Notices Roy. Astron. Soc., Geophys. Suppl.*, 6:253–271.

Parasnis, D.S., 1956. The electrical resistivity of some sulphide and oxide minerals and their ores. *Geophys. Prospecting*, 4(3):249–279.

Parasnis, D.S., 1961. *Magnetism – From Lodestone to Polar Wandering.* Hutchinson, London, 128 pp.

Parasnis, D.S., 1966. Electromagnetic prospecting – C.W. techniques. *Geoexploration* , 4(4):177–208.

Parasnis, D.S., 1967. Three-dimensional electric mise-à-la-masse survey of an irregular lead–zinc–copper deposit in central Sweden. *Geophys. Prospect.*, 15:407–437.

Parasnis, D.S., 1970. Some recent geoelectrical measurements in the Swedish sulphide ore fields illustrating scope and limitations of the methods concerned. In: L.W. Morley (Editor), *Mining and Groundwater Geophysics.* Geological Survey of Canada (Rept. 26), Ottawa, 290–301.

Parasnis, D.S., 1971. Analysis of some multi-frequency, multi-separation electromagnetic surveys. *Geophys. Prospect.*, 19:163–179.

Parasnis, D.S., 1972. *Principles of Applied Geophysics* (2nd ed.). Chapman and Hall, London 214 pp.

Paterson, N.R., 1961. Experimental and field data for the dual-frequency phase-shift method of airborne electro-magnetic prospecting. *Geophysics*, 26(5): 601–617.

Pemberton, R.H., 1962. Airborne e.m. in review. *Geophysics* 27(5):691–713.

Puranen, M., 1963. A geophysical investigation of the Satakunta sandstone area in south-western Finland. *Geoexploration,* 1(1):6–15.

Puzicha, K., 1942. Der Magnetismus der Gesteine als Funktion ihrer Magnetithaltes. *Beitr. Angew. Geophys.*, 9(2):158–186.

Ridland, G.C., 1945. Use of the Geiger–Müller counter in the search for pitchblende-bearing veins at Great Bear Lake, Canada. *Trans. A.I.M.E.*, 164: 117–124.

Romberg, F.E., 1958. Key variables of gravity. *Geophysics*, 23(4):684–700.

Roux, A.T., 1970. The application of geophysics to gold exploration in South Africa. In: L.W. Morley (Editor), *Mining and Groundwater Geophysics* Geological Survey of Canada (Rept. 26), Ottawa, 425–438.

Sato, M. and Mooney, H.M., 1960. The electrochemical mechanism of sulphide self-potentials. *Geophysics*, 25(1):226–249.

Schleusener, A., 1940. Nomogramme für Geländeverbesserung von Gravimetermessungen der angewandten Geophysik. *Beitr. Angew. Geophys.*, 8(4): 415–430.

Schlumberger, C., 1920. *Etudes sur la Prospection Electrique du sous sol.* Gauthiers-Villars, Paris, 94 pp.

Schmidt, G., 1959. Results of underground-seismic reflection investigations in the siderite district of the Siegerland. *Geophys. Prospecting*, 7(3):287–290.

Scott, H.S., 1957. The Airborne magnetometer. *Methods and Case Histories in Mining Geophysics.* Proc. 6th Commonwealth Mining and Metallurgical Congr., Ottawa, pp.26–34.

Seigel, H.O., 1959. A theory for induced polarization effects (for step-function excitation). In: J.R. Wait (Editor), *Overvoltage Research and Geophysical Applications.* Pergamon, London, pp.4–21.

Siikarla, T., 1966. Determination of gravity point elevations by means of liquid mercury elevation difference meter (levelling tube). *Geoexploration,* 4:113–138.

Slichter, L., 1955. Geophysics applied to prospecting for ores. *Econ. Geol.,* 50:885–969.

Smith, R.A., 1959. Some depth formulae for local magnetic and gravity anomalies, *Geophys. Prospecting,* 7(1):55–63.

Smith, R.A., 1960. Some formulae for interpreting local gravity anomalies. *Geophys. Prospecting,* 8(4):607–613.

Stam, J.C., 1962. Modern developments in shallow seismic refraction techniques. *Geophysics,* 27(2):198–212.

Starling, S.G., 1945. *Electricity and Magnetism for Degree Students.* Longmans, London, 2nd ed., 376 pp.

Thyer, R.F., 1963. Geophysical exploration – Australia. *Geophysics,* 28(2): 273–305.

Törnquist, G., 1958. Some practical results of airborne electromagnetic prospecting in Sweden. *Geophys. Prospecting,* 6(2):112–126.

Uhley, R.P. and Scharon, L., 1954. Gravity surveys for residual barite-deposits in Missouri. *Mining Engr.,* 6(1):52–56.

Vacquier, V., Steenland, N.C., Henderson, R.G. and Zietz, I., 1951. Interpretation of aeromagnetic maps. *Geol. Soc. Am., Mem.,* 47, 151 pp.

Vajk, R., 1956. Bouguer corrections with varying surface density. *Geophysics,* 21(4):1004–1020.

Volocyula, G.K., and Safronova, H.I. (Editors), 1971. *Borehole Mining Geophysics* "Nedra", Leningrad, 535 pp. (in Russian).

Wait, J.R. (Editor), 1959. *Overvoltage Research and Geophysical Applications.* Pergamon, London, 158 pp.

Werner, S., 1945. Determinations of the magnetic susceptibility of ores and rocks from Swedish iron ore deposits. *Sveriges Geol. Undersökn. Årsbok,* 39(5):1–79.

Werner, S., 1955. Interpretation of magnetic anomalies at sheet-like bodies. *Sveriges Geol. Undersökn. Årsbok,* 43(1949)(6):1–130.

Werner, S., 1958. Geophysical history of a deep-seated orebody in northern Sweden. In: *Geophysical Surveys in Mining, Hydrological and Engineering Projects.* European Assoc. Exploration Geophysicists, The Hague, pp.3–19.

Werner, S., 1961. Geofysiken i gruvindustrins tjänst. *Medd. Svenska Gruvföreningen,* 6(97):1–26.

Whetton, J.T., Meyers, J.O. and Smith, R., 1957. Correlation of rock density determinations for gravity survey interpretation. *Geophys. Prospecting*, 5(1): 20–43.

Yüngül, S., 1950. Interpretation of spontaneous polarization anomalies caused by spheroidal orebodies. *Geophysics*, 15(2):237–246.

Yüngül, S., 1956. Prospecting for chromite with gravimeter and magnetometer over rugged topography in eastern Turkey. *Geophysics*, 21(2):433–454.

Zachos, K., 1963. Discovery of a copper deposit in Chalkidiki Peninsula, northern Greece (in Greek with English summary). *Inst. Geol. Subsurface Res. Publ.*, 8(1):1–26.

Zietz, I. and Henderson, R.G., 1956. A preliminary report on model studies of magnetic anomalies of three-dimensional bodies. *Geophysics*, 21(3): 794–814.

Index